STANDARD INSTRUMENTATION
QUESTIONS AND ANSWERS

STANDARD INSTRUMENTATION
QUESTIONS AND ANSWERS
For Production-processes Control

STEPHEN MICHAEL ELONKA

Maintenance and Management Editor, Power *magazine. Licensed Chief Marine Steam Engineer, Oceans, Unlimited Horsepower. Licensed as Regular Instructor of Vocational High School, New York State. Member, Instrument Society of America, National Association of Power Engineers (life, honorary).* Author: The Marmaduke Surfaceblow Story, Plant Operator's Manual. *Co-author: Standard Plant Operator's Questions and Answers, Volumes I and II; Standard Refrigeration and Air Conditioning Questions and Answers; Mechanical Packing Handbook*

ALONZO RITTER PARSONS

Regional Training Director, Minneapolis-Honeywell Regulator Company, Industrial Products Group. Instrument Society of America: Executive Board, Vice-president, District 1; Chairman, Supplementary Education Committee; Past President, New York Section. Member, New York Academy of Sciences, American Rocket Society. Author: A Giant Step Forward in Oscillography, published by the New York Academy of Sciences

Volume I: MEASURING SYSTEMS

McGRAW-HILL BOOK COMPANY, INC.

New York   Toronto   London

1962

STANDARD INSTRUMENTATION QUESTIONS AND ANSWERS

19285

Dedicated to
the instrument technician of today, who must
keep the "little black box" working if
he is to advance in pay and prevent
costly production shutdowns

PREFACE

Today, industry's growth and efficiency are tied directly to its ability to instrument and control its production and process facilities. The tremendous growth in the field of automation and instrumentation over the past 10 years is evidence of industry's recognition of these basic tools of production and economic efficiency.

Men who understand and can apply the fundamental concepts of measurement, control, and process economics, who can engineer, install, and service instrumentation and control systems, are in greatest demand and command the top pay in industry.

The authors aim to accomplish three objectives with these two volumes: (1) provide information on the science of instrumentation so basic that these books will never be out of date, except for refinements and new developments, (2) answer questions in every important area of instrumentation detailed enough to explain what an instrument is, how it works, where it is applied, and what it will or will not do, and (3) supply the reader, with this *first* instrumentation book—his bible—with a cornerstone upon which to build his knowledge and mastery of this complex and highly vital subject.

If we have fulfilled these ambitious aims, then these volumes will be an important part of every instrumentation library and curriculum, from vocational school right up to technical institute and college level, for they answer numerous questions not now covered in any one textbook, regardless of level. Also, they give a quick panorama of the field of instrumentation and the fundamental concept involved, in easy-to-understand language and illustrations.

These volumes will greatly help not only instrument mechanics and technicians but also sales engineers, instructors, process and production engineers, machinery and equipment buyers, plant operators (both ashore, afloat, and in space), and everyone interested in any branch of this dynamic technology—for whatever reason.

The reader will soon discover that this library is not just "another set of question and answer books" but that these books so uniquely present each vital kernel of information that they just might start a trend in question-and-answer textbooks. Even as the use of the question and answer technique in programmed instructions (teaching machines) is proving highly successful, so the authors have selected their questions and answers to be of the greatest possible help to students and trainees, as well as to programmers.

Chapter 16 lists the educational opportunities offered in instrumentation by manufacturers and schools, on every level. Over 2,000 schools were surveyed—for the first time ever—to obtain these data. We hope that you, the reader, will help us keep this information up to date for each revision.

The two current volumes are the latest to be added to the highly modern and successful Standard Question and Answer library, which also includes the following:

Standard Plant Operator's Questions and Answers, vols. I and II
Standard Refrigeration and Air Conditioning Questions and Answers
Standard Electronics Questions and Answers, vols. I and II
(now being prepared for publication in early 1964)

The authors wholeheartedly thank all instrument manufacturers for their unselfish and generous contributions of technical information and illustrations ("we are happy to do anything we can to advance the working knowledge of instrumentation," as one manufacturer put it, "for we feel these basic books fill a very great need") and for checking the text for technical accuracy. Many firms also made valuable suggestions in the manuscript stages to improve these volumes.

We especially thank the editors of *Power* magazine: Lou Rowley, Jim O'Connor, Ben Skrotzki, Bob Marks, Ted Edwards, Norm Peach, Stewart Lawson, "Chief" Bender, and Ted Olive and Steven Danatos of *Chemical Engineering* magazine. Lloyd Slater, executive director of the Foundation for Instrumentation Education and Research, Inc., and Rufus Oldenburger, professor of mechanical engineering at Purdue were also very helpful. The Instrument Society of America, the only professional society dedicated exclusively to the science of instrumentation and control, was generous with materials and the counsel of its educational services director, Emil Minnar. ISA nomenclature, definitions, and *Recommended Practices* are used throughout. Howard K. Hogan and Frank J. Coyle of the U.S. Office of Education were extremely helpful.

Power magazine footed the expense of the school survey in Chap. 16 and first published it in the October, 1961, issue because of the great importance that instrumentation has for energy systems engineers.

The authors are most anxious to receive constructive criticism and suggestions for improving the next revision so that these volumes may always be of the greatest possible help to you, the reader.

Stephen Michael Elonka
Alonzo Ritter Parsons

CONTENTS

graphs · Stylus Galvanometer Oscillograph · Multichannel Photographic Oscillograph · Graphic Instrumentation Systems · Miniature Instruments: Pneumatic
and Electric · Digital Display Voltmeter · Integrators · Planimeters · Cathode-ray Oscilloscope with Polaroid Camera · Transmission Systems

CONTENTS OF VOLUME II

STANDARD INSTRUMENTATION
QUESTIONS AND ANSWERS

1

INSTRUMENTATION AND
PROCESS CHARACTERISTICS

Q　What is meant by plant and process instrumentation?
A　Instrumentation is the science of applying devices and techniques to measure, display, monitor, and control plant equipment and process operations.

Q　What are the objectives of instrumentation and control systems? Why are they needed in plants and industrial processes?
A　Instrumentation and control systems are applied to plant equipment and processes to optimize process efficiency; to produce a better product at lower cost in less time. Instrumentation is needed to (1) increase and control product quality; (2) increase process throughput and yield; (3) provide reliable data on raw materials, product quantities, and services related to process economics; (4) perform inspection and testing functions more rapidly and reliably; (5) simplify research and development projects and complex data gathering systems; and (6) provide safety systems for personnel, plants, and processes.

Q　How does an instrumentation or control system accomplish its objectives?
A　An efficient process plant represents a balance of energies into and out of dynamic processes. Instrumentation and control systems regulate automatically the flow of energy to the process units and the characteristics of process products to give stable operation at optimum efficiency. But attaining top efficiency is not easy. To succeed, it must combine all the know-how of process and equipment characteristics with that of instrumentation techniques and automatic control element techniques. And this must be done during the design stages of the process, then applied to the instrumentation and control system. Even greater efficiencies will result as market considerations and economic data are applied to day-by-day plant operations when a process control computer is added to the instrumentation and control system.

Q   What are the basic functions and elements of an instrumentation and automatic control system?

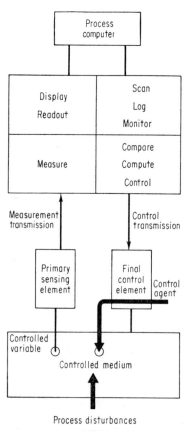

Fig. 1-1. Basic elements of instrumentation and control system.

A   Two prime components are (1) the process, and (2) the automatic controller (Fig. 1-1). The automatic controller performs the functions of (1) measuring the value of a process variable, (2) displaying the measured variable, (3) comparing the measured value with a preset desired value, and (4) manipulating another process variable to correct the measured value when a difference exists. It contains the measuring means (primary sensing element, measurement transmission means, measuring element, display, and often monitoring function) and the controlling means (control unit, control transmission means, final control element). The process is defined as the collective function performed in and by the equipment in which a process variable is controlled. It includes everything that affects the controlled variable.

Q   Illustrate a simple process control system and define its elements.

A   Figure 1-2 indicates a heat exchanger in which a product is heated to the desired temperature of 175°F by controlling the flow of steam through the heat-exchanger coils. The product is called the controlled medium, and the product temperature is the controlled variable (and the measured variable). The steam is called the control agent, and the manipulated variable is the rate of flow of steam, which is increased or decreased as the temperature of the product varies.

Q   Using Fig. 1-2, illustrate a typical automatic controller and define its elements.

A   The measuring means has these components: (1) primary sensing element (thermometer bulb to detect product temperature), (2) meas-

urement transmission means (thermal capillary tubing to connect thermometer bulb to spiral measuring element), (3) measuring element in
the recorder-controller case [pressure spiral which converts measured variable signal (pressure change in this case) to a recording pen motion on
a chart], (4) display means (a recording pen, ink, and paper chart
calibrated for a temperature range of 0 to 300°F).

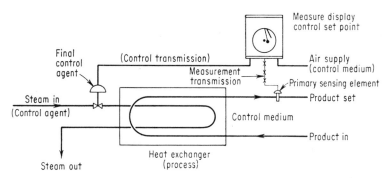

Fig. 1-2. Simple process control system.

The controlling means consists of (1) set-point adjustment unit (it
sets the desired measured-variable value), (2) controller with error detector (compares measured-variable value with desired set-point value and
produces an output control signal when an error or difference exists),
(3) control medium (medium used to transmit control signal to final
control element), in this case air under pressure, and (4) the final control element (operated by the control signal to control the manipulated
variable), in this case an air-operated steam control valve. In Fig. 1-2,
we control product temperature at 175°F with pneumatic (air-operated)
recording temperature controller. The set-point index is adjusted to 175°F
on a chart calibrated 0 to 300°F. As the thermometer bulb senses the
product temperature, its output signal is transmitted through the capillary
tubing and spiral and actuates the recording pen. The pen draws a continuous ink line on a round chart corresponding to the measured-variable
temperature. When the pen deviates from the set-point temperature of
175°F because of a process disturbance or load change, the error-detecting
control unit detects the difference. It produces a control signal which is
transmitted to the control valve in proportion to the error signal. When
the measured temperature is too high, the valve closes, decreasing the
steam flow; but with low temperature the valve opens, allowing more
steam to flow. This system can also be illustrated by the feedback control
loop diagram (Fig. 1-3).

Q   What are the basic characteristics of a process?
A   Every process exhibits these two effects which must be considered when instrumentation and control systems are applied to it: (1) load changes (changes in the controlled variable due to altered conditions in the process), (2) process lag (delay in time it takes the process variable to reach a new value when load changes occur). In rapidly responding processes, the dynamic response of the process variable is the important characteristic.

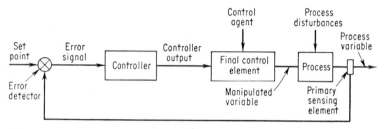

Fig. 1-3. Feedback control loop diagram.

Q   Define process load in terms of heat exchanger in Fig. 1-2. Name four sources of process load changes.
A   Process load is the total amount of control agent required by a process at any one time to maintain a balanced condition. In heat exchangers a flowing product is continuously heated with steam (control agent). It takes a certain quantity of steam to hold the product temperature at a given value when the product is flowing at a given rate. An increase in product flow takes more steam; an increase in inlet product temperature requires less steam. These are load changes. Any change in process load needs a change in final control-element setting to maintain a balance condition (keeps the controlled variable at set point). The magnitude and rate of load change are important in instrumentation and control systems.

Load changes occur from (1) greater or less demand for control agent, (2) a change in ambient conditions, (3) a change in quality of the control agent, and (4) a chemical reaction which generates or absorbs heat (exothermic or endothermic process).

Q   Name four sources of process lag.
A   Process: (1) capacity and capacitance (see next question), (2) resistance, (3) potential, and (4) dead time.

Q   Describe process capacitance and its effect on process lag.
A   Although capacity is a familiar term to measure the ability of a process to hold energy (measured in units of quantity), a more important

factor is the capacitance of a process. Capacitance is a measure of the ability of a process to hold a quantity of energy or material per unit quantity of some reference variable. It is measured in units of quantity divided by the reference variable. Figure 1-4 shows two tanks of dif-

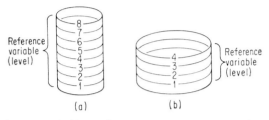

Fig. 1-4. Capacity compared with capacitance.

ferent shapes but of equal liquid volume capacity (128 cu ft). Each tank has a different liquid capacitance with respect to liquid level. The 8-ft-high tank has a liquid volume capacitance of 16 cu ft per ft of level (128 ÷ 8); while the 4-ft-high tank has a capacitance of 32 cu ft per ft. So always identify capacitance with the type of energy or material involved. Thermal capacitance of a liquid is defined in terms of the heat energy (Btu) needed to raise the liquid temperature per degree Fahrenheit.

Figure 1-5 shows a process with large thermal capacitance. Here a large amount of liquid is heated in a steam-jacketed kettle by controlling the steam flow through the jacket. Liquid temperature is measured by

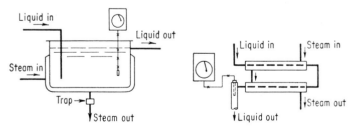

Fig. 1-5. Process with large thermal capacitance.

Fig. 1-6. Process with limited thermal capacitance.

a thermometer bulb. The liquid's mass resists changes in temperature which might be caused by variations in flow rate, heat input, and ambient temperature. This mass exerts a stabilizing influence and would make temperature control relatively easy. Conversely, Fig. 1-6 shows a high-velocity heat exchanger with limited thermal capacitance. The rate of flow through this process is identical to the rate through the kettle process. But there is a much smaller volume flow through the exchanger. With this small mass of fluid there is no stabilizing influence. Slight variations in feed rate or heat supply rate make it very difficult to control the temperature because the total volume of liquid in the exchanger at one time is so small compared with the rate of throughput and heat-transfer area. So although the over-all effect of large capacitance is favorable (acts like a flywheel), it does introduce a lag between the time a change is made in the control agent and the time the controlled variable reflects this change. It isn't easy to change the controlled variable in a large capacitance process to a new value. But it may also be difficult to maintain the controlled variable value in a small capacitance process because of its higher sensitivity to process disturbances.

Q   What is process resistance and its effect on process lag?
A   Process resistance is opposition to flow. It is measured in units of potential that is needed to produce a unit change in flow. Thermal resistance is the change of temperature which occurs per unit rate of heat flow through a process material or vessel (expressed in Btu per second). If a material is heated in a process with high thermal resistance, more control agent will be required to change the material temperature than in a low thermal resistance process. Potential represents a condition at a given point in the process which determines the energy at that point.

Q   How do you define dead time and its effect on process lag?
A   Dead time (also called transportation or transmission lag) is the interval from the time that a control agent change takes place until its effect is felt on the controlled variable. For example, in a tubular-type petroleum furnace, oil is pumped at a constant rate through hundreds of feet of tubing which line the furnace walls. It takes a long time for a given portion of oil to pass through the heater. This dead time causes more difficulty in automatic control systems than any other type of lag. During this period the controller is helpless, as it cannot initiate corrective action until the deviation is sensed.

Q   What are the basic characteristics of the measuring means?
A   Two basic characteristics considered in the evaluation of the measuring means are (1) speed of response, or lag, and (2) accuracy.

Q   What is meant by the measurement speed of response?
A   The time it takes a measuring system to respond completely to a change in the measured variable value is called the speed of response of the measuring system. Although ideally this time should be instantaneous, the primary sensing element, transmission system, and the measuring

element all respond to a process variable change in separate finite times. This time is often called lag.

Q How do you evaluate the primary elements' response?

A Response of most primary sensing elements, and especially temperature sensing elements, is expressed in terms of the lag coefficient. This is an arbitrary figure which expresses the response of a bare temperature primary element to an instantaneous (step) process variable temperature change in terms of how long it takes the element to reach 63.2 per cent of this total temperature change. Figure 1-7 shows speed-of-response curves for typical thermometer bulbs A and B. The response time of temperature elements is faster in moving liquid as compared with moving air (faster when unprotected than with a protecting tube). Some protecting tubes slow down speed of response more than others. Air space between a temperature element and protection tube slows response but can be improved by grounding (making contact) the tip to the protecting tube.

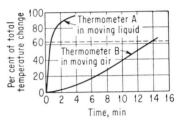

Fig. 1-7. Speed-of-response curves for thermometer bulbs.

Fluid velocity past the sensing element affects speed of response; the higher the velocity, the better the response. Thermal capacity has the same effect on speed of response as on process lag. Transmission lag defines the speed of response between the primary sensing element and the measuring element. Electric transmission means are much faster than thermal system capillary or pneumatic transmission systems.

Q Name four factors which influence measurement accuracy.

A Four factors are (1) static error, (2) dynamic error, (3) reproducibility, and (4) dead zone.

Q What is static error of measurement? How does it influence accuracy?

A Static error of measurement is the deviation of the instrument reading from the true value of the static measured variable. While large static error is undesirable, it is not detrimental to control when it is more important for the variable to be held at a constant value than at an exact absolute value. Accuracy is usually expressed in terms of the static error of the instrument and as a per cent of its range. When an instrument whose range is 800 to 1800° is said to have an accuracy within ±0.25 per cent, this means its static error at any point of the scale never exceeds 2.5° (0.25 per cent of 1,800 minus 800).

Q   What is reproducibility of a measuring system?

A   The degree of closeness with which the same value of the process variable can be measured at different times. In automatic control systems, reproducibility is more important than accuracy since it is a dynamic characteristic and is consistent.

Q   Explain the term dynamic error.

A   Figure 1-8 shows the difference between a gradual change of process

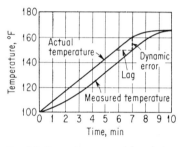

Fig. 1-8. Dynamic error and lag during a gradual change.

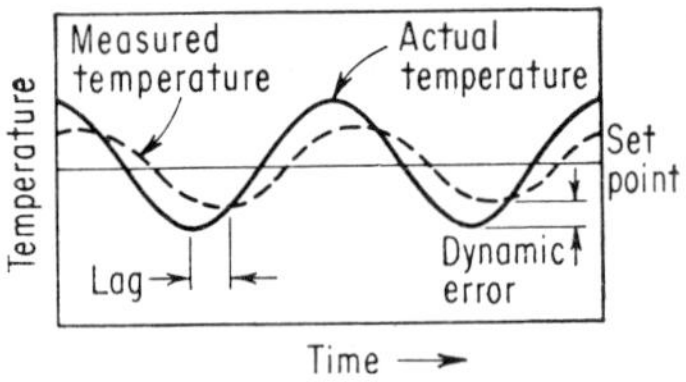

Fig. 1-9. Dynamic error and lag during a sinusoidal change.

temperature and the temperature measured by a temperature measuring system. Even with no static error the measuring system immediately lags behind the actual temperature; the lag increases with time until the actual temperature begins to level off and becomes steady. At this point there is no error; the temperatures are the same. The dynamic error is the difference between the actual and measured temperatures. Lag is the time between the actual temperature and the point at which the measured temperature reaches the value of the actual temperature. Dynamic error is in addition to static error. It influences control response as well as measurement response. Figure 1-9 shows dynamic error and lag during a sinusoidal change about the set point caused by the corrective action of a controller during a gradual change in measured variable.

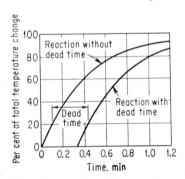

Fig. 1-10. Dead time is lag in detecting time.

Q   What is dead zone and dead time?

A   Dead zone is the largest range through which the measured variable can change without the change being detected by the measuring system. As Fig. 1-10 shows, dead time is the length of time which elapses before the instrument can detect a change in the variable. This is a function of the variable rate of change and measuring system sensitivity and response.

Q Name 26 of the most common and significant measured variables in industrial plants and processes.

A (1) Temperature, (2) flow, (3) pressure, (4) vacuum, (5) level, (6) chemical analysis, (7) humidity, (8) dew point, (9) moisture, (10) viscosity, (11) consistency, (12) density, (13) specific gravity, (14) speed, (15) stretch, (16) motion, (17) strain, (18) vibration, (19) electrical variables, (20) weight, (21) force, (22) thrust, (23) color, (24) gloss, (25) direction, and (26) nuclear radiation.

SUGGESTED READING

Eckman, Donald P.: *Industrial Instrumentation,* John Wiley & Sons, Inc., New York, 1950.

Elonka, Steve, and Joseph F. Robinson: *Standard Plant Operator's Questions and Answers,* vols. I and II, McGraw-Hill Book Company, Inc., New York, 1959.

Elonka, Steve: *Plant Operators' Manual,* McGraw-Hill Book Company, Inc., New York, 1956.

Elonka, Steve, and Julian Bernstein: *Standard Industrial Electronics Questions and Answers,* vols. I and II, McGraw-Hill Book Company, Inc., New York, to be published in 1964.

2

TEMPERATURE MEASURING SYSTEMS

Q   Why is the measurement of temperature so vital today?

A   Temperature measurement is vital to the control of quality and to the safe operation of machinery in every industry. This holds true for the pasteurizing of milk, roasting of coffee, heat-treating of metals, glass blowing, petroleum refining, pharmaceutical production, sterilization, power generation, missile-reentry experiments, as well as heating and cooling processes over a broad spectrum.

Q   What is temperature?

A   Temperature is the degree of hotness or coldness measured on a definite scale. The temperature of a body is its heat intensity (not heat quantity). All bodies are made up of a large number of small particles called molecules. The molecules are in constant motion. The faster they move, the hotter the body; the slower their motion, the colder the body. This condition can be described as the thermal potential or energy effectiveness of a body. When assigned a number, it is called the degree of temperature. The heat of one body can be transferred to another body.

Q   Define the units of temperature.

A   See Fig. 2-1a. The Fahrenheit temperature scale (°F) divides the temperature interval between the ice point and the steam point of water into 180 parts, or degrees. The ice point is given the value 32°F, and the steam point 212°F.

The centigrade temperature scale (°C) subdivides the temperature interval between ice and steam into 100 parts, or degrees. The ice point has the value of 0°C and the steam point 100°C.

The Kelvin temperature scale defines the absolute temperature scale. Absolute zero, or the lowest theoretical temperature, 0°K, is that condition where molecular motion ceases and there is therefore no heat. On the Fahrenheit scale this point has the value 459.6°F below zero (−460°F). On the centigrade scale it is −273°C. The ice point is +273°K, or 0°C. The boiling point is +373°K, or 100°C.

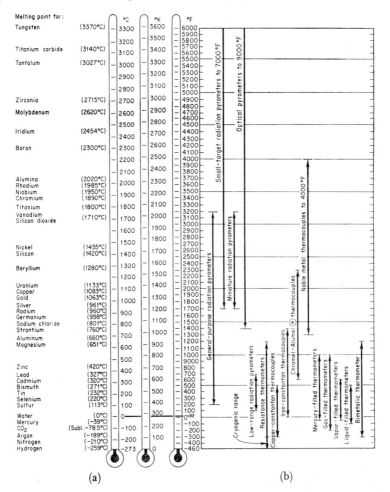

Fig. 2-1. Spectrum of temperature measuring devices. To convert Kelvin to centigrade, subtract 273 from °K. To convert centigrade to Fahrenheit, multiply °C times 1.8 and add 32. To convert Fahrenheit to Rankine, add 460° to °F.

Q How do you convert from degrees Fahrenheit to degrees centigrade and vice versa?

A To find degrees centigrade when given degrees Fahrenheit use the following:

$$°C = \tfrac{5}{9}(°F - 32)$$
$$°F = \tfrac{9}{5}°C + 32$$

Q What are the six reproducible equilibrium temperatures, or "fixed points," established as the basis for precise temperature measurements?
A (1) Boiling point of oxygen: −182.97°C. (2) Freezing point of water: −0.000°C. (3) Boiling point of water: +100.000°C. (4) Boiling point of sulfur: +444.60°C. (5) Melting point of silver: +960.8°C. (6) Melting point of gold: +1063°C.

Q What are the usual temperature ranges in plant and process applications?
A Ranges are from −200 to +4000°F. Research studies fluctuate more widely, from the extremely low cryogenic regions of −450°F up to the extremely hot temperatures of +7000°F.

Q Name five physical principles upon which temperature-measurement methods are based.
A See Fig. 2-1b. Temperature cannot be measured directly but must be inferred from its effect on a substance whose characteristics are understood. This inference is based on one of these basic physical principles: (1) Expansion of liquid, gas, or solid (filled thermal system). (2) Vapor tension of a liquid (filled thermal system). (3) Electrical potential produced by dissimilar metals in contact—thermoelectricity (thermocouples). (4) Change of electrical resistance (resistance thermometers). (5) Intensity of total radiation or of a particular band of wavelengths of radiation given off by a hot substance (radiation pyrometer).

Q How are filled thermal systems classified?
A As expansion and pressure-spring types. (1) Expansion type is the mercury-in-glass industrial thermometer. (2) Pressure-spring types are (a) liquid-filled (Class I), (b) mercury-filled (Class V), (c) vapor-pressure-filled (Class II, A, B, C, D), (d) gas-filled (Class III).

Q Where are filled thermal systems usually used?
A In plant and industrial processes to measure liquid, gas, air, and vapor temperatures in the following ranges: (1) Expansion-type (mercury-in-glass) thermometer −38 to +950°F. (2) Pressure-spring types: (a) Liquid-filled (hydrocarbon), −125 to +500°F. (b) Mercury-filled, −38 to +1200°F. (c) Vapor-filled, −50 to +600°F. (d) Gas-filled, −200 to +1200°F.

Q Describe a mercury-in-glass industrial thermometer.
A See Fig. 2-2. This thermometer has an evacuated glass tube with a bulb at the lower end of the glass tube filled with mercury and protected by a metal thermal well. The glass tube with bulb is mounted in a protective housing against a calibrated temperature scale. Standard scale sizes are 5, 7, 9, and 10 in. A temperature rise causes the mercury to

expand in the glass tube. The fixed or separable thermal well or socket contains mounting threads and union connections for easier mounting into a pipe, fitting, or vessel. Special well shapes (45°, 90°, straight, and sanitary), materials, and sizes are available.

Q   Where are mercury-in-glass thermometers commonly used?

A   As an inexpensive indicating device for measuring temperatures of flowing process fluids in open and closed conduits of limited fluctuations, where reading at the point of measurement is not a problem. Also where accuracies of 1 per cent of full range and slow response are tolerable. Using ethyl alcohol or pentane instead of mercury extends the range of measurement.

Q   What is a bimetallic thermometer? How does it work?

A   See Fig. 2-3. This temperature measuring device works on the

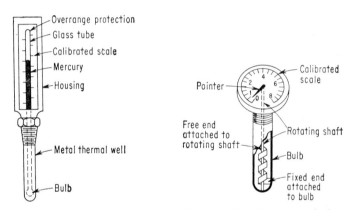

Fig. 2-2. Mercury-in-glass thermometer.

Fig. 2-3. Bimetallic industrial thermometer helical element.

principle that two different metals change size in different amounts when exposed to a change in temperature. The industrial bimetallic thermometer consists of strips of two or more metals laminated into a multilayer piece, usually in a helicoid form. As the temperature of this laminated metal strip changes, its different metals expand or contract different amounts, causing the helical coil to wind or unwind. One end of the helix is fixed and the other attached to a free-to-turn pointer. As the fixed end is subjected to a temperature change, the pointer indicates temperature on a calibrated dial scale. The useful temperature range is −300 to +1200°F. Accuracy is about 1 per cent of scale range. This thermometer is used for similar but more rugged jobs than liquid-in-glass stem thermometers.

Q Name four advantages of the bimetallic thermometer.
A (1) Relatively inexpensive, (2) rugged, (3) direct reading, and (4) needs no other equipment or outside power.

Q Name four disadvantages of the industrial bimetallic thermometer as compared with the liquid-in-glass thermometer.
A (1) It is read at the point of measurement and cannot be remotely indicated, (2) is not so accurate, (3) does not operate over so wide a total range, and (4) does not operate over so narrow a span.

Q Describe the Class I liquid-filled thermal systems.
A As Fig. 2-4 shows, this is a pressure-spring type. It has a bulb filled with a liquid (usually a hydrocarbon, but never mercury) in which the

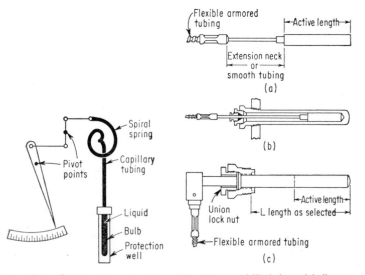

Fig. 2-4. Class I pressure-spring liquid-filled measuring system.

Fig. 2-5. Liquid-filled thermal bulb configuration.

liquid expands its volume as temperature rises. A thermal well protects the bulb from pressure or corrosion damage. A capillary tubing (with protective armor) transmits the pressure. A receiving element (spiral, Bourdon, or helix) is pressure-sensitive and converts the volumetric expansion into a motion through a linkage for temperature indication, recording, or transmission. Bulb sizes vary from $1\frac{1}{16} \times 8$ in. to $\frac{3}{8} \times 1\frac{1}{4}$ in., with tubing length as long as 150 ft. Bulb and tubing materials are often copper, steel, Monel, stainless steel, lead, or plastic covered.

Q Name three liquid-filled thermal bulb configurations and their purpose.

A See Fig. 2-5. (*a*) Plain bulbs; used where the measured medium is not under pressure and will not harm the bulb material. Can have adjustable fittings on the extension neck or smooth tubing for fit through walls. (*b*) Union-connected bulbs; used with separable wells for protection where the measured medium is harmful to the bulb material, where it is under pressure, or where the bulb must be removed without relieving the pressure. Fixed or adjustable union seats and bushings are used. Separable wells form a pressuretight connection in the wall of a vessel or pipe. (*c*) Rigid extension bulbs, either straight or right angle; used where the bulb is inserted through a rotating joint, is to be removed frequently, or is immersed in a viscous liquid.

Q What are the performance characteristics of liquid-filled thermal systems?

A (1) Range, -125 to $+600°F$; (2) minimum span, $25°F$ ($10°F$ special); (3) maximum span, about $250°F$ (some wider); (4) scale or chart, linear (evenly graduated); (5) accuracy, 1 per cent of full range; and (6) speed of response, poor (compared with other classes).

Q What is meant by the terms *case compensation* and *tubing* or *full compensation*?

A See Fig. 2-6. Because the entire thermal system is filled with a liquid, ambient temperature changes affect not only the liquid in the bulb but also the liquid in the capillary tubing and the spiral or Bourdon receiving element. This causes a false motion of the indicator or recording pen. Equalizing this error in the receiving element is called case compensation. There is enough case compensation when the bulb used has a short extension neck only, and when the ambient temperature change is negligible along the capillary. Case compensation is by a bimetal strip rigidly attached at the spiral's fixed end (Fig. 2-6*a*). As the ambient temperature varies around the spiral, the bimetal responds and adds to or subtracts enough from the motion of the spiral to cause the indicator to read correctly despite the ambient temperature effect.

Tubing and case compensation (full compensation, also capillary compensator) must be used with bulbs having long extension necks or those exposed to widely varying ambient temperatures along the capillary. For this type of compensation, two spirals and two capillary tubes are used (Fig. 2-6*b*). The measuring spiral is connected to the bulb in the usual way. The compensating spiral is connected to a capillary enclosed in the same armor as the measuring spiral capillary, but dead-ended at the bulb. The compensating spiral and its capillary are also filled with liquid. Temperature changes within the instrument case or along the tubing affect both spirals equally. Spirals are mounted in opposition, thus offsetting each other. Therefore, ambient temperature variations are added or subtracted from the movement of the measuring spiral, causing the instrument to read correctly.

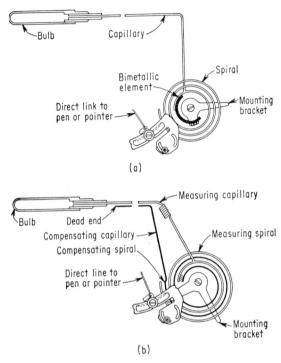

Fig. 2-6. Compensating thermal systems come in various designs.

Q What is meant by *overrange protection?*
A Overrange protection is the maximum temperature to which the bulb may be exposed indefinitely without damage to the system. Overrange protection on Class I thermal systems is between 100 and 200 per cent of full span for average tubing length. This decreases for very long tubing.

Q What is *bulb-elevation* error and what is its effect on liquid-filled systems?
A When the bulb of a liquid-filled system is raised above or lowered below the case, a pressure difference equal to the liquid heads develops

between the bulb and the spiral. This causes an erroneous reading. If the bulb is raised above the case, the indicator reads too high. This error can be calibrated and applied to correct the indicated reading.

Q Name four advantages of hydrocarbons in a liquid-filled thermal system.

A (1) Linear reading chart and scale, (2) narrow span of measurement, (3) small bulbs, and (4) low-temperature measurements.

Q Describe Class V mercury-filled thermal systems and how they work.

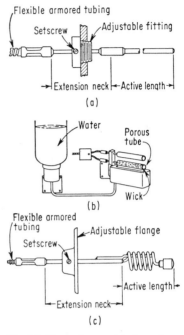
Fig. 2-8. Three of several bulb configurations used with mercury-filled systems.

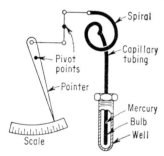
Fig. 2-7. Class V mercury-filled measuring system, pressure-spring type.

A See Fig. 2-7. This is a special form of liquid-filled thermal system where mercury is used as the fill. Bulb sizes vary depending on temperature span (some are $\frac{1}{2} \times 3\frac{1}{2}$ in. to $\frac{5}{8} \times 8\frac{1}{2}$ in.), with tubing lengths up to 200 ft. Bulb and tubing materials are steel, stainless steel, bronze, lead, or plastic covered.

Q Name seven bulb forms used with mercury-filled thermal systems.
A See Figs. 2-5 and 2-8. (1) Plain. (2) Union-connected. (3) Rigid extension. (4) Averaging bulbs, used to measure air or gas temperatures, with high speed of response. Long (300 in.) and thin, they sense the average temperature along the entire length. (5) Preformed capillary bulbs (c), used for measuring temperatures where air or gas velocities are low. The long capillary is formed into a coil supported rigidly by a strip attached to the extension neck. (6) Wet- and dry-bulb assemblies used to measure humidity with psychrometric methods (b). (7) Sanitary fittings and bulbs (a).

Q Name the performance characteristics of mercury-filled thermal systems.
A (1) Range, −65 to +1000°F (some to 1200°F); (2) minimum span, 40°F; (3) maximum span, 1000°F; (4) scale or chart, linear (evenly graduated); (5) accuracy 1 per cent; (6) speed of response, intermediate; (7) overrange capacity, 100 per cent of range; and (8) bulb-elevation error, negligible (except when exceeding 30 ft).

Q Must you use case-and-tubing compensation with mercury-filled thermal systems to compensate for ambient temperature variation?
A Only when the ambient temperature varies greatly along the capillary tubing, or when the bulb to be used has a long extension neck.

Q What are four advantages of mercury-filled thermal systems?
A (1) Linear scale, (2) stability, (3) ruggedness, and (4) speed of response.

Q Describe the Class II vapor-filled thermal systems.
A See Figs. 2-9 and 2-10. Vapor-filled thermal systems are similar to

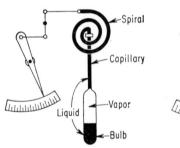

Fig. 2-9. Class II, A vapor-pressure measuring system.

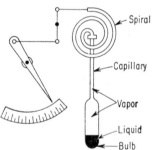

Fig. 2-10. Class II, B vapor-actuated pressure measuring system.

liquid- and mercury-filled systems, but the thermal system is partially filled with a volatile liquid. Methyl chloride, ether, butane, hexane, propane, toluene, or sulfur dioxide is used. All vapor-filled systems operate on the principle of vapor-pressure liquid-temperature relationship. Temperature is measured at the free surface between the liquid and vapor. Since the fill will always be in a liquid state at the coolest part of the system, the system must have enough fill so that the interface of the liquid and vapor will always be in the bulb.

Thermal systems are designed to operate under these conditions: (1) Class II, A operates with measured temperature *above* the thermal-system temperature. (2) Class II, B operates with measured temperature *below* the thermal-system temperature. (3) Class II, C operates with measured temperature *above* and *below* the thermal-system temperature. (4) Class II, D operates with measured temperature *above*, *below*, and *at* the thermal-system temperature. Here the volatile liquid is in the sensitive position of the bulb, and a fairly nonvolatile liquid transmits the vapor pressure to the receiving element. Bulb sizes vary from ⅜ × 3 in., ¾ × 5 in., to ⅜ × 10 in., depending on the temperature span. Tubing lengths are up to 200 ft. Most bulb and tubing materials are copper, steel, stainless steel, bronze, lead, and plastic coating.

Q Name the four types of vapor-filled bulb configurations.
A See Figs. 2-5 and 2-8. (1) Plain, (2) union-connected, (3) rigid extension, and (4) sanitary.

Q Explain the nine performance characteristics of vapor-filled systems.
A (1) Range, −50 to +600°F; (2) minimum span, 40°F; (3) maximum span, 300°F; (4) scale or chart, nonlinear (graduations increase as temperature rises); (5) accuracy, 1 per cent of full scale; (6) speed response, fast; (7) overrange capacity, usually small (less than 100 per cent); (8) bulb-elevation error, often large but can be canceled by calibration when the elevation difference is known; and (9) ambient temperature compensation, not needed.

Q What are four advantages of vapor-filled systems?
A (1) Narrow temperature span, (2) rapid response, (3) increased readability and control in upper range, and (4) low cost.

Q Describe a gas-filled thermal system.
A See Fig. 2-11. Gas-filled thermal systems are similar in design to those described except that the fill is an inert gas, usually nitrogen. Operation is based on Charles's gas law, $P_1/T_1 = P_2/T_2$, which states that if the gas *volume* is constant, absolute pressure will increase as the absolute *temperature* of all or part of the gas increases. So in this gas-filled thermal system, as the bulb containing a constant volume of gas is heated, the pressure thus created actuates the spring-tensioned receiving element.

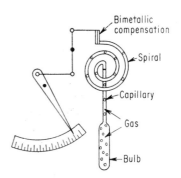

Fig. 2-11. Class III gas-expansion measuring system with compensator.

Bulb volume is very large in relation to the capillary tubing. This reduces ambient temperature variations. Bulb sizes are rather large (¾ × 10 in. and 1 × 5 in.) and tubing lengths run up to 200 ft. Materials include copper, steel, stainless steel, lead-covered metal, and bronze with plastic covering.

Q Name the four bulb designs used for gas-filled systems.
A (1) Plain, (2) union-connected, (3) averaging, and (4) preformed capillary.

Q List the performance characteristics of gas-filled thermal systems.
A (1) Range, −200 to +1000°F, (2) minimum span, 100°F; (3) maximum span, 1000°F; (4) scale or record, linear; (5) accuracy, 1 per cent; (6) speed of response, fastest; (7) overrange capacity, varies with range up to 300 per cent; and (8) bulb-elevation error, negligible.

Q Is case-and-tubing compensation needed?
A No, because bulb sizes are large compared with the tubing, but case compensation is necessary and furnished. A bimetal strip, rigidly attached to the mounting bracket, supports the spiral. The bimetal responds as the temperature around it changes and adds or subtracts from the spiral motion. This causes correct temperature readings regardless of ambient temperature changes.

Q What are the advantages of gas-filled thermal systems?
A Linear reading, simplicity, and fastest response.

Q What are the basic advantages of using filled thermal systems?
A (1) Simplicity, (2) inexpensive, (3) low maintenance, (4) rugged, (5) adequate performance characteristics for many process temperature measuring requirements, (6) self-contained measuring system eliminating power-supply requirements, (7) practical to separate point of measurement from point of readout and control unit by as much as 100 ft without using auxiliary transmission means, and (8) good accuracy and narrow spans are obtained with pneumatic transmitters.

Q What are six limitations of filled thermal systems?
A (1) Bulb size may be too large, (2) temperature range is limited in maximum and minimum, (3) spans not so narrow as in electrical temperature measuring techniques, (4) system failure means replacement of complete system, (5) sensitivity and accuracy not equal to electrical methods, and (6) tubing lengths over 100 ft not economical, with limit at 400 ft.

Q What points must you consider when selecting a filled thermal system for temperature measurement?
A (1) Type of filled system depends on (a) temperature range, (b) speed of response needed, (c) bulb size or configuration, (d) length of tubing required, and (e) type of chart or scale graduation desired. (2)

Type of bulb configuration depends on the measured-medium container (pipe, vessel, box, or room). (3) Type of protection well or socket depends on (*a*) measured medium, (*b*) corrosion, (*c*) viscosity, and (*d*) pressure characteristics. (4) Type of capillary tubing depends on atmosphere (corrosive) and vibration surrounding it. (5) Type of indicator, recorder, or controller depends on readout function desired. (6) Type of ambient temperature compensation depends on the thermal system selected and effect of temperature variations on its tubing and receiving element. (7) Bulb-elevation error recalibration depends on thermal system selected and effect of elevation difference on its accuracy.

Q   What method is mostly used to transmit a filled thermal system temperature reading beyond the practical maximum tubing length?
A   These system transmitters handle temperatures in process units as far as 2,000 ft from the point of measurement. This is done by metering air (3 to 15 psi) through ⅜-in. copper tubing to a receiver. Pneumatic transmission allows locating the receiving instruments (indicators, recorders, and controllers) at a safe distance from hazard areas. Pneumatic transmitters can be either transmitters only, or indicators or recorders.

Q   Describe a widely used nonindicating type of pneumatic transmitter for handling filled thermal system temperature measurements.
A   See Fig. 2-12. Modern nonindicating pneumatic temperature (filled

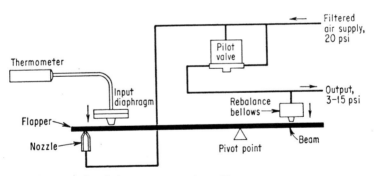

Fig. 2-12. Pneumatic force-balance temperature transmitter.

thermal system) type transmitters make use of the force-balance principle. This states that in a beam balance the moment of force on a beam is equal to the product of the force applied at right angles to the beam and its distance from the fulcrum. Force applied to a beam on one side of the fulcrum tends to move the beam. Balance is restored by applying forces to the other side, exerting a total moment equal and opposite to the original. Any difference in moment on either side of the fulcrum causes a very tiny motion. To produce a force, or a change in pressure with a change in temperature, a gas-filled thermal system is used. The resulting pressure is applied through a diaphragm, converted to a force on one side of the beam, which pivots about its fulcrum. As the beam moves, pressure to the output line is increased through a pilot relay. A balancing (or restoring) force is produced to bring the beam to rest. This action is instantaneous, moving the beam a maximum few thousandths of an inch. Bulb, tubing materials, and design are similar to gas-filled thermal systems. But smaller bulbs ($\frac{3}{8} \times 3\frac{1}{2}$ in. and tubing lengths up to 10 ft) are usually furnished.

Q Name six performance characteristics of a gas-filled thermal system pneumatic transmitter.
A These are: (1) over-all range, −370 to +1000°F; (2) minimum span, 50°F (adjustable); (3) maximum span, 400°F (adjustable); (4) accuracy, one-half of 1 per cent of span (a most important feature); (5) ambient temperature compensation, good, with bimetallic element or bellows; (6) speed of response, fastest (a rate action unit will overcome thermal lags in bulb and tubing).

Q Name seven advantages of a gas-filled thermal system type pneumatic transmitter.
A (1) Transmission distances up to 2,000 ft, (2) small size, (3) narrow span, (4) accurate, (5) dependable, (6) rugged, and (7) resistant to corrosive and hazardous atmospheres.

Q What is resistance thermometry?
A A method of measuring temperature which makes use of the property of metals to change electrical resistance as temperature changes (called temperature coefficient of resistance). This relationship is positive and linear for most metals.

Q Describe a resistance thermometer measuring system.
A Figure 2-13 shows a resistance thermometer. Components are a primary sensing device (resistance thermometer bulb), a measuring circuit (Wheatstone resistance bridge), and connecting lead wire. The measuring circuit is either a deflectional bridge or a balanced bridge. When the temperature changes at the resistance thermometer bulb, its resistance changes and unbalances the Wheatstone resistance bridge measuring circuit. This unbalance is measured and converted into a balancing action, which is an indication of the temperature. Simple indicating instruments use a deflectional bridge. Recording instruments use a balanced bridge. Conductor lead wire is used to eliminate bridge unbalance due to am-

bient temperature effects on the lead wire. Lead-wire lengths of up to 1,500 ft are practical.

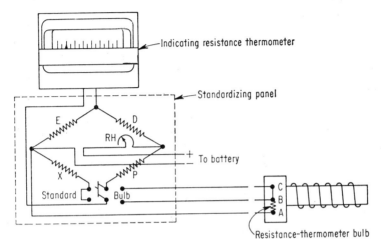

Fig. 2-13. Resistance thermometer measuring system.

Q What are some typical uses for resistance thermometers?
A Used in plants and for processes to measure temperature of liquids, gases, air, and surfaces from −200 to +900°C. Other uses are spot temperatures in small spaces in generator armature and field windings, pipes, junction boxes; average temperatures in rooms, spaces, vessels, process equipment; surface temperatures; and relative humidity, using wet- and dry-bulb temperatures. Platinum bulbs are used as temperature standards for calibration purposes.

Q Name the practical performance characteristics of resistance thermometer systems.
A These are: (1) temperature ranges of −258 to +900°C (platinum), −150 to +300°C (nickel), and −200 to +120°C (copper) with good reproducibility and accuracy (±0.3 to ±0.5 per cent of full span); (2) narrow temperature spans of 2 to 5°C are practical in industrial applications; (3) speed of response, about the same as thermocouples. They can vary from 1 sec in agitated water to several minutes in still air. These systems are very stable and sensitive.

Q Rocket and space vehicle testing and operational programs require the temperature measurement of such cryogenic fluids as liquid helium and hydrogen. What types of resistance thermometers are used for this service?

A   Platinum resistance thermometers measure down to 25°K. New low-temperature resistance thermometers measure temperatures between 0 and 100°K. They use the temperature dependence of resistance in doped germanium. Thermometer elements are precision-doped with two kinds of impurity to give convenient resistance and high thermometric sensitivity in their chosen range. Each thermometer is equipped with separate current and potential contacts (for measurement with standard potentiometric techniques) so that the long-term stability will be unaffected by any fluctuations in contact performance. Range is 4 to 40°K, or 0 to 100°K, with high sensitivity in the important liquid hydrogen range.

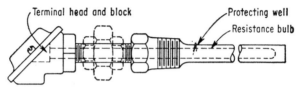

Fig. 2-14. Resistance thermometer bulb assembly.

Q   Describe a resistance thermometer bulb assembly.

A   Figures 2-14 and 2-15 show resistance thermometer bulbs for industrial use. Assemblies have (1) resistance element (or windings) in a tubular metal stem, (2) protection tube or separable well, and (3) ter-

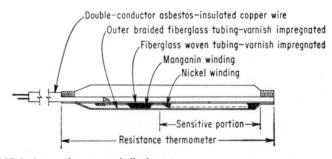

Fig. 2-15. Resistance thermometer bulb element.

minal block and housing. The tubular metal stem is sealed at the lower end while the upper end terminates in the terminal block and housing. In Fig. 2-15, the temperature-sensitive helical resistance winding is in the lower end of the metal stem, with which it is always in good thermal contact but from which it is electrically insulated. A separate Manganin winding in series with the sensitive winding is used to adjust the temperature resistance characteristic so that all bulbs are identical and interchangeable. Bulbs vary in size. A typical one is $3\frac{1}{2}$ in. long, $\frac{1}{4}$ in. in diameter, and an active portion of $1\frac{5}{8}$ in. in length. The windings terminate in a three-terminal insulated block, enclosed in a housing, or head, to which lead-wire connections are made. A threaded fitting is attached to the stem and head, to facilitate mounting the bulb in a wall or vessel. When the bulb must be protected from corrosive atmospheres or fluids, must withstand high pressure, or must often be removed from the process, it is mounted in a separable well or protection tube. Union connections connect the bulb to the well. The terminal housing has threaded connections on two ends for joining to the bulb stem and for lead-wire conduit connection. A screw cover speeds connecting the lead wires to the terminal block without removing the terminal housing from the conduit.

Q What features should resistance windings used in industrial resistance thermometer bulbs have? Why?
A (1) High temperature coefficient of resistance (the change per degree for a given value of resistance) for high sensitivity, (2) high resistivity (total resistance for a given length of wire) so that a high-resistance winding can be made in a small space, (3) stability over a long time and wide temperature ranges, (4) linear temperature-resistance relationship over wide ranges of temperatures and resistance, (5) ruggedness to withstand shock, vibration, and adjustment. Platinum (-258 to $+900°C$), copper (-200 to $+120°C$), and nickel (-150 to $+300°C$) windings are commonly used to meet these requirements. Tungsten and molybdenum elements have been used to $1500°C$.

Q Name a few configurations of resistance windings.
A (1) Space winding of bare wire over round insulating arbor; (2) insulated wire wound in smooth layers over ceramic, plastic, or metal arbor; (3) wire wound in small-diameter helix or coil which, in turn, is mounted on double-spiral grooves in the outer surface of a thin-walled insulated metal or ceramic tube or rod; and (4) woven-wire-mesh cloth. Common resistance values are 100 to 600 ohms for nickel bulbs at 100°F, 10 ohms for copper bulbs at 25°C, 25.5 ohms for laboratory platinum bulbs at 0°C.

Q What stem and protecting tube materials are used?
A Stainless steel, Monel, Inconel, bronze, brass, and copper. For high temperatures, glass, quartz, and silica stems are used.

Q How does lead-wire size vary with length and type of bridge measuring circuit?

A For lengths of 1,000 ft or less, 14-gage three-conductor insulated lead wire is used when connecting resistance bulbs to deflectional bridge instruments. For distances below 400 ft, 18-gage lead wire can be used. For lengths up to 1,500 ft, use 16-gage wire with balanced bridge instruments.

Q How does a balanced Wheatstone bridge resistance thermometer work?

A See Fig. 2-16. The resistance bulb, usually a coil of nickel or platinum wire, is hooked into opposite sides of the d-c measuring bridge

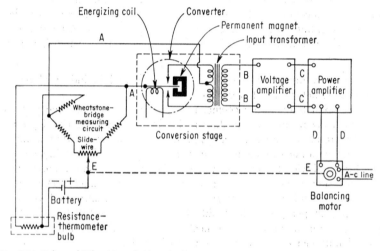

Fig. 2-16. Balanced Wheatstone bridge circuit.

circuit by two leads of equal resistance. A third lead fixes the bulb to the bridge battery (current supply), putting the other two leads in opposite arms. A variable resistance (slide-wire) is connected into the bridge circuit's other arm. When the bulb senses a temperature change its resistance changes and unbalances the bridge circuit. The self-balancing Wheatstone bridge spots the unbalance, its direction and magnitude, then moves the slide-wire contactor to rebalance the bridge. It also indicates or records the temperature on a scale or chart.

Q Five other types of balanced bridge circuits are used in resistance thermometry. Name them.

A (1) Collander, (2) Griffiths bridge, (3) double slide-wire bridge, (4) Mueller bridge, and (5) capacitance bridge.

Q How does a deflectional Wheatstone bridge resistance thermometer work?

A In the deflectional-type indicator (Fig. 2-13) points A, B, and C represent the bulb terminals, while D and E are ratio arms of equal resistance. P is a fixed resistance equal to the bulb's resistance at its highest reading on the temperature scale. X is a fixed resistance equal to the bulb's resistance at its lowest reading on the scale. The battery energizes the circuit, and RH is the rheostat for adjusting the battery current to the correct value. When the battery current is adjusted, the switch is thrown to standard to include X in the bridge circuit. The rheostat is then adjusted until the indicator deflects to the lowest temperature reading on the scale. After adjusting the current, the switch is thrown to the bulb position. The galvanometer pointer deflects to full scale on open circuit and to the proper temperature when the bulb is connected into the circuit and exposed to the measured medium.

Q Name six advantages of using resistance thermometers for temperature measurement.

A Resistance thermometers (1) have greater inherent accuracy than other temperature measuring methods, (2) can be used at greater distances from the point of measurement and recording than can the fluid-filled type of thermometer, (3) need no cold-junction reference compensation, (4) can be used in the room-temperature range where thermocouples are not dependable, (5) can measure lower temperatures than pressure-type thermometers, and (6) have a very rapid speed of response which is linear over its range.

Q What are some disadvantages of resistance thermometers?

A They are (1) relatively expensive, (2) more complex than filled thermal systems, and (3) more subject to damage from overranging than are thermocouples.

Q What are thermistors and how do they work?

A Thermistors are a variation of resistance thermometers gaining in use for industrial temperature measurements today. Whereas pure metals show an increase in resistance with temperature rise, solid semiconductors (oxides of iron, cobalt, copper, titanium, and manganese compressed into ceramic bodies) show a decrease in resistance with temperature rise, also a greater resistance change with a small temperature change. Wheatstone bridge measuring circuits are used with thermistors just as with resistance thermometers. The resistance-temperature relationship is fairly linear throughout the practical range of temperature measurement between -60 and $+400°C$. Spans as narrow as $1°C$ are practical.

Q Where are thermistors used today?
A To measure temperatures where small size is a factor in physiological applications, such as (1) intravenous blood thermometry, (2) industrial and military research applications, (3) surface temperature measurement by radiation techniques, (4) weather data, (5) automobile engine temperatures, (6) control of aircraft cabin temperatures, (7) electric cooking ranges, and (8) communication circuit temperature compensation.

Q In what forms are thermistors available?
A See Fig. 2-17. Thermistors are made in the form of beads as small as 0.015 in. diameter, disks 0.2 to 1.0 in. diameter, rods 0.03 to 0.25 in.

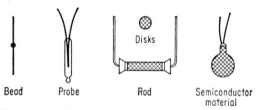

Bead   Probe   Rod   Semiconductor
                                                material

Fig. 2-17. Thermistors come in these forms.

diameter and up to 2.0 in. long, all with leads or pigtails embedded in the thermistor. They are mounted on probes, stacks, or in gas-filled bulbs. Physiological beads are often mounted in hypodermic needles or catheters.

Q What are six big advantages of thermistors?
A Thermistors (1) can be made and mounted in small sizes, (2) have high sensitivity and fast speed of response, (3) do not need lead-wire compensation, (4) have a narrow span, making long lead-wire lengths practical, (5) have low-temperature accuracy that approaches thermocouple accuracies, and (6) use a simple measuring circuit compared with thermocouples.

Q What are six limitations of thermistors?
A (1) Less stable, (2) less accurate and reproducible than resistance thermometers, (3) can change with use (but become more stable with age), (4) practical upper temperature limit is much less than with resistance thermometers and thermocouples, (5) less accurate in extremes of range, and (6) lack uniformity of calibration, thereby making interchangeability of probes impractical.

Q Describe a thermoelectric pyrometer.
A See Fig. 2-18. A thermoelectric pyrometer is a temperature measur-

ing system. It has a primary sensing element called a thermocouple, a millivolt measuring circuit called a millivoltmeter (or potentiometer), and connecting wires called thermocouple extension lead wires for attaching the thermocouple to the measuring instrument even when widely separated.

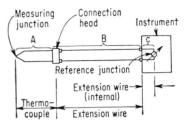

Q Name some typical thermoelectric pyrometer uses.

A Mostly used to measure (1) enclosure temperatures (vessels, pipes, compartments, furnaces, etc.), (2) material temperatures in an enclo-

Fig. 2-18. Thermoelectric pyrometer system measures temperature.

sure, (3) fluid stream temperatures, (4) surface temperatures (mostly for high temperatures and where high speed of response and accuracy are needed), (5) where point of measurement is some distance away, and (6) where a rugged, trouble-free system is important.

Q What is a thermocouple?
A See Fig. 2-19. A thermocouple is a temperature measuring device. It has two wires of dissimilar metals fused at one end (hot junction) and connected to a millivolt measuring circuit at the other (cold junction) by insulated lead wires. A thermocouple assembly is made up of

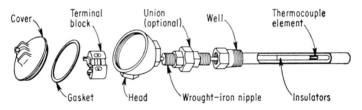

Fig. 2-19. Thermocouple assembly.

(*a*) the element, which is two dissimilar metals joined at one end with insulators to separate the wires electrically from each other and the protecting tube; (*b*) the terminal block, connected to the ends of the thermocouple (cold junction) and to the extension lead wire; (*c*) the terminal head for housing the terminal block and screw connections for protecting the tube and conduit. A gasketed screw cover (*d*) allows easy access for making connections, also protects the terminal block from the atmosphere; and (*e*) a protecting tube, or separable protecting well, for protecting the element from a harmful medium, from pressure, or if the element must be removed often without relieving the pressure. Various fittings are used to install the thermocouple at the point of measurement.

Q How does a thermocouple work?

A When the thermocouple's hot junction is exposed to a change in temperature, an electromotive force is developed (millivolts) proportional to the temperature change. The resultant electromotive force (emf) is measured on a millivoltmeter or potentiometer, then calibrated in degrees. The emf is dependent on (1) the difference in temperature between the hot and cold junctions of the single wires (called Thomson effect), and (2) the metallurgical composition of two dissimilar wires fused together at the hot junction (called Peltier effect). Since industrial thermocouple circuits have many junctions of many dissimilar metals (connectors, or terminals, extension lead wires, switches, compensators, etc.) all but *one* of the junctions must be maintained at a constant reference temperature, usually 32°F; then the net emf depends on the temperature of that one junction (usually the hot junction) only. Combinations of dissimilar metals are used in industrial thermocouples. Calibration curves using the reference temperature (32°F) as a base are

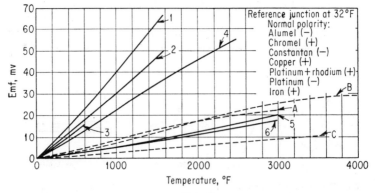

Fig. 2-20. Temperature emf thermocouple calibration curves. Tentative curves: A, rhenium-molybdenum; B, rhenium-tungsten; C, iridium–iridium rhodium. (1) Chromel-constantan; (2) iron-constantan (type J) (0.0290 mv per °F); (3) copper-constantan (type T) (0.0288 mv per °F); (4) Chromel-Alumel (type K) (0.0223 mv per °F); (5) platinum–platinum rhodium (type R) (0.0067 mv per °F); (6) platinum–platinum rhodium (type S) (0.0059 mv per °F).

produced, giving a table of temperature/emf values for each type of thermocouple. These curves (Fig. 2-20) deviate from a straight line over a wide temperature range, thus restricting their practical range to the curve's near-linear portions. Exact temperature/emf figures for each thermocouple are found in thermocouple manufacturers' conversion tables.

Q Describe a millivoltmeter pyrometer. How does it operate?

A A millivoltmeter pyrometer (Fig. 2-21, simple deflection-type pyrometer) is basically a d'Arsonval galvanometer connected to a thermocouple. A coil of wire, suspended by pivots and jeweled bearings, has a pointer attached and is surrounded by a magnetic field (from the permanent magnet and pole pieces). As temperature sensed by the thermocouple hot junction changes, a millivoltage is generated in the thermocouple. Current flows in the coil, thus setting up an opposing magnetic field. This action causes the coil to turn and the pointer to move across a scale. Hairsprings retard the movement of the coil and return the pointer to zero when there is no thermocouple current passing through the coil.

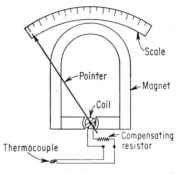

Fig. 2-21. Millivoltmeter pyrometer of the simple deflection type.

Q Describe an electronic null-balance, or continuous-balance, potentiometer pyrometer and how it operates.

A An electronic null-balance potentiometer (Fig. 2-22) measures and records temperatures by measuring the emf produced by a thermocouple,

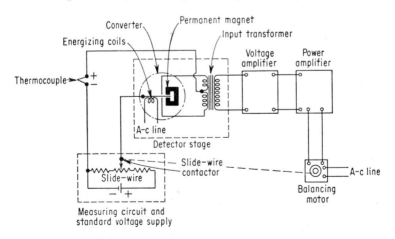

Fig. 2-22. Electric null-balance potentiometer.

or radiation pyrometer, hooked across its input terminals. It has a measuring circuit, current supply, detector, amplifier, balancing motor, and readout or recording section. The measuring circuit is basically a potentiometer, having a calibrated resistance slide-wire and a contact which moves along it. It has range-changing shunts, compensating resistors, and a means for range selection and suppression. Current supply, or constant emf source (usually a battery, standard cell, or zener diode constant voltage supply) is used as a reference, or standard known voltage. A thermocouple (unknown emf) is connected to the slide-wire circuit to oppose the standard reference voltage.

Current flows through the slide-wire only when the thermocouple voltage is different from the standard voltage. This difference, or unbalance voltage, is measured, or detected, by a converter, amplified in an electronic amplifier. The resultant power drives a reversible balancing motor (positions the slide-wire contactor to a balanced condition) and an

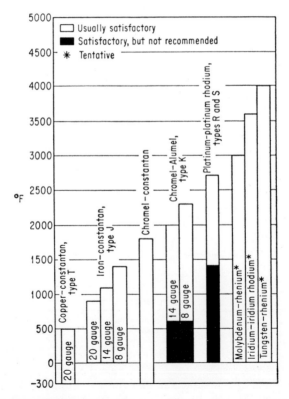

Fig. 2-23. Thermocouple temperature ranges.

indicator or pen to the correct temperature on the calibrated scale or chart. When no unbalance exists, there is no movement of the balancing motor, therefore no movement of the slide-wire contact or indicator or pen.

NOTE: See Chap. 8 for more details on recorders.

Q Conventional thermocouples are made of various base-metal and noble-metal element materials. Name these materials and the range of temperatures through which they operate.

A See Fig. 2-23. (1) Basic-metal thermocouples: (a) copper-constantan, −300 to +600°F; (b) iron-constantan, 0 to 1500°F (used intermittently to 1800°F); (c) Chromel-Alumel, 0 to 2000°F (intermittent service to 2300°F). (2) Noble-metal thermocouples: (a) platinum-platinum, 10 per cent rhodium, 0 to 2800°F (but not below 500°F); (b) molybdenum-rhenium, iridium–iridium rhodium, and tungsten-rhenium have been calibrated to ranges between 0 and 3000 to 4000°F.

Q What sizes of element wire are used? Why?

A Thermocouples are made from gage wire as small as 28 gage. For fast response and sensitivity, sizes are about 20 gage. But small-gage thermocouples are delicate and cannot respond to as high a temperature as the heavier-gage equivalent. Heavy-gage thermocouples (8-gage) are for higher temperatures and jobs where ruggedness and long life are needed. But they are slow in response, need more space, and are less sensitive at low temperatures.

Q What are the limits of error for conventional industrial thermocouples?

A See Table 2-1.

Q Name the eight types of thermocouples used in instrumentation systems. What atmospheric conditions can each withstand?

A (1) Copper-constantan thermocouples have high resistance to corrosion from atmospheric moisture or moisture condensation. Good for either oxidizing or reducing atmospheres. (2) Iron-constantan thermocouples, where there is little free oxygen. Heavier gages are used above 1000°F. (3) Chromel-constantan thermocouples, mostly for oxidizing atmospheres, not subject to corrosion in subzero temperatures. (4) Chromel-Alumel thermocouples for between 1000 and 2000°F in oxidizing atmospheres. (5) Platinum–platinum-rhodium thermocouples for oxidizing atmospheres having free oxygen (but easily contaminated in any other atmospheres). (6) Molybdenum-rhenium thermocouples for reducing and inert atmospheres or vacuum. (7) Iridium–iridium-rhodium thermocouples for oxidizing and inert atmospheres or vacuum. (8) Tung-

Table 2-1. Limits of Error for Commonly Used Thermocouples

Type	Thermocouples			Extension wires		
	Temperature range, °F	Limits of error		Temperature range, °F	Limits of error, °F	
		Standard	Special		Standard	Special
Copper-constantan	−300 to −75 −150 to −75 −75 to +200 200 to 700	..... ±2% ±1½°F ±¾%	±1% ±1% ±¾°F ±⅜%	−75 to +200	±1½	±¾
Iron-constantan	0 to 530 530 to 1400	±4°F ±¾%	±2°F ±⅜%	0 to 400	±4	±2
Chromel-Alumel	0 to 530 530 to 2300	±4°F ±¾%	....	0 to 400	±6	
Platinum–rhodium platinum	0 to 1000 1000 to 2700	±5°F ±0.5%	....	75 to 400	±12	

sten-rhenium thermocouples for reducing and inert atmospheres or vacuum (never for free oxygen).

Q If none of the above thermocouple characteristics is suitable for given atmospheric conditions, what steps would you take?

A Use the thermocouple most suitable for such temperature and atmospheric conditions. But insert in a protecting tube, or well, to prevent oxidation, corrosion, erosion, or contamination of the thermocouple. Special wells are made to withstand erosion and very high pressures. Use protection wells when thermocouples are to be withdrawn often from the process.

Q What are some typical protecting-tube characteristics?

A (1) High thermal conductivity resistance to reducing and oxidizing atmospheres and gases, (2) resistance to high temperatures and thermal shock, (3) resistance to erosion and corrosion from high velocity and corrosive fluids, (4) resistance against damage from mechanical shock and strain, (5) withstand high pressures and have low porosity to prevent gas leakage. Carbon steel, wrought and cast iron, stainless steel, Resisteat, nickel, Inconel, Kanthal, quartz, firebrick, mullite, Sillramic, silica, and beryllium oxide are just a few of the metal, ceramic, and metal-ceramic protecting tubes on the market. Manufacturers furnish characteristics and application data.

Q What physical forms are used in protecting tubes and wells?
A Closed-end metal and ceramic, open-end metal and ceramic, high pressure and velocity, short and deep immersion, pot and angle type, and double protecting tubes are used.

Q Name some typical thermocouple assemblies and their applications.
A See Fig. 2-24. (1) Straight assembly, for most common applications.

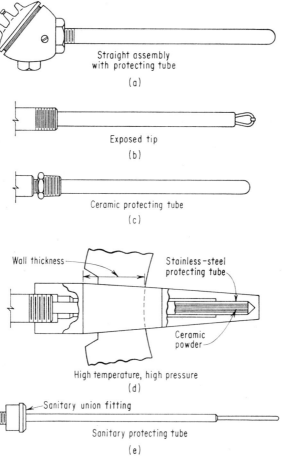

Straight assembly
with protecting tube
(a)

Exposed tip
(b)

Ceramic protecting tube
(c)

Wall thickness

Stainless-steel
protecting tube

Ceramic
powder

High temperature, high pressure
(d)

Sanitary union fitting

Sanitary protecting tube
(e)

Fig. 2-24. Typical thermocouple assemblies.

(2) Bare thermocouple, for rapid response and high sensitivity in non-corrosive atmospheres. (3) Exposed tip, for rapid response and rigidity.

(4) Pipe extended ceramic tube, for high temperatures. (5) Double protecting tubes, for high temperatures, and to protect the primary tube from breakage, corrosive atmospheres, and thermal shock. (6) Angle and bent thermocouples, for certain process vessels and furnaces. (7) Spring-loaded assemblies, for high speed and sensitive temperature measurement. (8) High-pressure high-velocity assemblies, for injection molding. (9) Lead covered, for pickling tanks. There are also assemblies for sanitary jobs, for molten-metal pot assemblies, portable assemblies for molten aluminum and steel, button-type assembly for surface temperatures, etc.

Q What factors affect the speed of response and sensitivity of a thermocouple?

A The mass of a thermocouple assembly (the hot junction and protecting tube). The thermocouple responds fastest when the protecting tube has the smallest outside diameter and thinnest wall thickness. Also when the hot junction's mass is reduced (a butt-weld junction). Metal-to-metal contact with the protecting tube's bottom improves heat transfer.

Q Why is thermocouple extension lead wire used instead of ordinary copper lead wire to connect the thermocouple to its measuring instrument?

A Lead wire of the same thermoelectric characteristics as the thermocouple is used. Ordinary copper lead wire would act as an additional thermocouple and change with temperature, thus adding a false emf into the circuit. That would cause an error in temperature reading. Lead wires of noble metal are not used with noble thermocouples because of the expense. Other wires of similar properties are substituted. Sizes of 14 and 16 gage are often used. Size is not too important unless millivoltmeter galvanometer-type indicators or recorders are used. Then lead-wire resistance should be kept to a minimum. Potentiometers are not affected by lead-wire size.

Q What are typical properties and characteristics of thermocouple lead wire?

A Thermocouple lead wire is usually furnished as matched pairs of iron-constantan, copper-constantan, Chromel-Alumel, iron-alloy, and copper-alloy materials. Insulations of polyvinyl plastic are used for chemicals, acids, hydrocarbons; asbestos-covered for high temperatures (200 to 400°F); lead-covered for certain corrosive acids; rubber-jacketed for waterproofing and resistance to certain chemicals. Each lead-wire combination is color-coded for easy identification.

Q List the limits of error for thermocouple extension lead wire.

A (1) Iron-constantan in the range 0 to 400°F, error of ±4°F for standard, ±2°F for special; (2) copper-constantan of −75 to +200°F, ±1.5°F for standard, ±0.75°F for special; (3) Chromel-Alumel of 0 to 400°F, ±6°F for standard; (4) copper alloy of 75 to 400°F, ±12°F for standard.

Q What factors must every instrument technician consider in selecting a thermocouple assembly and extension lead wire?
A (1) Thermocouple material used depends upon (a) temperature range, (b) maximum and minimum temperatures, (c) accuracy, (d) sensitivity, (e) speed of response, (f) atmosphere, and (g) measuring instrument used. (2) Type of protecting tube, well, or assembly configuration and material depends upon (a) the measured medium, (b) its container or enclosure, (c) space availability, (d) the atmosphere, (e) pressure and velocity conditions, (f) requirement for frequent removal of thermocouple element, and (g) any special installation needs. (3) Type of extension lead wire depends upon (a) the type of thermocouple, (b) distance, and (c) atmospheric conditions between the thermocouple and the measuring instrument.

Q What do's and don't's must every instrument technician know when installing a thermocouple assembly and extension lead wire?
A Thermocouple: (1) Select carefully both the location and depth of immersion in the process to avoid stagnant areas not representative of the temperature. (2) Consider the advantage of several thermocouples connected in parallel to give an average temperature reading. (3) Avoid direct flame impingement on the protecting tube as it reduces life and gives a false temperature reading. (4) Immerse the thermocouple in the measured medium deep enough to cut down on heat transfer along the protecting tube connection to the head (ten times the outside diameter of the tube is minimum immersion, except where immersed in high-velocity fluids). This distance can be reduced to cut down on tube erosion. (5) The protecting tube or well must extend far enough beyond the outer surface of the vessel or pipeline to bring the connecting head to near ambient temperature. (6) Prevent sagging of the tube when measuring high temperatures by installing the thermocouple vertically if possible. (7) When making thermocouples, clean wire's free ends thoroughly. Then check for correct polarity before inserting into the connecting terminal block.

Extension wire: (1) Use only the recommended type of extension wire for a given type of thermocouple. (2) Check the color coding of each wire and connect the negative wire to the negative terminal, the positive wire to the positive terminal on the terminal block. (3) Avoid splicing wire. If you must splice, solder and tape the joint. (4) Install wires in a conduit where possible and ground the conduit well to prevent electrical leakage from power installations. (5) Never run extension wires parallel to, or across, any line of 115 volts or more within a foot of the line. (6) Never run other electrical wires in the same conduit with extension wires. (7) Select the proper type of insulation to suit the installation conditions.

Q   What are standard thermocouple wire insulations and what temperatures do they withstand?
A   There are many types of insulated thermocouple wire to cover the temperature range from −190 to +2000°F. These insulations protect the wire from temperature, chemical action, abrasion, and moisture. There are tables showing correct insulation for most applications. Special insulation is engineered for unusual problems.

Q   *Cold junction* and *cold-junction compensation* are important. Why?
A   Each thermocouple has two junctions. The *hot junction* contacts the temperature being measured. The *cold junction*, or reference junction, is the free end of the thermocouple, or thermocouple extension lead wires, connected to the measuring instrument. Since the instrument measures the millivoltage generated by the temperature difference between the measuring and reference junctions, it is important (1) to maintain the reference junction at a constant temperature, and (2) that the measuring instrument be automatically and accurately compensated for temperature changes at this junction. When the reference junction is near the thermocouple, copper lead wire can be used between it and the measuring instrument (if the reference junction is kept at a constant temperature). This can be done by a temperature-controlled oven-type cold-junction system or an ice-bath type. In the temperature-controlled oven type, the cold-junction thermocouples are kept at a constant temperature, around 150°F. Hot-junction measurements are made relative to this 150°F, not 32°F. Accuracies are nominally ±1 to ±5°F. The ice-bath type uses a vacuum bottle as the "oven" while the control is the melting point of ice, 32°F. The cold-junction thermocouples are inserted in a test tube having 1 in. of mercury and surrounded by cracked melting ice. Accuracies are ±1°F, between 32 to 34°F. When the reference junction is in the measuring instrument, automatic cold-junction compensation is done with a wound copper coil. In a null-balance-type potentiometer, the electrical resistance characteristics of this coil change with temperature, directly in the measuring circuit. A bimetal spiral attached to the hairspring mounting in a deflection-type pyrometer does the reference junction compensation.

Q   How would you measure the temperature differential between two separated points?

A Figure 2-25 shows a practical way to measure the temperature differential between points T_1 and T_2. Similar thermocouples C and D are connected with the same thermocouple extension lead wire so the electromotive forces developed *oppose* each other. When a temperature calibrated millivolt measuring circuit is connected at E, it will measure the millivoltage equivalent to the temperature difference between T_1 and T_2.

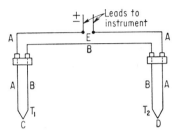

Fig. 2-25. Method of measuring differential temperatures.

Q Describe two methods often used to measure the average temperatures in large ducts or apparatus.

A Figure 2-26 shows two examples where the outputs of several thermocouples can be connected in series or parallel circuits to obtain an average temperature. In the parallel hookup, the emf developed at E is the average of the three thermocouples' output if they are measuring temperatures over the linear sections of the tempera-

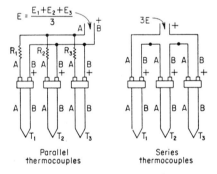

Fig. 2-26. Measurement of average temperatures with parallel and series thermocouples.

ture, or emf curves. Swamping, or equalizing, resistors R_1, R_2, and R_3 are needed in each thermocouple circuit to equalize the unequal resistance effect of circulating currents in each thermocouple when T_1, T_2, and T_3 are unequal. R_1, R_2, and R_3 are made high in comparison with the change of resistance in each thermocouple. Parallel connection of thermocouples for average temperature measurements has the advantage of using the same calibration as a single thermocouple. But, if a thermocouple burns out, it cannot be quickly detected.

In series connection, the emf developed at E is about three times that developed by one thermocouple. In this arrangement the measuring instrument does the averaging. When a null-balance potentiometer is used to measure the emf, the resistance in each branch does not have to be equalized. But the extension wires from each thermocouple must reach back to the reference junction in the instrument. If one thermocouple burns out, it is immediately detected since the emf at E disappears. The advantage of a series circuit is that it produces a greater emf output or more sensitivity when very small temperature changes are to be measured, or when the output of thermopiles (used in a radiation pyrometer) is to be measured. When using either parallel or series averaging circuits, be sure to avoid grounded measuring junctions unless an isolated or "true" differential input amplifier is used ahead of the measuring instrument.

Q Name three ways to transmit thermocouple signals from the point of measurement to a receiving indicator, recorder, or other readout system over distances not practical with thermocouple extension lead wire.

A Thermocouple signals are transmitted great distances by feeding into a millivolt measuring circuit (usually a potentiometer), which in turn actuates the transmitter. It uses (1) filtered air as a transmitting medium to distances of 2,000 ft, (2) continuous d-c (4 to 20 ma) or a-c (1 to 5 ma) electrical signals up to 10 miles, or (3) impulses over an impulse-type electrical system on commercial telephone lines as far as 100 miles.

Q Describe a thermocouple transmitter which transmits a d-c signal over two conductors.

A See Fig. 2-27. This type of temperature transmitter will transmit the output of any thermocouple or radiation pyrometer up to 10 miles over

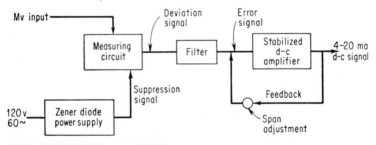

Fig. 2-27. Thermocouple electric transmitter.

two-conductor copper cable by transducing it to a 4- to 20-ma d-c signal. This d-c signal can be received by an indicating or recording milliampere measuring circuit, or by the input circuitry of a logger, scanner, or computer. The thermocouple output is connected into the measuring bridge circuit. Here the unbalance or error signal from the temperature change is compared with a standard reference suppression voltage from a zener diode constant-voltage supply. The deviation between the input signal and the suppression voltage is sent through a filter network to filter out a-c stray pickup. At this point a feedback signal fed through the span adjustment from the stabilized d-c amplifier output is subtracted from the filtered deviation signal, producing a resultant error signal. The error signal is fed into the stabilized d-c amplifier where a d-c milliampere output signal is developed for transmitting the millivolt (mv) or resistance input signal to the receiver over a two-conductor transmission system.

Q What are six advantages of thermocouples?
A (1) Relatively inexpensive, (2) accurate as compared with filled thermal systems and bimetallic types, (3) have high speed of response, (4) no practical limit to distances over which it can be connected to measuring instrument, (5) electrical output is convenient for connecting to many readout, logging, or computing systems, and (6) have wide operating range.

Q Name five thermocouple limitations.
A (1) Cold-junction compensation is needed, (2) needs a more expensive and complex measuring instrument than filled thermal systems or bimetallic thermometers, (3) response is not linear, (4) special extension lead wire is required, and (5) thermocouples deteriorate from contamination, corrosion, and erosion.

Q What is radiation pyrometry?
A The measurement of the temperature of an object by determining the quantity and characteristics of the radiant energy it emits. It makes practical use of the Stefan-Boltzmann law of radiant energy. This law states that the intensity of radiant energy emitted from the surface of a "black body" increases in proportion to the fourth power of the body's absolute temperature. A so-called "black body" radiates the maximum amount of heat energy for a given temperature, making it the reference or ideal condition for total radiation.

Black-body conditions do not usually exist in industrial applications. Instead, *non-black-body* conditions exist if the non-black body radiates less than the total radiation of a black body. Then an emittance correction factor must be applied to the measurement. An emittance correction factor is the ratio of the radiant energy emitted by a non-black body to that emitted by a black body at the same temperature. A black body has an emissivity factor of 1; non-black-body emissivity is always less than 1. These factors are applied as correction factors in calibrating the measuring instrument, usually by an adjustment on a calibrating rheostat.

Q   Describe a radiation pyrometer. How does it work?

A   See Fig. 2-28. A radiation pyrometer converts total radiant energy (not light) into electrical energy. This energy is calibrated to represent the temperature of the radiant body. The pyrometer's detector has a lens

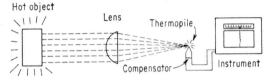

Fig. 2-28. Radiation pyrometers sighting into hot furnace.

which focuses the radiant energy emitted from the hot object to be measured, onto a thermopile (a number of small thermocouples in series in a circular pattern). The thermopile absorbs the radiant energy impinging upon it, thus increasing the temperature of the thermopile. This generates an electromotive force and a d-c millivolt output directly proportional to the radiant-body temperature. This temperature can be measured on a millivoltmeter or potentiometer measuring instrument.

Q   What effect do target distance and target size have on the radiation pyrometer output?

A   See Fig. 2-29. The output signal is independent of the distance to the target if the optical system field of view is completely filled by the

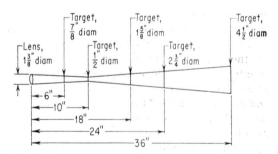

Fig. 2-29. Minimum target size is a function of distance to the target.

target. The minimum target size is a function of the distance to the target. Target size is expressed in terms of the diameter of an equivalent circle in a plane that is normal to the pyrometer's line of sight. Beyond certain minimum distances for each type of pyrometer, the relationship is a constant. This constant is expressed by the **distance factor** (the ratio of target distance to minimum target diameter, usually 70:1). Radiation pyrometers are made for a variety of target sizes, line-of-sight shapes, and target distances for specialized uses. When measuring under non-black-body conditions, restrict the sighting angle to a viewing at 45° or less from the perpendicular.

Q   What lens materials are used in the radiation pyrometer?
A   (1) Pyrex, (2) fused silica, and (3) calcium fluoride lenses are used since each transmits a different wavelength of radiant energy. Each is best for specific conditions. Pyrex glass has an upper limit of 2.7 microns and is for the high-temperature range. Because it is hard it can withstand shock, acid pitting, and etching. Pyrex is also used for filtering out higher-wavelength radiation reflected from water vapor and carbon dioxide, which would cause false readings. Fused silica is used for the very high temperature ranges, for intermediate ranges, and for small targets. Calcium fluoride is best for low-temperature ranges.

Q   What is the function of an auxiliary sighting lens?
A   This lens is in focus with the thermopile. It is a handy way to inspect a well-defined magnified image of both the thermopile and the target sighted upon.

Q   What is a safety shutter for a radiation pyrometer?
A   A fully automatic device mounted on the front of the radiation pyrometer. The shutter protects the lens against flame impingement.

Q   What method is used to compensate for ambient temperature variations around the thermopile?
A   Since the amount of radiant energy absorbed by the thermopile is dependent on the ambient (room) temperature as well as the target temperature, you must compensate the detector for changes in ambient temperature. This is done by connecting a nickel coil as a variable electrical shunt across the thermopile. As the ambient temperature varies, the resistance of the nickel coil varies, increasing or decreasing the head's emf output. This results in accurate compensation over the entire measuring range of the instrument.

Q   Name five ideal uses for radiation pyrometers.
A   (1) Where the surface temperature of hot objects within a furnace or process or of moving objects is desired, especially where the temperature sensing device cannot be in contact with the object. (2) Where temperatures are too high for thermocouples. (3) Where furnace atmospheres are harmful to thermocouples and cause false measurement and short life. Examples are hydrogen atmospheres in copper brazing and

bright annealing furnaces. (4) Where it is impractical to contact the material being measured. (5) Where thermocouples can't be used because of vibration, shock, or impractical mounting conditions.

Q   What temperature ranges do radiation pyrometers measure?
A   Ranges of 125 to 700°F, 200 to 1200°F, 800 to 2300°F, 1000 to 3200°F, and temperatures up to 7000°F can be measured. These pyrometers can respond to 98 per cent of the temperature change in 1 to 2 sec.

Q   How is the radiation pyrometer lens protected from direct flame impingement, heat damage, and smoke in the line of sight?
A   See Fig. 2-30. While the radiation pyrometer lens can be sighted directly onto the target, a closed-end target tube (either air-cooled or

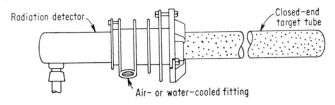

Fig. 2-30. Silicon carbide tube protects lens from flame impingement.

water-cooled) should protect it from flame impingement and heat damage to the lens and prevent dirt and smoke from obscuring the lens.

Q   What nine factors must be considered in selecting and installing a radiation detector?
A   (1) Target temperature and temperature of surrounding objects. (2) Target size. (3) Target distance from detector lens. (4) Target emittance and reflectance as well as the ability of the target to transmit the radiant energy it gives off. (5) Type of enclosure surrounding the heated object. If in the open, the percentage of heat emitted. (6) Sighting path and presence of smoke, vapors, and gases. (7) Sighting angle in a non-black-body application. (8) Ambient conditions of temperature and dirt. (9) Target speed, and whether stationary or moving.

Q   Name four advantages of radiation pyrometers.
A   (1) Highest upper temperature limit of any continuous measurement industrial temperature element (7000°F). (2) High speed of response. (3) No deterioration of element from corrosion, contamination, erosion, or metallurgical changes. (4) Can measure temperatures of objects without making physical contact.

Q What are four limitations of radiation pyrometers?

A (1) Must be calibrated in place, (2) need protection or sighting tubes when furnace atmospheres interfere with the line of sight, (3) radiation pyrometers are more expensive than other temperature measuring elements, and (4) it must "see" the temperature it is measuring.

SUGGESTED READING

Recommended Practices, sold by Instrument Society of America, 530 William Penn Place, Pittsburgh, Pa.

ISA—RP 1.1–.7, *Thermocouples and Thermocouple Extension Wires,* 31 pages

Books

Baker, H. D., and E. A. Ryder: *Temperature Measurement in Engineering,* John Wiley & Sons, Inc., New York, 1953.

Elonka, Steve, and Joseph F. Robinson: *Standard Plant Operator's Questions and Answers,* vols. I and II, McGraw-Hill Book Company, Inc., New York, 1959.

Elonka, Steve: *Plant Operators' Manual,* McGraw-Hill Book Company, Inc., New York, 1956.

Elonka, Steve, and Julian Bernstein: *Standard Industrial Electronics Questions and Answers,* vols. I and II, McGraw-Hill Book Company, Inc., New York, to be published in 1964.

3

FLOW MEASURING SYSTEMS

Q   What is flow?

A   Flow is fluid in motion. Fluids include liquids, air, gases, and steam.

Q   What basic principles must you know when measuring fluid flow rate?

A   When the energy state of a fluid is changed from a static condition (fluid at rest—potential energy, in the form of pressure head) to a moving condition (fluid in motion—kinetic energy, in the form of velocity) it is a flowing fluid. A force is needed to change this energy state. The force is usually applied by a pump or by creating a static head of fluid above its normal horizontal level. The force due to pressure on the liquid's surface is equal to the pressure times the surface area. The pressure in a fluid stream is least when the stream velocity is greatest and greatest where the velocity is least (Bernoulli's principle).

The velocity of a liquid flowing from an opening in the bottom of a tank can be expressed by Torricelli's theorem, which states that the velocity is equal to the square root of the product of two times the gravitational constant times the height of liquid times its density. The fundamental flow equation was developed from these basic concepts. It states that the quantity of flow is equal to a constant (made up of many related factors) times the square root of the pressure drop across a restriction in the flow line. Two types of flow in a pipe are (1) laminar flow and (2) turbulent flow. Laminar flow is streamlined (viscous flow) and occurs at low velocities. The velocity of the fluid is greatest along the pipe axis, decreasing sharply to zero at the pipe wall. As the velocity is increased the fluid motion becomes irregularly random and is called turbulent flow. As liquid increases in temperature it flows more easily, but as gas increases in temperature it tends to flow more slowly. This characteristic of flow readiness is called viscosity. The nature of flow depends on (1) pipe diameter, (2) density, (3) viscosity of flowing fluid, and (4) flow velocity. The numerical value of a dimensionless combination of these four variables is called the Reynolds number. Laminar flow is defined in terms of Reynolds numbers below 2,000. Turbulent flow has Reynolds numbers above 4,000.

Fluid flowing in pipes and ducts always drops in pressure along the pipe in the direction of flow. The drop is from friction between the fluid particles and the pipe. There are two basic fluid flow rate measurements: (1) Volume flow rate, where volume per time is expressed in units such as cubic feet per minute (air and gas), gallons per minute (liquids), barrels per hour (petroleum products), and pounds per hour (steam). Each of these measurements is made assuming that such factors as the fluid specific gravity, density, viscosity, temperature, barometric pressure, and supercompressibility remain constant. (2) Mass flow rate, where mass, or quantity, per time is expressed in such units as standard cubic feet per minute, tons per day, etc. Mass flow measurements are made taking the variation of all other factors into consideration with the volume flow rate measurement, either directly with the flow measuring device, or by continuously measuring and compensating for them.

Q Where are flowmeters used to measure fluid flow rates in plants and processes?

A Flowmeters are used for measuring flow rates of process product streams, plant steam, gaseous and liquid fuels, and process water. These measurements are made in pipes, air ducts, and open channels. Flow rate is one of the most important measurements in plants and processes.

Q Why is flow rate measurement important?

A Because fluid flow rate measurements establish proper ratios of process materials for production quality control. They also determine distribution of materials for cost control. Flowmetering is important in the control of stream pollution from industrial and municipal wastes, and also in municipal water plants.

Q Classify the five basic types of flowmeters.

A (1) Head flowmeters, (2) area flowmeters, (3) mass flowmeters, (4) positive-displacement flowmeters, and (5) flowmeters for flows in open channels.

Q On what principle does a head flowmeter work?

A See Fig. 3-1. A head flowmeter operates on the principle of a differential pressure created across a restriction in the flow line for each rate of flow. The restriction causes an increase in velocity, resulting in pressure drop which produces a differential pressure. The rate of flow in the flow line is directly proportional to the square root of this pressure differential.

Q   Describe a head flowmeter.

A   As Fig. 3-2 shows, the head flowmeter has a primary element which is the restriction in the flow line to produce a differential pressure (or head), a secondary element (called a manometer) which when connected

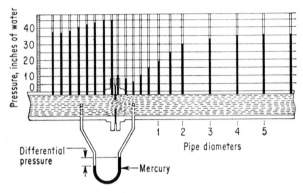

Fig. 3-1. Head flowmeter measures differential pressure.

to the primary element measures the differential pressure for determining the volume flow rate, and piping for connecting the primary element to the secondary element. The secondary element can be directly hooked to an indicator, recorder, or controller. Or it can be used as a flow rate transmitter. Head flowmeters are the most popular type.

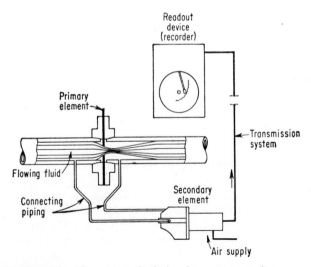

Fig. 3-2. Head flowmeter with manometer hooked up for constant recording.

Q   Name four types of head flowmeter primary elements.
A   (1) Orifice plate, (2) flow nozzle, (3) venturi tube, and (4) pitot tube.

Q   Describe three types of orifice plates.
A   The most commonly used orifice is a thin-plate square-edge concentric type (Fig. 3-3). Eccentric and segmental thin plates are also used. In the concentric type, the opening, or hole through which the fluid flows, is round and concentric to the center line of the pipe. Its edge is at 90° to the upstream flat face of the orifice. The circular bore in an eccentric orifice is tangent to the pipe's bottom. The base of the segmental orifice plate is a circular segment of the internal pipe diameter.

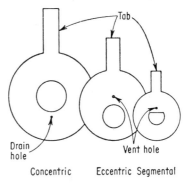

Fig. 3-3. Orifices come in three standard types.

All three types are usually used for pipe sizes from 1½ to 14 in. All three come in thicknesses of ⅟₁₆, ⅛, and ¼ in. Plate thickness at the orifice edge must not exceed one-thirtieth of the pipe inside diameter or one-eighth of the orifice base. If the thickness exceeds these figures, bevel the downstream edge to an angle of 45° or less to the plate's face. The upstream edge must be sharp and square to assure flow measurement accuracy. Concentric orifice plates for steam flow have a ⅟₁₆-in. hole drilled near the lower inside pipe wall for condensate drainage. Eccentric and segmental orifice plates have a small vent hole close to the upper inside pipe wall. The vent is for passage of gas usually associated with liquid flow. Orifice plates have a tab or holder for easier installation or removal. A calculation number is stamped on this tab. Orifice plates are made from rigid materials which will not change dimensions with use. Materials are stainless steel, Monel, and phosphor bronze.

Q   What are the applications for (1) concentric, (2) eccentric, and (3) segmental orifice plates?
A   (1) Concentric orifice plates are for any steady flow of clean homogeneous fluid (liquid, gas, steam, or air) which is in the normal turbulent flow region with Reynolds numbers of 500 or greater, liquids having a viscosity up to 300 SSU at 15°C, and for most gases and vapors. (2) Eccentric orifice plates are for steady flow of fluids containing some heavy material (such as sand or solids) that may build up against a

concentric orifice. Here place the bore near the bottom inside pipe wall. But if the fluid has floating solids or gases, place the base near the top inside pipe wall. (3) Segmental orifice plates are for fluids containing suspended solids. Here low, temporary, and permanent pressure drops are desirable at the cost of accuracy when a high orifice ratio is used. Segmental orifice plates also come in adjustable form, similar to a gate valve.

Q   What is a quadrant (quarter circle) orifice plate and why is it used?

A   A quadrant orifice plate (Fig. 3-4) is a new design using a rounded edge of definite radius which is a particular function of the orifice diameter. It is used to measure flows of high-viscosity fluids with Reynolds numbers between 300 and 25,000.

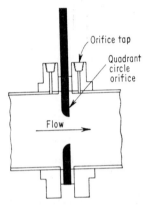

Fig. 3-4. Quadrant circle orifice plate and tap locations, welded-type flange.

Q   What factors must you consider when installing orifice plates in flow lines?

A   (1) Design of orifice flanges which position the orifice in the pipe, (2) orifice taps (tapped holes) through which the differential pressure measurement is made in the pipe and to which the secondary element piping connection is attached, (3) orifice location in the pipe configuration and straight-run requirements, and (4) effects of turbulent flow and straightening vanes for reducing these effects.

Q   Name and describe four types of orifice flanges.

A   Screw type or threaded flanges are screwed onto the pipe's end, then tack-welded. The orifice plate sandwiched in a pair of metal gaskets is placed between the flanges; then the flanges are bolted together for a pressuretight connection. Piping connections are then made through the flanges (flange taps), or directly into the pipe. Vena contracta, slip-on-type flanges are slipped over the pipe and welded at the flange's inside face and neck. The orifice plate and gaskets are held between the flanges as in the screw type. The welded-neck type butts against and is welded to the pipe's end, forming part of the meter run. Welded neck, or screw flanges, also have a ring gasket (usually soft iron). Here there is a groove in the flange face within which the gasket seats when the orifice is bolted into place. This is the ring type. Van Stone flanges, or lap-joint flanges, are used for high-pressure measurement, usually with pipe or vena contracta taps. The flange nipple is lapped on the flange's inside face and ground smooth, providing a seat for the gasket. The nipple's other end is welded to the pipe for easy or frequent removal. Use removable orifice fittings.

Q Name and describe three commonly used types of orifice taps.
A See Fig. 3-5. (1) Flange, (2) vena contracta, and (3) pipe taps.

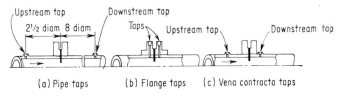

(a) Pipe taps   (b) Flange taps   (c) Vena contracta taps

Fig. 3-5. Three types of commonly used orifice taps.

Taps are in the pipe wall at a definite distance from the orifice plate. Holes are usually ¼ in. diameter through which the differential pressure is transmitted. Flange taps (*b*) are in the orifice pipe flanges at about 1 in. from the orifice plate, regardless of pipe size. The high-pressure connection is made upstream from the orifice plate, low-pressure tap downstream. Flange taps are accurately placed by the flange manufacturer. This feature eliminates errors inherent in other pipe taps. You don't have to recalculate if the orifice size is changed.

Vena contracta taps (*c*) are placed one pipe diameter upstream and at the point of lowest pressure (the vena contracta) downstream of the upstream orifice face. This feature gives the maximum pressure differential for a given flow. A tap is most accurate and inexpensive when properly installed. But this type is most ticklish to install properly and expensive if the orifice size must be changed often. Pipe taps (*a*) are usually located 2½ pipe diameters upstream and 8 pipe diameters downstream from the orifice plate. You must tap or weld pipe taps into the pipe accurately, with care, and with no protrusions or rough edges. Radius, corner, and elbow taps are sometimes used for special conditions. Select tap locations (all orifice taps) around the pipe to ensure that the flowing fluid always fills the piping and that sediment, entrained air or gas, and solids will not enter the taps.

Q Must you give careful consideration when locating the orifice plate in the pipe configuration?
A Yes, flow measurement accuracy is greatly affected by (1) the location of the orifice plate in relationship to the straight run of pipe up- and downstream from it, and (2) location of fittings such as valves, branch lines, elbows, curves, and bends. Each orifice flow measurement application requires a particular safe minimum straight run of pipe up- and downstream from the orifice. Other points are too varied to illus-

trate here, but detail requirements and recommended practice can be found in manufacturers' flow engineering handbooks and ASME, AGA, and ISA *Recommended Practices.*

Q How can you improve flow measuring accuracy when recommended practices for straight pipe run cannot be followed or turbulent flow is encountered?

A If all other methods have been tried, insert straightening vanes (Fig. 3-6) in the pipe upstream from the orifice plate. Take care to install straightening vanes securely to prevent the vanes from loosening and destroying expensive equipment. Tubular-type vanes are usually used on steam and liquids, fin-type on gases. Spool types are easy to install, inspect, and replace.

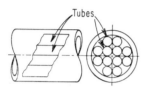

Fig. 3-6. Straightening vane bundle is welded to inside of pipe.

Q What factors must you consider when making head flowmeter calculations?

A To calculate proper primary element size, such as orifice plate bore dimensions with given flow conditions, or flow conditions from a given orifice size for specific head flowmeter installations, working equations with empirical constants are used. A factor called orifice ratio is used rather than orifice bore in the tables for determining (1) equivalent maximum flow, (2) permanent pressure loss, (3) straight pipe run requirements, (4) orifice tap location requirements, and (5) range differential factors. Flowmeter manufacturers have tables providing the needed constants and relationships for approximating orifice ratios and other installation factors without going through complex calculations. (Note—see flow engineering handbooks.) Three steps will help you make these approximations:

1. Orifice ratio, or beta ratio, d/D is the ratio of the orifice bore diameter d to the inside pipe diameter D. It is found by converting maximum flow into an *equivalent* maximum flow. The orifice ratio corresponding to this equivalent maximum flow in a given pipe size is found in a table.

2. An important factor needed to find the equivalent maximum flow is the differential range factor. This factor is a characteristic of differential pressure measuring devices (secondary elements) used with the primary elements. It is directly related to differential pressure range. Each secondary element is available in many different ranges (inches of water or inches of mercury); each range has a different range factor. Selection of range factor depends on minimum static pressure recommended, maximum static pressure upstream of the orifice available, and the possibility of changing the meter capacity. Try to select a range factor (and differ-

ential pressure range) which allows for increasing or decreasing the meter capacity without changing the orifice plate, but rather changing the range tube or bellows adjustment.

3. A percentage of the temporary differential pressure drop across the orifice restriction is never regained. Its value changes with the orifice ratio and is determined from a table. The amount of permanent pressure loss varies with the type of primary element and types of orifice taps. With an orifice plate, the permanent pressure loss varies between 50 and 90 per cent of the pressure differential for orifice ratios between 0.70 and 0.20.

Q Determining the orifice ratio for steam flow requires what specific factors?
A For steam flow, (1) maximum steam flow rate (lb per hour), (2) operating pressure (psig), (3) degrees superheat (°F), (4) pipe size and weight are known conditions. The range differential (inches of water) is selected and the range factor determined; the correction factor for steam condition (pressure and superheat) is determined from a table. These factors are substituted in the formula

$$\text{Equivalent flow (lb per hour)} = \frac{\text{required flow (lb per hour)}}{\text{steam condition} \times \text{range factor}}$$

Check the resultant equivalent flow in another table to determine the orifice ratio. For most accurate flow measurement, keep the orifice ratio below 0.75 to 0.80.

Q What factors are important to find the orifice ratio for water flow?
A For water flow, (1) maximum water flow rate (gph at operating pressure psi), (2) operating temperature (°F), (3) pipe size and weight are known conditions. To measure incompressible fluids, the relationship between differential and static pressures is not critical. But follow standard recommendations for this relationship to ensure low permanent pressure loss. With this in mind and allowing for changes in meter capacity, select the range differential and factor. Substitute these factors in the formula

$$\text{Equivalent flow (gph)} = \frac{\text{required flow (gph)}}{\text{range factor}}$$

The orifice ratio and equivalent flow figure can be determined from the table.

Q Finding the orifice ratio for gas or air flow involves what specific factors?
A For gas flow, (1) maximum rate of flow (cfh at operating pressure

and temperature), (2) operating pressure (psig), (3) specific gravity (referred to air), (4) operating temperature (°F), (5) pipe size and weight (inches), (6) condition of gas (dry or saturated). Substitute in the formula

$$\text{Equivalent flow (cfh)} = \frac{\text{required flow (cfh)}}{\text{operating factor} \times \text{range factor}}$$

The gas flow operating factor is determined from a double interpolation in a table which provides the operating factor from specific gravity, operating pressure, and operating temperature. Presume that conditions remain constant during measurement. Important in gas flows is that maximum pressure differentials (inches of water) do not exceed operating pressure (psig). With proper values inserted in the gas flow approximation formula, you can solve for equivalent flow and orifice ratio from data in the table.

Q Determining the orifice ratio for oil flows requires what specific factors?

A For oil flow, (1) maximum rate of flow (gph)—if given in barrels (bbl) per day, 42 gal per bbl, (2) operating pressure (psi), (3) specific gravity at 60°F, (4) operating temperature (°F), (5) pipe size and weight (inches) are known factors. Substitute in the formula

$$\text{Equivalent flow (gph)} = \frac{\text{required flow (gph)}}{\text{specific gravity factor} \times \text{range factor}}$$

The specific gravity factor is determined from a table, using specific gravity at 60°F and the operating temperature. Then find the orifice ratio in the same way as in preceding questions.

Q What piping connections are needed between the primary element and secondary element of head flowmeters?

A The arrangement of piping between primary elements, such as orifice plates from taps, and the secondary element (a differential pressure measuring device) is so important because most flow measurement errors occur because of faulty piping. Piping or tubing should be large enough to be self-draining (copper tubing minimum ½ in. outside diameter) and should slope at least 2 in. per ft of horizontal run. Connections should not leak, and the tubing runs must be smooth without peaks or valleys and kept filled with liquid from all fluids except air and gas. Materials should resist corrosive atmospheres. Use seal chambers if the measured fluids might corrode the secondary element or corrode, clog, or vaporize in the connection lines. Use a liquid, gas, or air purge system where metered fluid must be kept from the connection lines. Vapor traps are needed on liquid service at high points in the connecting pip-

·ing. In each connection line on steam and condensable vapor flows, use condensing chambers adjacent to the orifice plate to provide an equal liquid head. Three types of valve-manifold assemblies provide shutoff facilities around the secondary element and thus speed installation and maintenance. Figures 3-7, 3-8, and 3-9 show typical piping arrangements for gas, steam, and water in horizontal and vertical flow lines.

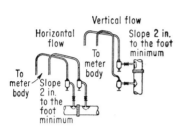

Fig. 3-7. Gas piping arrangements.   Fig. 3-8. Steam piping arrangements.

Q Name five advantages of orifice plates.
A (1) Low cost, (2) need little space, (3) complete and accurate data available for computing flow rate, (4) easily interchanged, (5) come also in adjustable orifice.

Q What are four big disadvantages of orifice plates?
A (1) Low efficiency (greater permanent pressure loss than other devices), (2) poor accuracy on high orifice ratios above 0.75, (3) subject to wear (not very strong), and (4) obstruct flow of dirt or sediment.

Q Name three types of flow nozzles or flow tubes. Describe one type.
A (1) Flow nozzle, (2) Gentile flow tube, and (3) Dall flow tube.

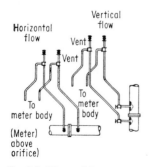

Fig. 3-9. Water piping arrangements.

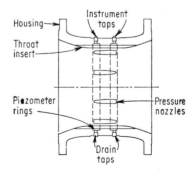

Fig. 3-10. Gentile flow tube has two groups of pressure nozzles.

Flow tubes and nozzles are primary elements inserted directly in flow lines to measure the differential pressure developed by their restriction to flow (Fig. 3-10). A flow tube has a short spool piece, the inner periphery of which has two groups of pressure nozzles. One group is directed upstream, the other downstream. Nozzle groups are interconnected by common pressure rings from which standard pipe taps are connected. Piping assemblies similar to those used for orifice plates connect the flow tube to a secondary element.

Q Where are flow tubes used? Why?

A Flow tubes are best for fluids having moderate amounts of solids in suspension. Gentile and Dall tubes are best for clean fluids, gases, or liquids with solids, for lowest head loss. Because they present less obstruction to flow, solids do not build up in the throat section. Flow tubes are made of steel, stainless steel, or Monel. The throat is made of bronze and stainless steel. Both flow tubes and nozzles are used to measure high-velocity flows (usually water and steam) beyond the capacity of an orifice. These need less straight run of pipe.

Q Compare the performance of a flow tube with that of an orifice.

A The flow tube, or nozzle, will handle 60 per cent more flow than an orifice plate under the same conditions. Its permanent pressure loss will vary from 30 to 90 per cent of the differential pressure, depending on the diameter ratio. Flow tubes can handle higher-velocity flows than orifices because they can handle greater flows for the same pipe size. Flow tubes are made for pipe sizes as large as 60 in.

Q List the factors for flow tube flow calculations.

A Flow approximations can be made using the same flow information factors, and formulas, as used for orifice flow calculations. The exception is that a factor of 1.6 should be inserted in the denominator to recognize the 60 per cent greater capacity of the flow tubes. Get calibration tables, range factors, and coefficients from flow tube manufacturers.

Q What are the four important advantages of flow tubes and nozzles?

A (1) Good efficiency, less permanent pressure loss than orifice plates, but more than venturi tubes, (2) higher capacity than orifice, effective on high-velocity flow, good accuracy at higher orifice ratios, (3) needs less space than a venturi tube and needs a minimum straight pipe run, and (4) has good resistance to wear.

Q Name two disadvantages of flow tubes.

A (1) Higher cost than orifice plates, and (2) empirical data are not definitive or complete.

Q Describe a venturi tube.

A See Fig. 3-11. A venturi tube is another type of pressure differential producing head meter primary element for flowmetering in pipes. A venturi tube combines into a single unit a throat or constricted portion between two tapered sections. Three parts are made of one or more sections fitting between flanges of the pipe. The entrance cone and throat have about the same characteristics as a nozzle, while the discharge cone recovers most of the temporary pressure drop. The high-pressure tap is through the piezometer ring. The low-pressure tap is through the throat. Design is varied for fluids with suspended material, and for special applications. Some designs have handholes for cleanout facilities. A streamlined entrance and exit eliminate pockets in which solids can be trapped. Venturis are made of bronze, stainless steel, and cast iron. You can coat or line the inside of a venturi with rubber, cement, or plastics to give erosion and corrosion resisting properties. There is a venturi insert which is smaller and less expensive than the standard venturi tube. Sizes as large as 72 to 84 in. in diameter and 40 ft in length are not uncommon. Piping connections to the secondary element from venturi tubes are similar to those from orifice plates and flow tubes.

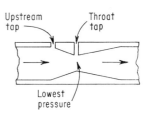

Fig. 3-11. Venturi tube also measures flow.

Q Where should you use venturi tubes?

A (1) Where measured fluid contains large amounts of suspended solids, (2) where its favorable pressure recovery characteristics justify high expense, and (3) where maximum accuracy is desired to measure highly viscous fluids. Common uses are for pulp, stock flow, where there are crystals in liquor, sewage flow, and for many water flow measurements.

Q Compare the performance of a venturi tube with that of an orifice plate.

A As with the flow tube, the venturi tube handles 60 per cent more flow than an orifice plate. Its permanent pressure loss is only 10 to 20 per cent of the differential pressure. As in all flow measuring devices, abrasive fluids affect flow measurement accuracy. Published coefficients are accurate to plus or minus 0.75 per cent over orifice ratios from 0.30 to 0.75.

Q What factors pertain to flow calculations for venturi tubes?

A You can make flow approximations with the same factors, flow information, and formulas used for flow tubes. But venturi manufacturers are responsible for correct dimensions, machining, and recommended straight pipe runs. Hydraulic laboratory tests are often made for each venturi tube to ensure accurate flow measurement.

Q What are four significant venturi tube advantages?
A (1) High efficiency, high differential pressure recovery; (2) high accuracy, the most accurate primary element, especially at high orifice ratios (above 0.75); (3) resistance to abrasion and trapping dirt or sediment; and (4) overall best element for very large liquid flows and big pipelines.

Q What are the three main disadvantages of venturi tubes?
A (1) Very expensive, (2) large and awkward size, (3) difficult to change once installed.

Q Describe a pitot tube.
A A pitot tube (Fig. 3-12) is another differential pressure measuring primary element used for measuring flow. It measures the difference between the static pressure and the total of static and velocity head at the same point in a flow stream. Most pitot tubes are built for various special purposes, or to make their insertion into pipes or ducts through pressuretight glands. A pitot tube has two pressure passages; one faces into the flowing fluid, giving the high-velocity or impact point reacting to total pressure (static and kinetic). The other passage is perpendicular to the axis of flow and reacts to the low or static pressure only. The pitot tube enters the flow line through a pressuretight gland which allows moving the tube across the flow-line cross section. Differential pressure can be connected to a secondary element through an ordinary tubing connection. Pitot tubes are brass or stainless steel.

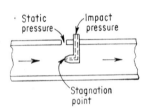

Fig. 3-12. Pitot tube with independent static tap.

Q Where are pitot tubes used?
A Pitot tubes are mainly used for temporary tests where (1) a rough measurement is acceptable, (2) the fluid is clean, (3) the line is large and the velocity high, and (4) size and expense of an orifice plate prohibit its use. Uses are mostly for large air or gas flows and velocity surveys in ducts, especially in air conditioning and aerodynamic studies. Calibration is normally made during installation.

Q What are some limitations of pitot tubes?
A Foreign material (dirt, sediment, or solids) clogs the tube and causes

faulty measurement. This makes continuous measurement without frequent cleaning unreliable. Accurate flow measurement is difficult with pitot tubes.

Q Name five types of head flowmeter secondary elements used in plants and processes.

A (1) Mercury float-type manometers, (2) bell-type meters, (3) mercuryless bellows meters, (4) mercuryless force-balance-type meters and (5) weight-balance, or ring-balance meters.

Q Describe a mercury float-type manometer. How does it work?

A See Fig. 3-13. This type of head flowmeter secondary element is
used for flow rate measurements in
plants and processes more than any
other type. It has two forged steel
chambers connected at the bottom
by a mercury-filled U tube. The high-
pressure tap is hooked to a chamber
where a steel float on the mercury
detects its level. Another chamber is
connected to the low-pressure tap.
This chamber has a range tube whose
size can be varied by substitution, to
change the meter's differential pressure range. As the differential pressure goes up, the mercury is forced
from the float chamber into the
range tube chamber, thus moving
the float from top to bottom. Float
motion is transferred through a pressuretight bearing shaft, to a lever,
then to a pointer or pen arm for
indicating or recording the flow rate
on a square-root-graduated scale or
chart (divisions are close together
near zero and farther apart at full
range). Float motion can be me-

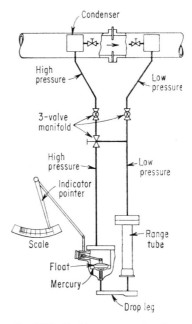

Fig. 3-13. Float-type manometer flow-meter uses mercury.

chanically, pneumatically, or electrically transmitted to the pen arm or
pointer. When the differential pressure range of a U-tube manometer
must be changed, you must also substitute a different range tube. Each
range tube has a specific amount of mercury. A three-valve manifold with
two shutoff valves and an equalizing valve usually comes as a part of the
manometer. These make installation and servicing easier.

Q What are the performance specifications of mercury float-type manometers?

A Pressure differential ranges of 20 to 400 in. of water at maximum static pressures of 5,000 psig are often met. You can have low ranges between 1 and 10 in. of water at about 150 psig by using a low-pressure bell-type manometer. A flow range of $3\frac{1}{2}$ to 1 can be covered on a mercury manometer. You can measure wide range flows by combining a high-range and a low-range meter operating continuously, and connected to the same orifice. Range tubes often provide increases in flow range in increments of about 25 per cent and accuracies of 2 to 5 per cent on flow rates for the upper 75 per cent of the range. Accuracy is less in the low 25 per cent.

Q Where are mercury float-type manometers used?

A To measure, indicate, record, transmit, and control general-purpose plant and process fluid flows in pipelines. They are the workhorse of all the flowmeters. But mercuryless and magnetic-type secondary flowmeter elements are increasing in use today.

Q What type of mercury meter body is needed to measure reverse flows?

A For reverse flow jobs, use what is known as a "dropped range tube." This measures the differential pressure in proportion to maximum flow in one direction to zero flow to maximum flow in the reverse direction. Charts and scales come with zero in the center.

Q Since mercury float-type manometers respond to the differential pressure of the flowing media across a restriction in the line (so that the flow rate is directly proportional to the square root of the differential), how can an evenly graduated scale or chart be used?

A You can obtain an evenly graduated chart, or a linear relationship, by shaping one leg in the U-tube meter body, by using (1) a Ledoux bell construction, or (2) a square root extraction cam in the recorder. Evenly graduated charts are very useful for flow accounting jobs.

Q Describe a Ledoux bell, evenly graduated meter body. How does it work?

A A Ledoux bell (Fig. 3-14) is a meter body so shaped that it responds to a change in differential pressure by giving a linear motion directly proportional to the flow rate. The meter body is a pressure chamber containing the characterized bell which floats in mercury. Low pressure is applied to the bell's inside and high pressure to the outside. Mercury is the seal between the two pressures. As the differential pressure varies the bell moves up and down. Its motion may be transmitted electrically to a recording pen or indicator by the movement of an armature attached to it in an inductance bridge transmission circuit. Direct linkage through a pressuretight bearing on the pen arm is also used.

The record chart, or scale indication, is linear and evenly graduated. Different-sized bells are used for different ranges.

Q Where are Ledoux bell meters used?
A The evenly graduated response to flow-rate characteristics of the Ledoux bell meter makes it very convenient for measuring plant steam, water, fuels, and air. Process flow lines are also measured where an accurate accounting of flow rate is needed.

Q List the typical performance characteristic of Ledoux bell flowmeters.
A Ledoux bell flowmeters have differential ranges from 0 to 50 in., up to 0 to 212 in. of water up to 1,500 psig. Accuracies of flow rates are about 2 per cent of full range over the upper 80 per cent of the range. Speed of response is sometimes expressed as 2 sec for 63.2 per cent of full range change. A flow range of 4 to 1 can be covered by bell flowmeters.

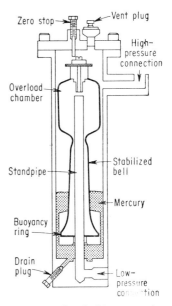

Fig. 3-14. Ledoux bell flowmeter also uses mercury.

Q Name two types of mercuryless head flowmeter secondary elements. Why are they growing so rapidly for use in plant and process flow measurements?
A (1) Bellows type and (2) force-balance diaphragm type. These mercuryless head flowmeters are replacing mercury head flowmeters. They do away with the bother associated with mercury, the need of changing range tubes, and the lack of enough overrange protection.

Q Describe a mercuryless bellows head flowmeter. How does it work?
A The bellows meter body (Fig. 3-15) converts differential pressure changes (through a dual bellows design) into motion to work a flow indicator, recorder, controller, or transmitter. It has a steel (or stainless steel) pressure body with high- and low-pressure connections, two stainless-steel measuring bellows (filled with a sealing liquid) connected by a stabilizing spring, a range spring assembly, and a motion-transmitting torque tube. Differential pressure connections are made to high- and low-pressure taps. As the differential pressure increases, the liquid-filled high-

pressure bellows compresses. This forces its liquid fill through a rectangular orifice into the low-pressure bellows, until the bellows position
balance is reached. When the bellows move, a connecting rod and
torque tube assembly move a corresponding amount, carrying this motion
outside of the meter body to the instrument or transmitter it operates.
Shaft position is thus directly proportional to differential pressure. The

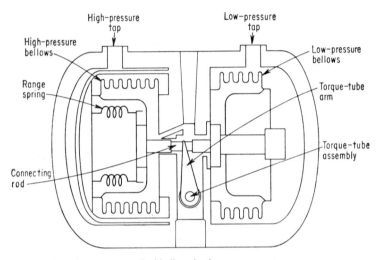

Fig. 3-15. Bellows flowmeter uses dual bellows hookup.

range spring determines how far the bellows move for a given differential
pressure. There are different range springs for each differential range.
Bellows meters give positive overload protection up to full line pressure.
Three-valve manifolds and simplified piping assemblies are used with
bellows meters for connecting to the primary element.

Q What are typical bellows meter performance characteristics?
A Differential ranges can be measured from 0 to 20 in. of water to
0 to 400 in. of water with unevenly (square root) graduated charts and
scales with maximum static pressures of 2,500 psig. Remember that
bellows meters have a calibrated accuracy of ±0.5 per cent of full scale.
They are not affected by static pressure and temperature variations over
a range between −90 and +250°F. The meter will respond in 1 to 2
sec to 63 per cent of a full-scale differential change. Sensitivity is within
±0.05 per cent of full scale.

Q Name the five advantages of bellows-type head flowmeters compared
with the mercury manometer type.

A (1) No mercury needed. This saves money and eliminates mercury contamination from blowouts and the inconvenience of handling mercury on range changes. (2) More accurate. (3) Easier to install. Simple piping assemblies, no wiring or power supply required. (4) Needs little maintenance. (5) Insensitive to vibration and pulsation.

Q Describe a mercuryless force-balance diaphragm-type head flowmeter pneumatic transmitter. How does it work?

A See Fig. 3-16. This unit measures differential pressure and transmits this measurement pneumatically to a flow receiver (indicator, recorder, controller). It does this job by using a balance principle similar to an ordinary beam balance. The meter body converts the difference between the high and low pressure connected to it into a force which acts on one end of the beam. This compares with force of an unknown weight on one scale pan of a balance, while known calibrated weights are added to the other scale pan until the unknown weight is balanced and the scale arm is level. Then a pneumatic balance system in the transmitter develops an opposing force (due to air pressure) to exactly balance the force caused by the differential pressure in the meter body. Output air pressure from the transmitter is directly proportional to the measured differential pressure and is transmitted directly in terms of flow or

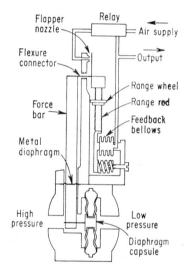

Fig. 3-16. Force-balance diaphragm-type pneumatic flow transmitter flow tube.

differential pressure to a pneumatic receiver. No mercury is needed. There is very little motion, and nearly zero displacement.

In a typical example of a force-balance flow transmitter, the differential pressure is applied at the high- and low-pressure sides of a diaphragm capsule. This is held between the two pressure chambers. Change in pressure causes the capsule to exert force on the lower end of a force bar. This force is balanced through a simple lever system consisting of (1) force bar, (2) range bar, and (3) flexure connectors. Metal diaphragms attached to the force bar and the range wheel act as fulcrums. Force exerted by the capsule is opposed through this lever system by the feedback bellows. Now to convert the minute motion of the force bar into a suitable pneumatic signal, a flapper is attached to the force bar so that it moves against a nozzle, changing the air pressure behind it. This flapper-nozzle combination compares the measured forces developed at the diaphragm capsule with forces exerted by the feedback bellows. Air pressure from the air supply relay connected to the feedback bellows maintains balance between the two forces. Any change in differential pressure across the capsule produces a tiny movement of the flapper. This movement causes a change of output pressure at the relay, and a simultaneous balancing action at the feedback bellows.

The meter differential pressure range is continuously adjustable by positioning the range wheel along the range rod. Zero adjustment is also continuously adjustable. The meter body material is stainless steel. Diaphragm materials are stainless steel, Viton-A on glass cloth, Teflon on glass cloth, or Buna N. Simplified piping connections are used and standard recommended practices apply. Condensate "pots," seals, and purges are not needed.

Q   Can force-balance diaphragm-type flowmeter transmitters transmit their flow signals electrically, as well as pneumatically?
A   Yes. These transmitters are designed to transmit a low-level electrical signal over a two-conductor cable to distant receivers and controllers.

Q   Where are force-balance diaphragm flowmeter transmitters used?
A   Chief use is as a general-purpose fluid flowmeter secondary element for plant and process uses where flow rate is transmitted from the point of measurement to a centrally located readout and control panel. Using this type of meter is efficient because it is simple and small and works well in hazardous and corrosive atmospheres.

Q   Name the performance characteristics of a typical force-balance diaphragm flow transmitter.
A   Differential pressure ranges are continuous and adjustable from 0 to 20 in. of water to 0 to 1,000 in. of water, with static pressures as high as 1,500 psi. Accuracy is ±1 per cent of full differential range. Process fluids temperatures can be as high as 350°F and ambient temperatures around the transmitter as high as 250°F. The meter will respond in less than 1 sec to 63 per cent of a full-scale differential pressure change.

Q   List the seven advantages of a force-balance diaphragm-type head flowmeter.
A   (1) High speed of response, (2) easy installation and piping, (3) small size, (4) no mercury needed, (5) easy maintenance, (6) easy range change, and (7) insensitive to vibration.

Q   Describe a ring-balance-type head flowmeter secondary element. How does it work?

A   A ring-balance flowmeter (Fig. 3-17), also called a radial torque-meter, uses a hollow ring body to convert the differential pressure meas-ured across the primary flow element into a rotational movement. The ring body is mounted on a knife-edge bearing, thus permitting rotation about the axis of the ring. The ring is divided into two pressure compartments by a baffle at the top, and by sealing liquid (usually mercury) which fills the ring's lower part. Two ring com-partments are connected to the pressure taps by a flexible piping assembly which permits free rotation as the differential pressure changes. Ring rotation movement is transmitted to an indicator, recording pen, or transmitter assembly through a cam and linkage. Cam contour permits a linear response to flow rate by extracting

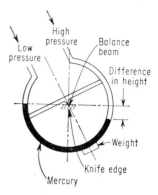

Fig. 3-17. Ring-balance-type head flowmeter secondary element.

the square-root function of the differential pressure measurement. Then an evenly graduated chart or scale may be used as readout. Ring torque is a function of the differential pressure acting on the baffle. Torque is resisted by a leaf-spring system above the ring. Thus the meter is in equilibrium when ring torque is balanced by spring force.

Q   What are the performance characteristics of typical ring-balance flowmeters?

A   Typical differential ranges for low ranges are from 0.5 to 20 in. of water at a working pressure of 75 psig, for high ranges, 20 to 140 in. of water at 15,000 psig working pressures. When two or three rings are placed in series, ranges up to 560 in. of water are obtainable. Basic dif-ferential ranges are obtained by varying the ring cross-sectional area and the specific gravity of the sealing liquid. Range changes within these basic ranges are made by a calibration adjustment. Sensitivity of 1 part in 1,000 is common.

Q   What are the three major applications for ring-balance-type flow-meters?

A   (1) Boiler and furnace flow measurements (steam, gas, air, and feedwater flows), (2) liquid flow measurements, and (3) air flow meas-urements in test cells.

Q   What factors affect the accuracy of head flowmeters?

A   The more common factors are: (1) Faulty orifice plate installation (reversing bevel, off center, rounded base edge, accumulation of sediment or dirt on upstream face, warped plate, wire edge). (2) Errors from orifice taps due to projecting nipple beyond inside pipe wall, burrs from drilling and tapping, flash or icicle from welding flanges plugging nipples. (3) Faulty installation of piping assemblies. These are off-level condensate traps, dirt in the lines, leaks, connecting tubing peaks and valleys that collect condensate or trap gas, improper configuration which differs from recommended practice for specific fluids. (4) Meter body troubles arise from dirt in range tube, dirty mercury, improper zero adjustment. (5) Excessive purge rates, pipe roughness, turbulent or pulsating flow, not enough straight run of pipe, incorrect internal pipe diameter, and thermocouple well or pipe fittings protruding in the flow stream near the primary element.

Q   Name five advantages of head flowmeters.
A   (1) Direct reading in volume rate of flow; (2) square root calibration very good for automatic control uses; (3) adaptable for remote transmission, recording, indicating, and totalizing readout devices; (4) low cost; and (5) easy to operate, install, and maintain.

Q   In what major category of flowmeters is flow measurement directly proportional linear to orifice area rather than proportional to the square root of differential pressure as in orifice flowmeters?
A   Area flowmeters. Here the flow rate is inferred from the change in area of an orifice in the flow line across which the pressure differential is constant.

Q   Name two types of area flowmeters.
A   (1) Rotameters and (2) cylinder and piston types.

Q   Describe a rotameter. How does it work?
A   Figure 3-18 shows that a rotameter has a weighted plummet or float inside a tapered tube. This tube has screwed or flanged pipe connections for mounting in a vertical position directly in the fluid flow line. The small end is down, through which the fluid flows from bottom to top. Annular clearance between the plummet and the varying diameter inside the tube is a variable-area orifice. The plummet reaches an equilibrium position proportional to flow rate when the upward force of the fluid passing through the annular orifice equals the downward force of the plummet. Flow rate may be read directly from the plummet position in the fluid against an evenly graduated scale on the tube or attached to it. Plummet motion may also be transferred through an extension-rod linkage to actuate an indicator pointer, a recording pen arm, or a pneumatic or electric inductance bridge transmitter-receiver system.

Rotameter tubes are made from borosilicate glass and various metals such as stainless steel. Plummets are made of the harder, corrosion-resistant metals such as stainless steel, Hastelloy, Monel, and nickel in several differential shapes and flow characteristics.

Float extension rods are made in various lengths, depending on readout device. Direct reading scales are usually 2-, 5-, 10-, and 24-in. lengths. Typical rotameter sizes range from ⅟₁₆-in. pipe to special designs for 24- and 36-in. pipe sizes.

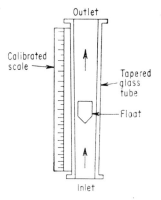

Fig. 3-18. Rotameter has a float inside tapered tube.

Q What are typical rotameter performance characteristics?

A A rotameter can measure water flows from as little as 0.08 cu cm per min to over 6,000 gpm. Heavy-walled glass tubes can withstand over 500 psig and temperatures of 200°F for small sizes. Some metal-tube types can withstand as high as 10,000 psig and temperatures of 1000°F. Accuracies are ±1 to 2 per cent of instantaneous flow reading over ranges of 10 to 1. This means that flows as low as 10 per cent of full-scale range can be measured accurately. Permanent pressure loss through rotameters is practically constant and can be kept to a low figure.

Q What are the five major uses of rotameters?

A (1) Measurement and metering of small and special flows in purging and blending systems, (2) frequent on-off service, (3) measurement of fluid flows having a variety of high densities, viscosities, and volatility, (4) fluid streams subject to freezing or congealing, and (5) for measuring flow rates of acids and corrosive fluids or slurries.

Q What steps must you consider in selecting and sizing a rotameter?

A Manufacturers of rotameters provide capacity tables and conversion tables for selecting and sizing rotameters. Steps to follow are: (1) Select a meter tube, float type, and material for the needed flow conditions and readout requirements. (2) Determine the maximum flow rate needed, and select a meter range to allow for an increase of 100 per cent, or decrease of 20 per cent without changing the rotameter. (3) Select the applicable conversion equation and change the desired maximum flow to an equivalent flow for liquid on which the capacity table is based. (4) Determine the correct capacity table and select the proper tube taper, float shape, and weight, considering viscosity effects. (5) Meter factor, pressure loss, and viscosity effects can then be determined from a formula. You can change flow rate capacity by varying the float weight and shape. Effects of viscosity can be compensated by changing the float shape; effects of density are compensated by a change in float weight (or material).

Q How is a rotameter mounted in the flow line?

A As Fig. 3-19 shows, a rotameter is always mounted vertically with the outlet (downstream) connections at the top of the meter and the

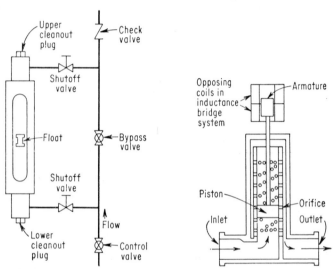

Fig. 3-19. When mounting, rotameter must be vertical.

Fig. 3-20. Area flowmeter of the
cylinder and piston type.

inlet (upstream) connections at the bottom. The highest scale gradua-tions and the largest part of the metering tube are at the top. Flow accuracies of rotameters are usually independent of upstream piping fittings such as elbows and control valves if no closer than five pipe diameters upstream. Connecting horizontally allows using vertical plug connections as cleanout ports. The check and bypass valving shown is needed around a rotameter for installing and servicing.

Q Name seven advantages of rotameters.

A (1) Wide linear flow range of 10 to 1, (2) flexibility for all types of fluids and simplicity of piping assemblies, (3) excellent and accurate for very small flows, (4) constant and small permanent pressure drop, (5) easy cleaning and maintenance, (6) almost unaffected by viscosity effects, and (7) low cost in pipe sizes below 6 in.

Q What are three limitations of rotameters?

A (1) High cost in large sizes, (2) accuracy is affected by dirt, needing frequent cleaning, and (3) accuracy is affected when the meter tube is not installed normal to the flow axis.

Q Describe a cylinder and piston-type area flowmeter. How does it work?

A A piston-type area flowmeter (Fig. 3-20) has a sleeve held rigidly in a cast-iron or steel body, and a fitted piston (or metering plug). The meter body is mounted vertically in the flow line with flange connections. The flowing fluid enters the meter body horizontally, is deflected against the floating piston, and then passes through an orifice opposite the inlet. The orifice is rectangular in shape and fixed on the bottom and sides. The top of the orifice is formed by the piston, which moves up and down, thus varying the orifice size. A bypass leads from the low-pressure side of the meter to the top of the piston so that its pressure is always the same as that on the downstream side of the orifice.

The piston moves up and down to uncover the orifice enough to maintain a constant differential pressure between the up- and downstream sides of the orifice. Piston movement is therefore directly proportional (linear) to the flow through the meter body. Piston movement is limited by either weights or a spring. An adjustment of this loading changes the capacity of the meter within certain limits. Piston-type meters come in 1-, 2-, and 4-in. pipe sizes and a variety of flow capacities. This type of area flowmeter usually is read out on an evenly graduated indicator or recorder, which has an induction-bridge-type electric receiver. The meter body is a transmitter which transmits the flow measurement in terms of piston motion across a three-conductor a-c electrical inductance bridge circuit. The meter body may have a steam jacket for maintaining highly viscous fluids at a flowing temperature.

Q What are the performance characteristics of piston-type area flowmeters?

A Piston area flowmeters are used to measure liquid flows in ranges of 0 to 270 gpm (water) to as high as 13,800 gpm at pressures up to 600 psi and temperatures up to 600°F. Meters can be paralleled for higher flow rates. Pressure drops are as great as 2 psi for the heaviest piston. Capacity varies with specific gravity and viscosity. Accuracies are of 1 to 2 per cent.

Q Where are piston-type area flowmeters used?

A For water, kerosene, gasoline, oils, tars, chemicals, refrigerants, and many corrosive chemicals.

Q What are the piping and installation requirements for piston-type area flowmeters?

A Piston-type meter bodies are installed directly in the flow line in a vertical position. The flow line is supported to prevent sagging, and a strainer upstream of the meter prevents dirt from clogging the orifice. There should be a minimum of 20 pipe diameter of straight pipe run upstream, and at least 5 diameters downstream of the meter body.

Q What are three advantages of piston-type area flowmeters?

A (1) Ease of installation, (2) measures corrosive fluids, and (3) measures high-viscosity fluids, fuel oils, and tars.

Q Name a major category of flowmeters using positive-displacement methods to measure total flow quantity.

A These are known as positive-displacement flowmeters. There are six major types: (1) nutating disk, or piston, (2) rotary vane, (3) sealed-drum, (4) lobe-impeller, (5) bellows meter, and (6) reciprocating piston meters. All these meters measure volume of flow and register the total flow volume.

Q Where are positive-displacement flowmeters used?

A Positive-displacement flowmeters are usually used for metering liquids and gases in plants and chemical processes. They are well suited to their purpose, and widely used, because they are very accurate, simple, have small pressure loss, and can be shut off positively after a desired quantity has been metered.

Q How does a nutating-disk-type positive-displacement meter measure?

A As Fig. 3-21 shows, this meter has a nutating (wobbling in rotation) disk pivoted in the center of a circular wedge-shaped measuring chamber. Liquid enters through the inlet connection on one side of the meter and leaves through an outlet on the other side while completely filling the spaces above and below the disk. The advancing volume of liquid moves the disk in a nutating motion around a center pivot, until the liquid discharges through the outlet port. Since the disk fits tightly in the measuring chamber, its nutations are a direct measure of the volume passing through the meter. A pin attached at the disk's pivot point on one end and to a counter gear train on the other actuates the counter register as the disk rotates, giving a reading of total quantity of flow through the meter. The meter is usually made of cast iron with a carbon-steel or brass disk. For corrosive liquids, materials of bronze, aluminum, or Monel are used. A 4-in. pipe size is about the largest meter size.

Q What is the chief use of nutating-disk flowmeters?

A This positive-displacement type is the most widely used flowmeter.

Its chief use is for domestic water service because it is simple, low-cost, and compact. This meter is also used for fluids (fuel oil) under high temperature and pressures.

Q   What are the performance characteristics of typical nutating-disk meters?

A   Flows from about 1 to 375 gpm can be measured to an accuracy of ±1 per cent in pipe sizes from ½ to 4 in. Pressures as high as 1,000 psig are common.

Q   Describe briefly a rotary-vane positive-displacement meter, its operation and major use.

A   In a rotary-vane meter (Fig. 3-22) the meter body is shaped like a closed drum, with a shaft carrying a smaller rotor arranged to rotate in-

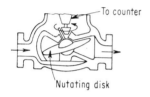

Fig. 3-21. Nutating-disk-type positive-displacement meter.

Fig. 3-22. Rotary vane positive-displacement meter.

side the meter body. This shaft is mounted eccentrically in relation to the center of the meter chamber. The rotor usually holds four spring-loaded sliding vanes between it and the cylinder wall. Liquid entering the measuring chamber builds up pressure against vane 1, causing the rotor to turn. As vane 1 is moved by the liquid, it seals off the inlet port. As the rotor turns on its shaft, vane 2 moves into the position formerly occupied by vane 1. Between vanes 1 and 2 is a definite volume of liquid. Vanes move around the measuring chamber until the liquid between vane 1 and 2 is discharged through the outlet port. Then the process repeats without pulsations. A counter register is attached to the shaft of the rotor so that flow volume is directly proportional to shaft rotation. Rotary-vane meters are used chiefly for metering liquids. Accuracy is ±0.3 per cent.

Q   (1) What is mass flow measurement, (2) where is it used, and (3) why is it important in plant and process measurements?

A   Mass flow measurement is (1) measurement of the quantity of flowing fluid, expressed in tons per day, pounds per hour, etc. It is independent of the physical properties of the fluid itself, or of the ambient conditions in which the measurement is made. (2) Mass flow measurement is widely used in modern plants and processes.

EXAMPLE: (*a*) a chemical process where the reaction is governed by the mass of the materials, not volume; (*b*) where the heating or cooling effects of the steam, air, or gas stream are proportional to mass flow, not volume flow; or (*c*) for cost accounting, yield measurement, energy Btu, blending, and bulk loading, fueling procedures, and basis weight determination.

(3) It is important to measure mass flows because tighter control, better quality, more accurate accounting, and more precise energy balance can be obtained.

Q   What are the two major categories of mass flowmeters?
A   (1) The mass flowmeter, in which the reaction of the sensing element is proportional to true mass flow rate, and (2) the mass flowmeter in which volumetric flow rate is measured. Here the output is converted to mass flow by compensating for such physical properties of the flowing material as pressure, temperature, Reynolds number, density, viscosity, and such ambient conditions as temperature, barometric pressure, and humidity.

Q   What is the fundamental equation for mass flow?
A $M = ApV$

where M = mass flow rate
    p = flowing density
    V = flowing velocity
    A = the cross-sectional area of the channel
If the channel area A is constant, the flowmeter detects the product pV. This product is also the momentum m of the stream per unit of cross-sectional area. If the flowmeter detects this instantaneous momentum m, it is a "true" mass flowmeter. If the flowmeter measures the quantities of density p and velocity V and multiplies them to give the product pV as its output, it is an inferential, or compensated mass flowmeter.

Q   Upon what principle are direct ("true") measuring mass flowmeters based?
A   Direct mass flowmeters work on the principle of transverse momentum measuring. Here the reaction of the primary element is proportional to the momentum of the flow stream. The meter imposes on the fluid stream a momentum (velocity) transverse (at right angles) to the longitudinal (axial) flow of the stream.

Q   What are the three classifications of transverse momentum meters, or direct mass flowmeters?

A (1) Axial flowmeters, (2) radial flowmeters, and (3) gyroscopic flowmeters.

Q How does an axial-type mass flowmeter work? Describe it.

A The axial-type mass flowmeter (Fig. 3-23) works on the principle of conservation of angular momentum. An impeller and a turbine are mounted on separate shafts in the meter housing or conduit. All the fluid passes through the impeller and turbine. The impeller is driven by a motor at constant angular velocity, so that as fluid enters the impeller the fluid receives an angular momentum equal to that of the impeller. Now the fluid stream has both an angular (transverse) momentum proportional to the impeller's velocity and mass rate of fluid flow and an axial momentum. The turbine, or torque sensing wheel, downstream from the impeller is spring-restrained and does not rotate. The turbine removes the angular momentum from the fluid at the same rate that the fluid has gained momentum from the impeller. Both the

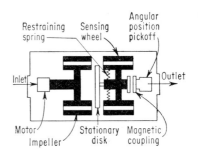

Fig. 3-23. Axial-type mass flowmeter uses angular momentum principle.

impeller and the turbine have several straight vanes located along their rims and parallel to the conduit's center line. The turbine, as it removes the angular momentum from the fluid, acts as a torque measuring device. An angular position sensing device which is magnetically coupled to the turbine measures the turbine shaft torque. Therefore, the output represents instantaneous angular momentum and is proportional to true mass flow. There are stationary disks between the impeller and the turbine which reduce viscosity coupling. An electrical signal from the angular position sensing device is read out on an electric current indicator or recorder or integrator counter. Flow capacity is directly proportional to the nominal pipe size of the flowmeter and fluid to be measured. Manufacturers furnish capacity tables for many sizes and fluids.

Q What are the performance characteristics of a typical axial-type mass flowmeter?

A Axial-type mass flowmeters are used for liquid and gas flow measurements. Density and velocity variations do not affect the mass flow measurements. They (1) have relatively low pressure drop, (2) can operate over a broad temperature range, (3) are chiefly used for low temperatures (−320°F), and (4) are available over wide flow ranges and pressures (as high as 2,000 psig).

Q   Where are most axial-type mass flowmeters used?
A   For aircraft, missile, and rocket fuel and cryogenic fluid flows. Also for petrochemical liquids and gases, and industrial fuels.

Q   Describe a radial-type mass flowmeter and how it works.
A   See Fig. 3-24. Sometimes called a *Coriolis* flowmeter, a radial mass flowmeter has a meter body with its impeller and downstream guide vane driven at a constant angular velocity within the meter housing. Fluid enters the meter body inlet through a torque tube, then flows out through the radial vanes of the impeller at an angular velocity equal to that of the impeller. Impeller moment is proportional to the mass flow rate through the meter and is detected by measuring the torque-tube reaction to the impeller rotation.

Q   What are the advantages of a radial mass flowmeter?
A   There are only two advantages: (1) the torque tube detects the mass flow rate in either direction, thus making this a bidirectional flowmeter; and (2) since angular momentum is recovered, the meter needs little power, just enough to overcome bearing and seal friction and viscosity losses.

Q   What are the three major categories of inferential, or compensated, type mass flowmeters?
A   (1) Velocity mass flowmeters with density compensation, (2) head flowmeters with density compensation, and (3) head flowmeters with velocity compensation.

Q   Define an inferential mass flowmeter.
A   A flow measuring device which determines the mass flow by compensations to the volumetric flow rates of the device. Density and velocity are the factors for which compensation is made.

Q   Name four types of velocity mass flowmeters with density compensation.
A   (1) Turbine flowmeter, (2) vortex-velocity flowmeter with densitometer, (3) magnetic flowmeter with densitometer, and (4) ultrasonic velocity flowmeter with densitometer. In all these mass flowmeters mass flow measurement is obtained as the resultant of the product of the fluid stream velocity and density.

Q   Describe a turbine-type velocity flowmeter with densitometer.
A   A turbine-type velocity flowmeter (Fig. 3-25) is based on measuring the speed of a turbine's rotation in a fluid stream. Because the speed of rotation is proportional to stream velocity it is an indication of volumetric flow. Volumetric flow is combined with a measurement of stream fluid density in a computing device whose output is mass flow rate. This

flowmeter (Fig. 3-26) has end fittings to match the piping in which it is installed. A permanent magnet is sealed inside a stainless-steel rotor which rotates in the fluid stream. As the fluid flows through the meter housing, the rotor spins at a speed determined by the fluid velocity and

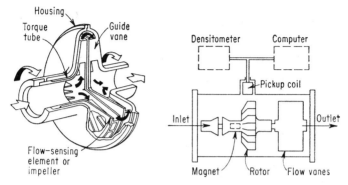

Fig. 3-24. Radial-type mass flow-meter; also called a Coriolis flow-meter.

Fig. 3-25. Turbine-type velocity flowmeter.

the angle of the rotor blades, thereby inducing an a-c voltage in a magnetic pickup coil mounted outside the housing. A pulse is generated in the coil for each rotation of the rotor. This signal frequency is directly proportional to the flow rate of the fluid through the meter. When the

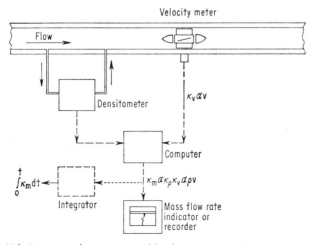

Fig. 3-26. Velocity meter, when compensated by densitometer, reads out in mass flow rate.

output is read out directly as pulses, the total number of pulses is proportional to the total quantity of flow. But when the total number of pulses is integrated over discrete time periods through a frequency converter, a continuous flow rate is read out.

In some models the design of the rotor and its supporting members is such that the rotor spins freely without thrust friction midway between its upstream and downstream supports. In other designs, the rotor spins in ball-bearing races, and the fluid enters the meter through straightening vanes and a sharp-edged orifice. Density can be measured by several methods. Most direct is with a float densitometer where the buoyant force on a float submerged in a side stream of the fluid is measured and transduced into a continuous electrical signal. This signal is fed to the mass flow computing circuit where volume flow is multiplied by density to give mass flow rate.

Q What are the performance characteristics of typical turbine-type flowmeters?

A Turbine flowmeters have calibrated flow rates starting from $\frac{1}{16}$-in. to as high as 12-in. pipe size. Digital outputs are linear with flow rate within ±0.5 per cent over ranges as great as 20 to 1. Repeatability of rate indication is 0.1 per cent of flow rate; speed of response is as fast as 5 msec. Normally turbine meters operate over static pressure ranges to 4,000 psig, special models to 40,000 psi, and temperature ranges from −300 to +1200°F. Viscosity effects can be compensated during calibration. Fluids of viscosities below 1 centistoke do not greatly affect linearity accuracy. Horizontal, vertical, and bidirectional flows are measured.

Q How do you select the size of a turbine flowmeter?

A Manufacturers furnish liquid flow rate tables showing meter sizes vs. volumetric flow, maximum and minimum linear ranges and low repeatable flow, and gravimetric flow range for 0.8 specific gravity. For fluids of different specific gravities, a calculation factor is applied. Gas flowmeter size selections are made from curves showing maximum and minimum volumetric flow rates vs. velocity. Factory calibration curves are furnished with each meter.

Q What are the eight major advantages of turbine-type flowmeters?

A (1) High flow rate accuracy, linearity, and repeatability; (2) fast speed of response; (3) wide flow rangeability; (4) flow accuracy not affected by adjacent piping shapes; (5) simple and rugged; (6) operates over wide temperature and pressure ranges; (7) used for bidirectional flow measurements; and (8) used for pulsating flows.

Q Name five applications for turbine flowmeters.
A (1) Transient fluid flow studies, (2) aircraft and rocket fuel flow measurement in engine test facilities, (3) in-line product blending, (4) batch flow control, and (5) flow measurements of slurries, molten metals, and other dense liquids.

Q Describe a vortex-velocity flowmeter with densitometer and how it operates.
A A vortex-velocity flowmeter (Fig. 3-27) consists of a piece of straight pipe (steel or stainless steel) with an offset cylindrical chamber. When fluid flows through the pipe an eddy or vortex forms in the chamber. The principle of operation of this flowmeter is based on coupling together the rotary flow of the vortex and the linear main flow. Measuring the velocity of the rotary flow indicates the velocity of the main flow. The rotor positioned in the vortex maintains its stability and rotates at a speed equal to the vortex speed. Since this vortex is locked to the main flow, the vortex velocity is directly proportional to the main flow velocity.

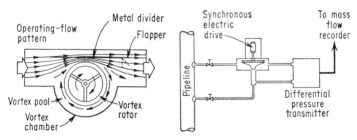

Fig. 3-27. Vortex-velocity flowmeter has rotor.

Fig. 3-28. Dynamic densitometer is a gas sampling blower.

The rotor rides with the vortex and is used to count its revolutions. A magnetic coupling on the rotor shaft provides the means for transmitting electrically rotor revolutions to a counter register, recording instrument, or computing device. A flat metal divider is inserted along the axis of the main flow stream above the rotor to form a more orderly channel for the rotor. A flapper attached to the downstream end of the bypass can divert some of the flow. The flapper is used for calibration and can be used to change the meter's range. This meter provides a volume flow rate or volume total of the fluid flowing through the flowmeter.

Continuous density measurement for compensating the volume flow for temperature, pressure, and compressibility to provide mass flow rate is done with a dynamic densitometer (Fig. 3-28). This type of densitometer is a gas-sampling blower driven at constant speed by a synchronous motor. It operates on the principle of the fan law, which states that a fan, or blower, driven at a constant speed and coupled to a fixed system, will provide a pressure differential proportional to fluid density. Pressure differential developed across the sampling blower varies linearly with the density of the gas sampled. When the densitometer is mounted directly in the flowmeter pipe and a differential pressure measuring device is connected across the densitometer blower, the differential pressure meter's output signal is directly proportional to gas density. This density measurement and the volumetric flow measurement from the vortex-velocity flowmeter are multiplied mechanically or electrically in the computing device. Product of the two signals is mass flow rate. Total mass flow can also be computed in an integrating device.

Q   What are typical vortex-velocity flowmeter performance characteristics?

A   While these flowmeters measure both liquid and gas flows, they are most effective for gas flows. Sizes are from 2- to 16-in. pipe size, working pressures from 1,500 to 5,000 psi, temperature ranges from 32 to 200°F, liquid flow ranges from 20 to 200 gpm, gas flow ranges from 10 to 100 fpm, accuracies of plus or minus one-half of 1 per cent of reading over full flow range, rangeability of 10 to 1, and fast response. Pressure drop across the meter varies with the density. Pulsating flow does not materially affect the accuracy. The densitometer has an accuracy of ±0.05 per cent of the reading over a range 0 to 25 lb per cu ft.

Q   How do you select the size of a vortex-velocity flowmeter?

A   Manufacturers furnish flow rate tables for liquid and gas meters. Liquid flow rates are based on water flow where the maximum rate (high range) is given for the flapper fully open, and the minimum rate (low range) with the flapper closed; the rate depends on dynamic viscosity and density. For liquids other than water, the maximum rate is universally proportional to the square root of the density; flow rate tables are furnished. You only need to select the proper meter size from the maximum and minimum flow rates required. When more than one liquid meter is used on the same flow run, all should be somewhat oversized. Then when one meter is taken out of service the remainder can meter the total flow.

To select a meter for gas flow, first determine which size covers the full range of maximum and minimum gas flow rates required. Next see if it creates a pressure drop within the allowable limit. Maximum and minimum flow rate curves are furnished where the flow rate is in terms of standard line conditions, line pressure in terms of psig and based on a gas specific gravity of 0.6. If the specific gravity of the gas differs from

0.6, multiply the minimum flow rate by a factor determined by dividing 0.600 by the square root of the specific gravity.

Q Name four advantages of vortex-velocity flowmeters.
A (1) Simple construction and simple installation, (2) economical and rugged, (3) does not need strainers in the flow stream, and (4) is easily combined in systems having temperature, density, and pressure compensation.

Q Where are vortex-velocity flowmeters used?
A Chiefly for measuring quantities of gas, hydrocarbons, water, air, fuel oils, ammonia, and slurries, especially where mass or compensated flow is desired.

Q Describe an electromagnetic flowmeter with densitometer for mass flows and explain how it works.
A As Fig. 3-29 shows, this unit has a magnetic flow transmitter which is installed directly in the process flow line, an electronic volume flow

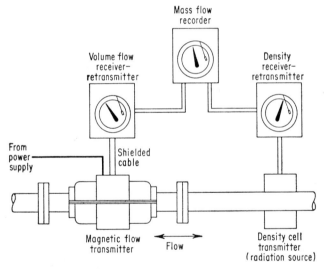

Fig. 3-29. Magnetic flowmeter system with densitometer.

receiver, density cell, density receiver transmitter, and mass flow recorder with density and volume flow computing circuit to give mass flow rate.

The magnetic transmitter (Fig. 3-30) has a nonmagnetic metal tube (through which liquid flows) bolted directly in the flow line, a pair of button electrodes on the tube's wall in contact with the flowing liquid, and an electromagnet mounted on the tube's outside in a protective housing. As in power generators, the transmitter operates on the prin-

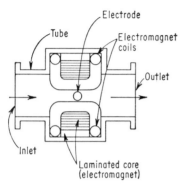

Fig. 3-30. Magnetic flow transmitter with details of electrode.

ciple of Faraday's law of magnetic induction. It states that, when a moving conductor cuts across lines of force in a magnetic field, a voltage is induced in the conductor. If the dimensions of the conductor remain constant, the induced voltage is directly proportional to the velocity of the conductor, and velocity × area = volume rate of flow. In this case, the measured liquid itself is the conductor. As long as the flow line is full during measurement, the conductor's diameter is constant and is determined by the inside diameter of the transmitter tube.

An electromagnet encircling the tube generates an alternating uniform magnetic field. Thus the voltage induced in the flowing liquid varies only with changes in its velocity. Changes in the voltage are sensed by the electrodes and are transmitted to the receiver by a two-wire shielded cable. So the voltage transmitted to the receiver is directly proportional to the flowing liquid velocity and volume flow rate. The receiver, usually located up to 1,000 ft from the transmitter, has an a-c circuit consisting of an auxiliary power supply, a preamplifier unit with phase shift adjustment, an a-c error detection circuit, a balancing motor, and a servo amplifier. Receiver and transmitters operate on 120- or 240-volt 60-cycle power, depending on pipe size.

The metering tube in smaller sizes is made of nonmagnetic stainless steel. In larger sizes corrosion-resistant linings of Teflon, Kel-F, Neoprene, etc. and fiberglass are used. Sizes range from 0.1 to 72 in. nominal pipe size. End connections are flanged. Meter housings can be waterproof and explosionproof. Electrodes are usually stainless steel or other corrosion-resistant materials. The radiation-type densitometer works well with a magnetic mass flowmeter system because it measures the density of liquids with entrained solids and slurries. Installing it directly in the flow line does not cause an obstruction.

Q   What are typical performance characteristics for magnetic flowmeters?

A   Magnetic flowmeters measure volumetric flow rates from minimum flows of 0.1 gpm for 0.1-in. sizes to flows of 32,000 gpm (no maximum limit) for 72-in. sizes, over line pressure ranges from 250 psig to 14 in. vacuum. Special meters are good for as high as 3,000 psig, and temperatures up to 600°F.

Q   What information do you need for sizing magnetic flowmeters?

A   Magnetic flowmeters come individually calibrated, according to the following requirements: (1) flow line size, (2) desired transmitter tube size, (3) maximum and minimum flows and units of measurement, (4) end connections, (5) tube lining, (6) maximum and minimum flow temperatures and pressures, and (7) fluid conductivity in microhms.

Q   Name eight applications for magnetic flowmeters.

A   Although magnetic flowmeters are limited to conductive liquid flow measurements, they are widely used for metering (1) paper pulp, (2) sewage, (3) corrosive acid, (4) water, (5) tomato and other vegetable pulp, (6) rayon viscose, (7) detergents, and (8) many slurries and dry solids. Single flow, flow difference, total flow, and flow ratios are measured with magnetic flowmeters.

Q   Name six advantages of magnetic flowmeters.

A   (1) Measure flow in vertical or horizontal pipes in either direction, (2) linear transmitter output, (3) very low flow rate, (4) no limit on maximum flow rate, (5) high sensitivity and accuracy, and (6) no measuring errors with high-conductivity fluids and very low pressure drop.

Q   How does an ultrasonic mass flowmeter work?

A   An ultrasonic mass flowmeter (Fig. 3-31) was recently developed for rocket and missile flowmetering. Several types are used but each uses sound waves in either the acoustic or ultrasonic range. In one, an ultrasonic pulse generated by a transmitter in a section of pipe is directed from one side of the pipe to one or two receivers on the other side. Sound wave is reflected back and forth through the fluid while it is carried downstream with the fluid flow, thus decreasing in

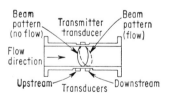

Fig. 3-31. Ultrasonic mass flowmeter works on sound-deflection principle.

amplitude. Pulses are timed so that a new one is transmitted only after the previous echo train dies out. As a pulse is transmitted, the upstream receiver voltage level increases. Volumetric flow rate is measured by determining the ratio of these two voltages. The output of the receiver transducers can be read out on any voltage indicator, recorder, or into a computing circuit. Temperature changes in the fluid will change the sound velocity. A thermistor temperature probe measures temperature for proper compensation. Density is measured with an acoustical impedance device. Mass flow rate is computed using these measurements in a computing circuit which multiplies temperature compensated volume flow by density.

Q   Where can ultrasonic flowmeters be used?
A   Ultrasonic flowmeters are valuable for flow measurement of fluids which are dangerous because of high pressure or high temperature, are corrosive, or have radioactive characteristics. They can be applied to a variety of conventional process flows as well.

Q   Describe a mass flowmeter which makes use of a head flowmeter with density compensation.
A   A mass flowmeter (Fig. 3-32) consists of (1) a head flowmeter to produce a volume flow rate measurement from the square root of differ-

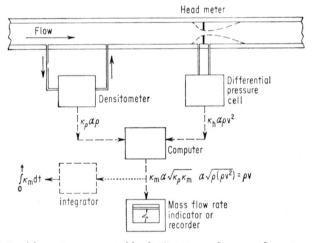

Fig. 3-32. Head flowmeter compensated by densitometer produces mass flow rate.

ential pressure (differential pressure is created with any of the primary sensing elements described earlier in this chapter), (2) a differential pressure measuring element which translates differential pressure into an electrical signal, (3) a densitometer to measure the fluid density and translate it into an electrical signal proportional to density, and (4) an electrical computing circuit which extracts the square root of the product of volume flow and density. The computed output is proportional to mass flow rate, which is indicated, recorded, or integrated for total mass flow. A more conventional method of handling head flow rate with density compensation records instantaneous differential pressure across the head meter and the density on a chart. The chart record is integrated and the density measurement is used as a correction factor in computing total mass flow.

Q Where would you use head flowmeters with density compensation?
A Use for process flow measurements where head flowmeters are used to advantage and where mass flow is needed. Head flowmeter limitations also limit the applications here as a compensated flowmeter. Often existing head flowmeters are transformed into mass flowmeters by adding a densitometer and compensating the circuit with minor modifications.

Q Describe a mass flowmeter which makes use of a head flowmeter with velocity compensation.
A A mass flowmeter (Fig. 3-33) has the same elements as the system described with density compensation. The exception is that the densi-

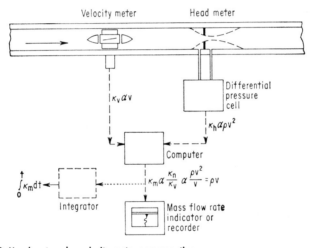

Fig. 3-33. Head meter plus velocity meter compensation.

tometer is not used and a velocity-type flowmeter acts as the compensating element. A volumetric flow signal is combined with the velocity flow signal in a mechanical or electrical compensating circuit. This mathematically divides the head meter signal by the velocity meter signal to produce a resulting signal proportional to mass flow rate. Often these flow signals and the resultant mass flow are recorded on the same chart.

Q What major category of flow measuring primary devices is used to measure liquid flow in open channels?
A (1) Sharp-edged weirs, and (2) Parshall flumes. These primary de-

vices are acted upon directly by the liquid to produce a changing head. This head is measured by a float-actuated instrument (indicator, recorder, or transmitter) which converts liquid head in inches to equivalent flow readings in volume or weight limits.

Q Name and describe three widely used types of sharp-edged weirs.
A (1) Rectangular weir, (2) triangular, or V-notch weir, shown in Fig. 3-34, and (3) Cipolletti weir. All three kinds vary only in the type of notch in the weir's plate. A notched metal weir plate through which the liquid stream flows is installed at right angles to the flowing stream in a weir box. This box provides a stilling chamber on the upstream side of the weir plate. The stilling section is sized so that the liquid approaches the weir plate in a smooth stream at a mean velocity of no greater than ½ fps through a straight channel distance, at least ten times the width of the weir crest. The weir plate is smooth on its upstream side. The weir box should be free from sediment and solids. The crest (bottom edge of the weir notch) and sides of the notch are no thicker than ⅛ in.

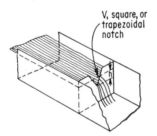

Fig. 3-34. Sharp-edged weir is most accurate and simple method of measuring flow in open channels.

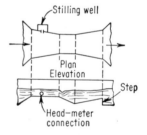

Fig. 3-35. Parshall flumes measure large flows in open channels.

Locate the weir crest higher than the maximum possible downstream liquid surface elevation to avoid submergence of the weir. The height of crest above the bottom of the upstream stilling chamber is at least twice the maximum head to be measured. So also the distance from the sides of the weir notch to the sides of the stilling chamber is at least twice the maximum head. Distance from the weir to the place where the head is measured should be enough to prevent any effect from the down curve of the liquid surface. When these critical distances are great enough to cause the liquid to "pond" above the weir so that the liquid approaches the weir notch at low velocity, the weir is said to have complete contraction and the rate of flow is directly proportional to the head of liquid measured on its surface in the stilling chamber. The shape of the weir notch determines the weir flow capacity and the exponent n of head h in the fundamental flow equation ($Q = a$ constant $\times h^n$).

Q What are the flow ranges of the three types of weirs?
A (1) A rectangular weir has a flow range of 0 to 250 to 10,000 gpm, (2) a V-notch weir a range of 0 to 150 to 2,000 gpm, and (3) a Cipolletti weir a range of 0 to 250 to 10,000 gpm.

Q Where would you use weirs for flow measurements?
A Weirs are used for flow measurement of liquid streams in open channels and partially filled pipes. The chief use is for large flows of water or liquids where other commonly used differential type primary elements might impede the flow of liquids containing solids in suspension, abrasives, or corrosive materials. But sediment accumulation in the weir pond may become a problem since it affects accuracy. In that case frequent cleaning is required.

Q Describe a Parshall flume and how liquid flow is measured with it.
A A Parshall flume (Fig. 3-35) has a converging upstream section, a throat, and a diverging downstream section. The flume is made of wooden timbers or cement in the stream bed, or channel. All sections have vertical side walls, with the floor in the throat inclined downward. Discharge through the flume is considered free-flow when the liquid elevation downstream from the throat is low enough to prevent the flow from being retarded by the effect of the backwater. When this downstream liquid elevation is high enough to affect the rate of flow, the critical point is reached and a condition of submerged flow exists. With free flow the actual flow is a function of the upper head h alone. A flume of free-flow design is used with a float-actuated meter. The fundamental flow equation for a flume is the same as that for a weir ($Q = a$ constant $\times Wh^n$). But for a flume, the constant and the head exponent n vary with flume throat width W. Flow rate through the flume is still directly proportional to the liquid surface head measured by a float resting on the surface. With submerged flow the flow rate is a function of both upper h_u and lower h_d heads.

Q Where are Parshall flumes used?
A Parshall flumes are used for large liquid flows (1) where flowing liquid may carry excessive solids or sediments which cannot be tolerated in a weir stilling chamber, (2) where there may not be a large enough head of water for free flow, or (3) where it is impossible to construct a large enough stilling section upstream.

Q Describe a float-actuated flowmeter used with weirs and flumes and its operation.

A Since the exponential relationship between head and flow varies with each primary element, the measuring system must determine the head and extract the exponential function for each type of weir or flume. To do this a float-actuated flowmeter uses a cylindrical or spherical copper float which rides the surface of the liquid in a stilling well connected to the primary element. The float is attached to a counterweighted stainless-steel cable which passes over a friction-free pulley in a housing on the back of an instrument case. The pulley is on a common shaft with a characterized cam which moves the recording pen or indicating pointer across an evenly graduated chart or scale as the liquid level in the stilling well rises or falls with changes in flow rate. Each cam is designed to extract the particular head exponent characteristic of the type of weir or flume. The instrument is usually an indicator, recorder, or flow transmitter.

SUGGESTED READING

Recommended Practices, sold by Instrument Society of America, 530 William Penn Place, Pittsburgh, Pa.

ISA—RP 2.1, *Manometer Tables*, 31 pages

ISA—RP 3.1, *Flowmeter Installations Seal and Condensate Chambers*, 6 pages

ISA—RP 3.2, *Flange Mounted Sharp Edged Orifice Plates for Flow Measurement*, 7 pages

ISA—RP 11.1, *Mercury Handling*, 7 pages

ISA—RP 16.4, *Nomenclature and Terminology for Extension Type Variable Area Meters (Rotameters)*, 2 pages

ISA—RP 16.5, *Installation, Operation, Maintenance Instructions for Glass Tube Variable Area Meters (Rotameters)*, 4 pages

ISA—RP 16.6, *Methods and Equipment for Calibration of Variable Area Meters (Rotameters)*, 6 pages

ISA—RP 31.1, *Terminology and Specifications for Turbine-type Flow Transducers (Volumetric)*, 2 pages

Books

Cusick, C. F.: *Flow Meter Engineering Handbook*, Minneapolis-Honeywell Regulator Company, Philadelphia, Pa., 1961.

Elonka, Steve, and Julian Bernstein: *Standard Industrial Electronics Questions and Answers*, vols. I and II, McGraw-Hill Book Company, Inc., New York, to be published in 1964.

Elonka, Steve, and Joseph F. Robinson: *Standard Plant Operator's Questions and Answers*, vols. I and II, McGraw-Hill Book Company, Inc., New York, 1959.

Elonka, Steve, and Quaid W. Minich: *Standard Refrigeration and Air Conditioning Questions and Answers*, McGraw-Hill Book Company, Inc., New York, 1961.

4

PRESSURE AND VACUUM
MEASURING SYSTEMS

Q What is pressure?

A Pressure is the force exerted against a given surface area. Pressure is measured in terms of the force applied to an area or in terms of the height to which pressure will raise a column of a given liquid. The pressure is equal to the height times the liquid's density.

Atmospheric pressure is the force exerted on a unit area of the earth's surface by the atmosphere's weight. Plant and process pressure measuring devices show the difference between the pressure of a confined (enclosed) fluid and that of the atmosphere. If the measured pressure is greater than that of atmosphere, the difference is known as gage pressure. The gage pressure reading added to the atmospheric pressure reading equals absolute pressure. Pressures below atmospheric are expressed in terms of vacuum, or as absolute pressure. The absolute pressure is zero when in a state of (near) perfect vacuum.

When the pressure is expressed as vacuum (negative pressure), you find the equivalent absolute pressure by subtracting the vacuum reading from the atmospheric pressure.

Q Define the units of pressure.

A Pressure is expressed in units of force per unit area, such as pounds per square inch (psi), kilograms per square centimeter, and in units of height of a column of liquid, such as feet and inches of water, and inches and centimeters or millimeters of mercury. Vacuum is often expressed in terms of microns (one-thousandth of a millimeter of mercury). Roughly, 1 ft of water is equal to 1 in. of mercury and weighs $\frac{1}{2}$ psi. The standard atmospheric pressure at sea level is defined as 14.7 psi, and is equivalent to the pressure needed to support a column of mercury 29.92 in. or 760 mm high. This (14.7 psi) is also called 1 atmosphere. These sea level (zero altitude) conditions are defined at a temperature of 0°C (centigrade).

Pressure is exerted by the weight of a confined volume of fluid. Pressure depends on a characteristic of the fluid, which is density, or weight per unit volume. Density (and pressure) of the fluid increases with temperature rise and decreases when the altitude increases above sea level. Therefore, temperature and altitude must be defined when expressing pressure. A "perfect vacuum" would be at 0 in. of mercury vacuum, at 0 psi absolute pressure (completely out of the earth's atmosphere).

Q   How do you convert 1 in. of mercury into (1) inches of water, (2) millimeters of mercury, and (3) pounds per square inch?
A   One inch of mercury equals (1) 13.6 in. of water, (2) 25.4 mm of mercury, and (3) 0.491 psi.

Q   What pressure ranges are usually encountered in plant and process applications?
A   See Fig. 4-1. Plant and process pressure needs range from as high as 40,000 psi pressure to as low as 10^{-4} mm of mercury (0.1 micron),

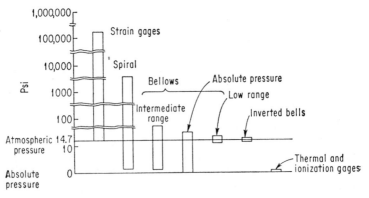

Fig. 4-1. Ranges of elements and gages.

vacuum. Research laboratories work with measurements from 300,000 psi to 10^{-12} mm of mercury.

Q   Why are pressure and vacuum measurements important? What are some specific examples of pressure measurement applications?
A   With the exception of temperature, pressure and vacuum measurements are the most important and common in plants and processes. Control from pressure measurement is often much more effective than from temperature. In some processes a change of $\frac{1}{2}°$ temperature may cause a change of 20 in. of water pressure. Modern synthesis processes in the chemical and plastic field operate under very high pressures, and

the electrode disposition of metals is done under high vacuum. Cooking time is reduced under high pressure in the paper, textile, and food industries. Evaporators are more efficient under higher-vacuum conditions. Rocket and missile applications require many very high pressure and vacuum measurements. Use of absolute pressure gages is often confined to the accurate measurement and control of pressure low enough to be seriously affected by variations in barometric (atmospheric) pressure. An example is in distillation towers and evaporators.

Q Name three major categories of pressure and vacuum measuring systems. How are they classified?

A Pressure measuring systems are usually divided into (1) mechanical pressure transducers, (2) electrical pressure transducers, and (3) high-vacuum measuring systems. Mechanical pressure transducers are classified as (*a*) liquid column elements, and (*b*) elastic elements. Electrical pressure transducers are classified as (*a*) strain gage, (*b*) resistance, (*c*) force-balance (oscillator), (*d*) magnetic, and (*e*) capacitance pressure transducers. Vacuum systems are classified as (*a*) high range and (*b*) low range.

Q On what principle do liquid column pressure elements work? How are these columns classified?

A The principle is that a hydrostatic pressure exerted by a liquid at the lower end of a column is directly proportional to the height of liquid in the column. Liquid columns are classified as (1) absolute pressure gage, (2) McLeod gage, (3) fixed-cistern barometer, (4) manometers, and (5) bell-type elements.

Q What liquids are used in liquid column pressure elements?

A Liquids such as mercury, colored water, organic liquids (densities less than water), and bromide compounds (densities greater than water). The exact liquid (and density) selected depends on the pressure range needed.

Q Sketch an absolute pressure liquid column gage. How does it work?

A This gage (Fig. 4-2) measures absolute pressure by admitting the pressure to be measured into the open end of a U tube containing mercury, while the closed end is under vacuum. Absolute pressure P is measured by observing the liquid level difference h in the two legs and multiplying by the density d of liquid ($P = hd$). This is a laboratory instrument.

Q Describe another type of absolute pressure liquid column gage for low absolute pressures.

A The McLeod gage (Fig. 4-3) measures gases at absolute pressures in the range of 1 to 5,000 microns. Gas is trapped in a measuring tube by mercury as the instrument is rotated about a pivot through 90° from the horizontal of the mercury column. The final volume of compressed gas in the measuring tube is indicated by the height of mercury against a calibrated scale. This, also, is a laboratory instrument.

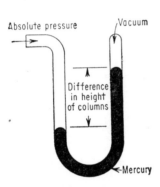

Fig. 4-2. Absolute pressure gage.

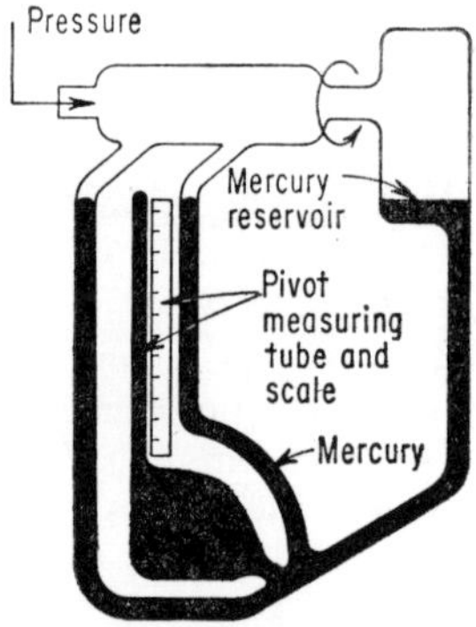

Fig. 4-3. McLeod gage.

Q   Describe a liquid column element used for measuring atmospheric pressure.

A   The fixed-cistern barometer (Fig. 4-4) measures atmospheric pressures. It consists of an evacuated glass tube filled with mercury and closed at one end. The open end is inverted in a container of mercury.

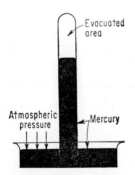

Fig. 4-4. Fixed-cistern barometer.

Atmospheric pressure is found by measuring the difference in height between the top of the mercury column and the level of mercury in the container. This type of barometer is widely used.

Q   How does a U-tube manometer work?

A   A U-tube manometer (Fig. 4-5) is a type of liquid column pressure element; it measures differential pressures. A U-shaped pyrex glass tube is open at both ends and filled partially with mercury. When two different pressures are admitted to the open ends the mercury seeks different levels in the tubes, indirectly proportional to the pressure. The pressure differential is read on a calibrated scale between the glass tube as a function of the difference in mercury levels in the two columns. Pressure is independent of tube cross section. U-tube manometers can be filled with any type of liquid, depending on the desired pressure range. They are mounted in banks of up to 150 tubes on one panel with ranges as high as 200 in. Individual precision calibrated scales and backlighting are used for very precise pressure measurement.

Q Where are glass U-tube manometers used in industry?
A As primary pressure standards for calibrating other industrial pressure gages. They are used in wind tunnels, engine and rocket test stands, and for precise pressure measurements in process and plant uses.

Q Name an industrial differential pressure element which uses the U-tube principle.
A The head flowmeter manometer described in Chap. 3, Fig. 3-14, measures flow rate by sensing the differential pressure across a restriction in the pipeline. In this instrument a range tube and float chamber hold the mercury instead of the glass U tube. Float motion is converted to an indicator pointer or pen arm motion on a chart or scale. These instruments are used for differential pressure indication as well as flow rate.

Q Describe a well manometer.
A A well manometer (Fig. 4-6) works on the same principle as the

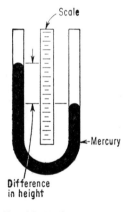

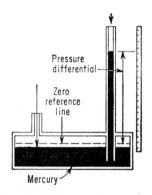

Fig. 4-5. U-tube manometer.   Fig. 4-6. Well manometer.

U tube except that one leg of the U tube is replaced by a large shallow well. When the well and other leg are filled with mercury the difference between pressures P_1 and P_2 is indicated on a scale behind the leg as the height of the column of mercury above the zero line in the well. The error from the difference in areas of the well and leg is negligible when the well diameter is much greater than the tube diameter.

Q   What liquid column pressure element measures accurately very low pressure differentials over an expanded scale?

A   The inclined-tube manometer (Fig. 4-7) is similar to the U-tube liquid column type, except that one leg is inclined. A small change in mercury level in the vertical tube causes a large change of mercury position in the inclined tube. The distance is equal to the vertical liquid height times the cosecant of the angle that the sloping tube makes with the horizontal position. There are two pressure connections. For low-pressure measurements the liquid used is normally lighter than water. The gage's scale can be graduated to 0.01 in., which gives accurate readings to 0.005 in.

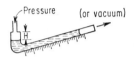

Fig. 4-7. Inclined-tube manometer.

Q   Where are inclined-tube manometers used?

A   Mostly for low-pressure differential measurements of boiler draft, static pressures in air-conditioning systems, and furnace pressures.

Q   Describe a ring-balance manometer used for differential pressure measurement.

A   The ring-balance manometer (Fig. 4-8) is a liquid column pressure element, but the liquid column is circular and split. Like a wheel, the circular unit pivots on a knife-edge at the center and is balanced by a weight at the bottom. Pressures P_1 and P_2 are applied to the ring through flexible connections. The amount of rotation of the ring indicates the differential pressure. Ring-balance manometers indicate differential pressure on a scale, or record it on a chart. Its application as a head-type flowmeter is described in Chap. 3, Fig. 3-17.

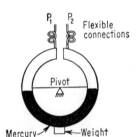

Fig. 4-8. Ring-balance manometer.

Q   Sketch and describe the operation of three bell-type liquid column pressure gages.

A   (1) Sketch *a* (Fig. 4-9) shows how a single liquid seal bell can replace the inclined U tube to indicate, record, or control pressure. The inverted bell is immersed in a container of seal liquid (usually oil). When pressure is applied to the bell's inside, the bell moves against a restricting spring or counterweight. The bell motion positions an indicator pointer or recording pen on a pressure scale. This type of pressure element is very sensitive to the measurement of low pressures and vacuums (as low as 0 to 10 in. of water). The same principle is used for differential pressure measurement (sketch *b*). In this element the bell is sealed within another container and the two pressures are applied to the bell's inside and outside. The bell moves in direct proportion to the pressure difference between inside and outside. The bell's motion is restricted by an opposing spring and is transferred to an indicator pointer through a pressuretight shaft.

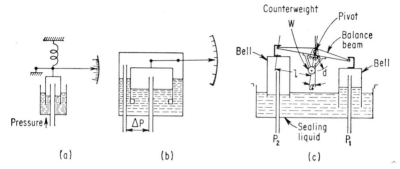

Fig. 4-9. Three-bell-type liquid column pressure gages.

Sketch *c* is a variation of the inverted liquid seal bell. In this differential pressure element two inverted bells immersed in oil are connected by a beam balance. Pressures are introduced, one under each bell. The bell is moved by the changing pressures but restrained by a counterweight on the beam. In effect, this arrangement weighs the minutest difference in pressure between the two pressure lines. A pointer attached to the balance beam indicates the pressure difference between the two measured pressures on a scale. A double bell system can be used to measure small static pressures when atmospheric compensation or a reference pressure is introduced to one bell and pressure to be measured to the other bell. This instrument is sensitive to within ±0.0005 in. of water. It comes in scale ranges of 0 to 2 in. of water.

Q Where are bell-type pressure gages used?
A To measure and control furnace and heater draft conditions. They especially apply when atmospheric pressure compensation is needed.

Q What general category of mechanical pressure transducers is widely used in industrial plants and processes? Classify them.
A Elastic elements: (1) Bourdon-spring, (2) bellows, and (3) diaphragm.

Q Why are these three so important in industrial applications?
A Pressure elements described as liquid column elements, especially

those using glass measuring tubes, are normally used in laboratories because they are fragile and cumbersome. But elastic elements are rugged,
small, simple in operation, and free from maintenance problems, making
them more suitable for industrial use.

Q   On what principle do all elastic pressure elements work?
A   They follow Hooke's law, which states that stress is proportional to
strain, or that deflection of the elastic element and resulting motion is
proportional to the pressure applied to it.

Q   Describe three types of Bourdon-spring pressure gages. How do they
work?
A   Sketch *a* (Fig. 4-10) shows the C-type Bourdon-spring pressure
gage. It is the sensing element for nonindicating and indicating pressure

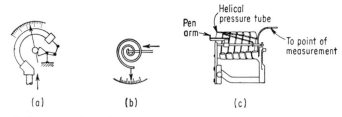

(a)   (b)   (c)

Fig. 4-10. Three types of Bourdon-spring pressure gages.

controllers and transmitters. The gage consists of a metal thin-walled
tube, flattened on diametrically opposite sides to produce an elliptical
cross section, and bent into a circle's segment. One end is fastened to
the gage socket and pressure source; the other end is closed and free to
move. Pressure in the tube causes the ellipse to approach a circle and
the segment to unwind. Because this motion is slight, a sector and pinion
gear amplify it enough to rotate a pointer shaft across an evenly graduated scale, calibrated in pressure units. A Bourdon-spring gage is not
used with recording pressure gages unless it is long enough to provide
enough tip movement for the recording pen motion.

Sketch *b* shows a spiral gage. Rather than use a long circular Bourdon tube, recording gages use a flattened Bourdon tube, wound in a
spiral of several turns. Then as pressure is applied to the open end, the
spiral tends to uncoil, thus providing a large movement of the free end.
Movement is translated to a pen arm motion through a single link. No
sector and pinion are needed as with the Bourdon tube. Friction and lost
motion are reduced, while accuracy is increased.

The helix gage (sketch *c*) shows the helical type of pressure-
actuated element. This is similar to the spiral type except that the

flattened Bourdon tube is wound along a shaft inside four or five turns. One end of the tube is fixed. The other end is attached to the central shaft, which moves as pressure is admitted to the fixed end. Circular movement of the helix is transmitted only from the central shaft rotation through a linkage to the pen arm, in proportion to pressure change. This type of pressure element (also the spiral type) is widely used in recording thermometers (described in Chap. 2) and in recording pressure gages.

Q What materials and pressure ranges are common for Bourdon-tube pressure elements?
A For low pressures: minimum range is 0 to 12 psig and maximum range 0 to 400 psig; use trumpet brass and phosphor bronze. (Vacuum range is 0 to 30 in. of mercury.) For medium pressures: minimum range is 0 to 30 psig and maximum range 0 to 400 psig; use beryllium copper, steel, stainless steel, and Monel (Monel for corrosive service). For high pressures: minimum range is 0 to 50 psig and maximum range 0 to 100,000 psig (single Bourdon).

Q How accurate are Bourdon-tube pressure elements?
A Commercial-type indicating gages and recorders are accurate to $\pm\frac{1}{2}$ per cent of full scale. Precision pressure gages are guaranteed accurate within one-fourth of 1 per cent of full scale.

Q Name and describe briefly three special Bourdon pressure gages.
A (1) The compound-pressure and vacuum gage; uses a center-zero calibrated scale to indicate either pressure or vacuum with a conventional Bourdon element. Use where sudden or vacuum reversals are expected. (2) The suppressed zero pressure gage uses a spring that counterbalances the Bourdon tube's force and holds the pointer at a specified pressure value above zero. The pointer moves off the scale's lower end when the pressure exceeds this value. (3) The duplex pressure gage is really two gages in one case with two pointers to indicate related pressure on the same dial. As many as three or four Bourdon, spiral, or bellow units can be assembled in a recording pressure gage case with four pens.

Q What is the most sensitive elastic pressure element?
A The bellows pressure element is more sensitive than the Bourdon or diaphragm types. There are two types of bellow elements: (1) spring-opposed bellows and (2) dual spring and bellows.

Q Describe a spring-opposed bellows element and tell how it works.
A The spring and bellows element (Fig. 4-11) is used for lower pressure ranges than spiral elements. It has a spring-loaded metal bellows

enclosed in a shell, which is connected to the pressure source. Pressure compresses the bellows, forcing its lower end upward against the spring's opposing force. The rod resting on the bellows' bottom transmits this vertical movement through linkage to the pen arm or pointer. This intermediate-range type is usually mounted inside the instrument case. For low pressure ranges, a larger bellows element is used with an internal connection. The result is a much greater force against the opposing spring per unit pressure, thus allowing enough pen motion for smaller pressures. This unit is usually mounted on the instrument case's back.

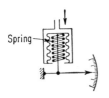

Fig. 4-11. Spring-opposed bellows element.

Q Can you measure a combination of pressure and vacuum with a spring-opposed bellows unit?

A Yes. The gage for measuring both pressure and vacuum has a second spring which opposes the collapsing of the bellows caused by the vacuum. This gage works exactly like the low-range spring and bellows unit.

Q For what ranges are spring-opposed bellows elements used?

A The intermediate-range type is used for pressures with full-scale values between 100 in. of water and 15 psig, or for vacuums with full-scale values between 10 and 30 in. of mercury. The low-pressure element can be used for pressures of 5 to 75 in. of water full range, and for vacuums with full-scale range as low as 5 to 50 in. of water. Positive pressure ranges can be changed by replacing the spring. An entirely new element is needed for the other ranges. All charts and scales are linear and evenly graduated.

Q Describe a spring-opposed bellows element used for absolute pressure measurement.

A The dual spring and bellows element is used to measure absolute pressure. It has two opposing bellows (similar to Fig. 4-11) in one unit. The yoke connects the two bellows in series to the pen shaft or pointer. The upper bellows, which contains the actuating spring, is evacuated and sealed at near perfect vacuum. The lower bellows is not evacuated and is connected to the pressure source. As pressure decreases within the lower bellows, the resultant upward force is decreased. The spring thus causes the lower bellows to collapse. This movement is then transmitted through the lever arm to the pen or pointer. Since the barometric pressure is the same on both bellows, the unit compensates automatically for barometric pressure variations. So, because barometric pressure changes do not move the pen, the pen records only true absolute pressure changes. Reverse-reading charts, having the lowest value at the outer edge, are used. Use for ranges of 0 to 100 mm, to 0 to 760 mm of mercury (60 in.). Lowest range is 0 to 10 mm.

Q Why are absolute pressure measurements in process applications important?

A Absolute pressure gages are best for measuring and controlling pressures that are low enough to be seriously affected by variations in barometric (atmospheric) pressure. Here is an example of barometric pressure compensation: Let's say that pressure in a distilling column is to be controlled at 50 mm of mercury absolute. If you used a vacuum gage to control, the control set point would be 710 mm of mercury with a barometric pressure of 760 mm of mercury $(760 - 50 = 710)$. Should the barometer rise to 775 mm, the vacuum gage would read 725 mm $(775 - 50)$, and the control system would function to decrease the gage pressure by 15 mm. But this action would raise the absolute pressure to 65 mm, or 20 per cent over that desired. Such an error can seriously affect a process. While you can correct it by periodic readings of a barometer, this is a manual procedure and cancels the advantages of automatic control. That is why you should use an absolute pressure gage to measure and control automatic barometric pressure compensation.

Q Bellows elements are made of what materials?

A Bronze, brass, steel, stainless steel, Monel, and beryllium copper. The material used depends upon the corrosive conditions, pressure range, and sensitivity required.

Q Name and classify elastic elements used for low-pressure measurements.

A Diaphragm elastic elements. They are classified as (1) metallic and (2) nonmetallic diaphragms.

Q Describe the metallic diaphragms of pressure elements. How do they work?

A Metallic diaphragms are made as a single flat or corrugated metal shell, or as a capsule of several shells rigidly bonded together and connected through a rod to a pointer. As pressure deflects the diaphragm, the motion positions the pointer along an evenly graduated pressure scale (Fig. 4-12). A small change in pressure causes a large diaphragm deflection. Diaphragms are made from phosphor bronze, beryllium copper, trumpet brass, stainless steel, Ni-Span C, and Monel.

Q Describe nonmetallic diaphragm pressure elements and how they work.

A Nonmetallic diaphragms (Fig. 4-13) are used for very low pressures.

They are made of leather, Teflon, Neoprene, and polyethylene so they are limp and flexible. The diaphragm is usually opposed by a spring, which is deflected by an amount directly proportional to the applied pressure. Linkage connecting the diaphragm to a pointer moves the

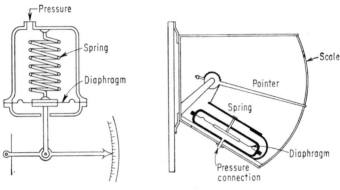

Fig. 4-12. Diaphragm gage.   Fig. 4-13. Diaphragm pressure element.

pointer across the scale during pressure changes. This type of gage usually comes as an assembly of several adjacent indicator scales in the same housing, but often with different ranges.

Q   What are the pressure ranges of diaphragm pressure gages?
A   Pressure ranges of 0 to 0.2 in. of water (minimum), 0 to 400 psig (maximum); vacuum ranges of 0 to 0.2 in. of water (minimum), 0 to 30 in. of mercury (maximum); compound pressure and vacuum ranges have a total span of 0.2 in. of water.

Q   What factors determine the selection and application of elastic element pressure and vacuum gages?
A   (1) Full-scale pressure and/or vacuum range, (2) measured fluid's corrosive properties, temperature, and density, (3) degree of range suppression, (4) barometric effects on the pressure measurement (ambient temperature and barometric pressure), (5) pulsation and overload protection needed, (6) dynamic pressure change, (7) readout requirements, and (8) transmission needs.

Q   What is the maximum speed of response of most mechanical pressure transducers?
A   Full-scale response to pressure changes for mechanical transducers and their indicating or recording system is no greater than 0.1 sec. And, response to fast-changing pressure requires leak-free pressure piping and nearness to pressure source.

Q How should you protect mechanical pressure transducers from damage due to pressure overrange and underrange?

A When the pressure at the range's low end produces a deflection of the element greater than the normal deflection at zero, you must provide underrange protection by preventing element deflection with a rigid stop. Overrange protection is often done by (1) restricting deflection with a rigid backing, (2) using spring-release linkages, and (3) selecting an element for 100 per cent above operating range.

Q How can a pressure measuring element be protected from corrosive or congealing viscous fluids and from inaccuracies caused by sharp changes in static head and overloads?

A By inserting protecting seals between the pressure measuring element and the process fluid (Fig. 4-14). Seals are a flexible diaphragm or

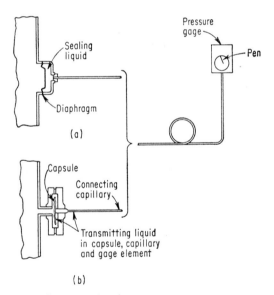

Fig. 4-14. Protecting seals in measuring element.

bellows of corrosion-resistant material in contact with the process fluid. They are connected to the pressure element by pressure tubing, filled with a pressure transmitting liquid fill. Liquid fill to the liquid seals or to the nonmetallic diaphragms is used for the lower pressure ranges. Seals include cleanout, flushing, and removable features. Careful thought to pressure range, process fluid corrosion properties, response time, and mounting facilities is needed when applying protecting seals.

Q How can you protect mechanical pressure transducers from damage caused by extreme pulsating pressure?
A A common method to dampen pulsations is to install a shutoff valve ahead of the gage and throttle it until pulsation disappears. Another method is to use a pulsation dampener or snubber.

Q Name seven major advantages of mechanical pressure transducers.
A (1) Rugged and simple in construction, operation, and maintenance, (2) relatively inexpensive, (3) have industry acceptance and experience, (4) use very simple readout and control devices, (5) inherently accurate, (6) have adequate dynamic response, and (7) cover the most common ranges adequately.

Q Name four limitations of mechanical pressure transducers.
A (1) Do not cover the extremely low and high pressure ranges, (2) are slow to respond to fast-changing pressures and shock waves, (3) are too large for many jobs, and (4) their transducer output signal is not convenient in the electrical form needed in large data systems.

Q What is an electrical pressure transducer?
A A primary measuring element which converts an input pressure to an electrical output signal proportional to pressure.

Q What are (1) the character of the output electrical signal and (2) the signal conditioning equipment associated with electrical pressure transducers?
A The output signal from electrical pressure transducers is an electrical signal of specific amplitude (millivolts or milliamperes: 1/1,000 volt or ampere), frequency response (cycles per second), or pulse duration (milliseconds). This is caused by changing a specific electrical property of the transducer (resistance, reluctance, inductance) when the transducer is energized from a power supply (a-c or d-c).

Signal conditioning equipment takes the form of any of the following components, or combinations of components, depending on the type of transducer used: (1) resistance bridge circuit and gage power supply, (2) bridge balance facilities, (3) d-c amplifier, (4) carrier amplifier, (5) analog to digital converter and (6) calibration facilities. Signal conditioning equipment is required to modify the transducer output so it conforms to the signal needs of the desired readout equipment in a pressure measuring system.

Q Name seven types of readout equipment used for recording or indicating pressure signals from electrical transducers.
A (1) Indicating and recording null-balance electronic potentiometers, (2) multichannel recording oscillographs, (3) indicators (ammeters and

voltmeters), (4) oscilloscopes, (5) magnetic tape recorders, (6) digital indicators, and (7) digital printers and paper-tape machines.

Q Why are electrical pressure transducers important as measuring elements in today's industrial applications?

A High pressures (to 150,000 psig) at high-frequency responses (to 20,000 cps) under difficult ambient conditions can be measured with these transducers. Their electrical output signal is convenient to transmit over a long distance to a variety of readout devices. Their form is suitable for use in computing circuits.

Q How are electrical pressure transducers classified?

A (1) Strain gage, (2) resistance, (3) magnetic, (4) capacitative, (5) force balance (oscillator), and (6) piezoelectric pressure transducers.

Q What is the principle of a strain gage? Describe two types and how they work.

A See Fig. 4-15. The strain gage operates on the principle that a wire element will change its resistance as a function of applied stresses,

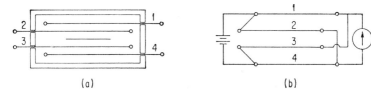

(a)   (b)

Fig. 4-15. Strain gage.

strains, or elongation. Strain is defined as the change in length divided by the original length ($\Delta l/L$). The unit resistance change that the strain produces is the change in resistance divided by the original resistance ($\Delta r/R$). The relation between the unit strain and the unit resistance change is defined as the gage factor $GF = (\Delta r/R)/(\Delta l/L)$.

Strain gage transducers are classified as (1) unbonded and (2) bonded. Physically, the strain gage consists of a short length, or grid, of fine (0.001 in.) diameter wire of high electrical resistance. In the unbonded type, the transducer is electrically and mechanically symmetrical. An armature is supported rigidly in the center of a stationary frame, in a plane perpendicular to the longitudinal axis (Fig. 4-15a). Four filaments of strain-sensitive wire, equal in length, are wound between rigid insulators mounted in the frame and the armature. As the armature is moved to the left by an external force, elements 1 and 4 increase in length, while elements 2 and 3 decrease in length. The resistance change of the filaments is proportional to their change in length. In the bonded-type strain gage, a grid or helix of fine strain gage wires is cemented between paper (to protect it and simplify mounting) and then to the member which is to be subjected to stress or strain. When a force is applied to the member, the strain gage wires change length with it, and the change in wire resistance is proportional to the change in length.

Electrically these two types of strain gages are usually arranged in the form of a Wheatstone bridge (Fig. 4-15*b*). Active elements are placed so that opposite legs of the bridge change their resistance at the same rate for a given direction of displacement of the force summing member. When an a-c or d-c voltage is applied to the bridge, and the force summing member is displaced, the bridge is unbalanced to produce an electrical output directly proportional to the applied force. The specific amount of electrical output depends on the gage voltage, gage factor, and the amount of applied strain. Strain gage elements are physically arranged on a force member to measure (1) bending strain only, (2) axial strain only, (3) torsion, (4) loading (in compression or elongation), and (5) combinations in arrays (rosettes).

Q   Sketch and describe the operation of (1) an unbonded and (2) a bonded strain gage pressure transducer.

A   A strain gage is used as the transducer in an electrical pressure transducer when attached directly to a mechanical pressure element such as a metal diaphragm, or a metal bellows, or when the pressure is transmitted to the strain gage by an armature from the mechanical pressure element.

(1) In the unbonded-type pressure transducer (Fig. 4-16), the armature is connected to a metallic bellows or diaphragm. When a diaphragm is used, the strain gage measures the displacement of the diaphragm center, due to process pressure exerted on the diaphragm. This is done in one modern design by two four-legged springs intermeshed in a stainless-steel ring, with each leg attached to the ring. Pins extending through the springs are binding posts for the strain windings. Any movement of the armature extending from the pickup diaphragm to the center of the two springs will cause a simultaneous extension of one set of windings and relaxation of the other. Thus the resistance of the windings varies proportionally to the gage pressure applied. When a gage voltage is applied, an electrical signal proportional to the applied pressure exists at the pressure transducer output terminals. This pressure

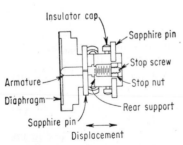

Fig. 4-16. Unbonded pressure transducer.

transducer is made in a compact cylindrical stainless housing with pressure connections on one end and electrical connections on the other.

(2) (The bonded pressure transducer (Fig. 4-17) works much the same as the unbonded type, except that the strain gage filaments are bonded directly to a pressure-sensitive tube (closed at one end) encased in a metal housing. When fluid pressure enters the tube, it expands the tube circumferentially and stretches the strain gage filaments. The resulting change in resistance unbalances the bridge circuit. When a fixed gage voltage is applied at the input terminals, the bridge unbalance is reflected as a change in pressure transducer output voltage (millivolts) proportional to applied gage pressure. When either bonded or unbonded strain gage transducers use a bellows (which is partially evacuated and sealed) absolute pressure is measured. If two pressure connections

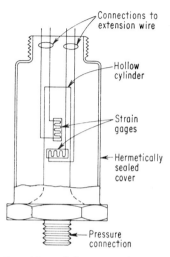

Fig. 4-17. Bonded pressure transducer.

are provided (one to each side of the bellows on the diaphragm) differential pressure is measured.

Q   What are typical performance characteristics of strain gage pressure transducers?

A   Unbonded pressure transducers operate in a range of from ±1 to +5,000 psig or psia. Bonded types go as high as 300,000 psig. They usually require a 5-volt d-c or a-c gage power supply. Output signal is as high as 20 mv per volt gage power input. Frequency response is as high as 20,000 cps.

Q   Name four types of signal conditioning equipment that modify the output signal from strain gage pressure transducers for recording with (1) potentiometers, (2) oscillographs, (3) data handling systems, and (4) magnetic tape machines.

A   Recording potentiometers have a special built-in amplifier and bridge circuit which respond to d-c pressure measurements. Carrier amplifiers provide gage voltage regulation, bridge circuit, gain control, provision for making the mechanical and electrical zero coincident, and calibration circuits. When a d-c amplifier and bridge balance unit are used a separate gage power supply is required. Use a carrier amplifier system in the dynamic range from d-c to 1,000 cps, and a differential input d-c amplifier and bridge balance unit for a dynamic range from d-c to 10,000 cps.

Q   How do you compensate for temperature variations across the strain gage elements? Remember that resistance of the wires varies with temperature and thus eliminates the resulting zero shift or drift.

A   Compensating resistors are placed in the bridge circuit to counteract any unbalancing effect due to temperature variations.

Q   Name four advantages of unbonded pressure transducers.

A   (1) Excellent frequency response (static or dynamic), (2) can be used at high fluid temperatures and are easy to compensate for ambient temperature effects, (3) excited by direct or alternating current, and (4) continuous resolution.

Q   Name two limitations of unbonded pressure transducers.

A   (1) Lower pressure range than bonded type, and (2) low millivolt output signal.

Q   Name four advantages of bonded-type pressure transducers.

A   (1) High pressure range, (2) a-c or d-c excitation, (3) high frequency response (dynamic and static), and (4) excellent linearity and hysteresis characteristics.

Q   What are three limitations of bonded pressure transducers?

A   (1) Lower pressure range limited, (2) low sensitivity, and (3) limited temperature range.

Q   Sketch and describe two types of potentiometric pressure transducers. Show how each works.

A   Pressure is first converted to mechanical motion. This motion positions a contacting brush on a precision resistance element. Figure 4-18 shows a transducer in which the unwinding motion of a Bourdon tube actuates a pivoted arm. The brush attached to the arm's end wipes along an accurate resistor. These elements are all mounted in the same compact cylindrical metal housing.

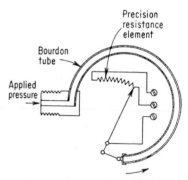

Fig. 4-18. Transducer with wound Bourdon tube.

Figure 4-19 shows a transducer in which the rectilinear motion of a metal diaphragm assembly moves an elongated brush attached to the diaphragm. The resistance element is at an acute angle to the brush, so that a long resistor may be covered with a short mechanical motion without a linkage. In the illustration the contact point is between the brush and the winding. The resistance element in the best types is wound of fine (.0007 in. diameter) precious metal wire. The brush is of precious metal. When either an a-c or d-c power is applied to the resistance element, an electrical signal is produced at the output terminals. This signal varies continuously with a change in the applied pressure.

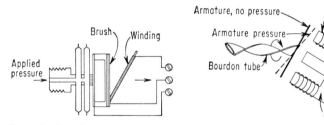

Fig. 4-19. Transducer with metal diaphragm.

Fig. 4-20. Inductive pressure transducer.

Q What are typical performance specifications of potentiometer instruments?

A They have full-scale ranges from several inches of water to many thousand psig, differential or absolute pressure. Transducers are linear with flow, altitude, or almost any arbitrary curve. Typical performance specifications may be: linearity ±0.3 per cent, resolution 0.15 per cent, temperature effect ± 0.5 per cent over most field temperature ranges. Transducers can be thousands of feet from readout equipment. They can usually handle most corrosive pressure mediums.

Q What are the major advantages of potentiometric instruments?

A (1) Often the simplest and most reliable electrical pressure devices; (2) capable of high output, will run most meters, recorders, controllers, computers without need for amplifiers; (3) low in cost compared with other types; and (4) resistance element is capable of wide variation, thus provide taps at fixed or adjustable points. These instruments provide shaped forms or other techniques to produce output linear with flow, altitude, depth, etc.

Q What are the limitations of potentiometric instruments?

A Frequency response is limited in most cases to about 10 cps.

Q Sketch and describe two types of magnetic pressure transducers.

A (1) Figure 4-20 is an inductive pressure transducer, also called a reluctance transducer. Force is measured by the change in the inductance ratio of a pair of coils. The force member, or pressure element, is either a metallic diaphragm, or a twisted metal Bourdon tube, opened at one end for pressure and closed at the other end. An armature is attached to the closed end and hangs suspended between magnetic coils. As pressure is applied, the Bourdon tube rotates and causes the armature to rotate, thus changing its relative position between the coils. The tube rotates in one direction for positive pressure, the opposite for negative pressure. Rotation causes air gaps in an electromagnetic bridge circuit to change, thereby changing circuit inductances. Gage voltage is supplied from a-c power. This inductance change can be used to amplitude-modulate a carrier voltage, determine an f-m telemetering oscillator frequency, or in some other way provide an electrical signal proportional to the measured pressure.

(2) Figure 4-21 is a linear variable differential transformer transducer (LVDT). It is an electromechanical transducer which produces an

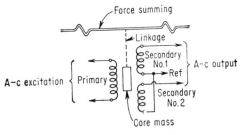

Fig. 4-21. LVDT transducer.

electrical output proportional to the displacement of a movable magnetic core inside a differential transformer. The differential transformer has three coils equally spaced on a cylindrical coil form. A rod-shaped magnetic core positioned axially inside the coil assembly provides a path for magnetic flux linking the coils. When the primary coil (center) is energized with alternating current, voltages are induced in the two secondary coils (outer), which are connected in series opposing. This means that the two voltages in the secondary coils are of opposite phase. The net output of the transformer is the difference in these voltages. The output is zero volt at one central position of the core. When the core is moved from this center (null or balance) point, the voltage induced in the coil toward which the core moves increases while it decreases in the opposite coil. The output signal is therefore directly proportional and linear with the differential voltage produced by the core position. As the core passes the null position, the output signal is equal to, but 180° out of phase with, the signal produced by the corresponding core position on the other side of null. The LVDT transducer becomes a pressure transducer when a Bourdon tube, or diaphragm, is attached to the magnetic core (Fig. 4-22). When pressure is applied to the nonmovable open end, the closed end is free to move the magnetic core in the LVDT. Thus pressure changes produce a corresponding linear electrical output signal into a carrier amplifier, a-c to d-c demodulator, or directly into an a-c readout device.

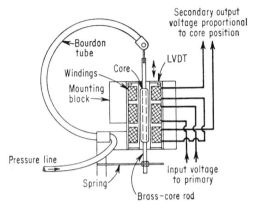

Fig. 4-22. LVDT transducer becomes a pressure transducer.

Q Name the typical performance characteristics of both types of magnetic pressure transducers.

A (1) Inductive pressure transducers have pressure ranges from 0 to 5 psig to as high as 5,000 psig, continuous resolution, frequency response up to 1,000 cps, and output signals as high as 80 mv per volt excitation. (2) LVDT pressure transducers measure pressures in ranges from 0 to 15 in. of water, up to 0 to 10,000 psig continuous resolution, frequency response up to 200 cps, and output signals as high as 1.5 volts with 10-volt 110-cps excitation.

Q What are the advantages and limitations of inductive pressure transducers?

A Advantages: (1) High output signal, (2) continuous resolution, (3) used for static or dynamic response, and (4) can be connected directly into f-m telemetering systems. But they must be (1) a-c excited only, (2) reactively and resistively balanced, (3) used for relatively low frequency response, and (4) they give erratic performance when near magnetic fields.

Q What are the advantages and limitations of LVDT pressure transducers?

A Advantages: (1) Continuous resolution, (2) high output signal, and (3) low hysteresis. But they (1) must be a-c excited only, (2) have low frequency response, and (3) must be read out by a-c instrument or through an a-c to d-c demodulator.

Q Show a capacitive pressure transducer and describe how it works.
A See Fig. 4-23. A capacitive pressure transducer uses the principle that the capacitance between two conductors, or plates, separated by a dielectric material, changes when the distance separating the plates is changed. In the pressure transducer, a stiff metal diaphragm is one plate of a variable capacitor. The other plate is mounted on an insulated electrode in the transducer case near the diaphragm separated by a dielectric. Under pressure, the diaphragm flexes and moves closer to the inner plate, thereby decreasing the capacitance reactance of the capacitor. This change in capacitance is used to unbalance a capacitance bridge circuit, amplified and used in phase-, frequency-, or amplitude-modulated carrier systems.

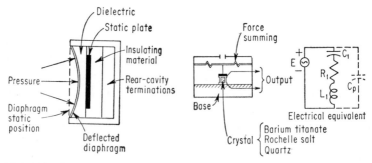

Fig. 4-23. Capacitive pressure transducer.

Fig. 4-24. Piezoelectric pressure transducer.

Q What are the advantages of capacitive pressure transducers?
A (1) Excellent frequency response, (2) simple, compact, inexpensive construction, (3) low "gravity" response—important in pressure transducers, and (4) continuous resolution.

Q Do capacitive pressure transducers have any limitations?
A Yes: (1) high output impedance, (2) long leads give erratic signals, distortion, capacitance unbalance, (3) must be reactively and resistively balanced, and (4) very sensitive to temperature variations.

Q Describe a piezoelectric pressure transducer and how it works.
A See Fig. 4-24. The piezoelectric element is made from an asymmetrical crystalline material such as barium titanite, quartz, or tourmaline. These produce an electrical potential when a force of stress or strain is exerted on the crystal. When a piezoelectric element is attached to a

stiff metallic pressure diaphragm and encased, it is called a piezoelectric pressure transducer. It will produce a small electrical output signal directly proportional to a change in applied pressure, without need of external gage power supply. The output signal is high in voltage amplitude and high in frequency response. The crystal has a very high output impedance (low current output) and cannot measure d-c or static pressures.

Q What signal conditioning equipment is needed to use a piezoelectric pressure transducer with readout systems such as analog or digital potentiometers, recording oscillographs, and magnetic tape recorders?

A Since piezoelectric transducers do not respond to static conditions, an a-c amplifier is needed to increase the crystal output signal strength for readout devices. Often an a-c cathode follower preamplifier ahead of the amplifier is desirable to match the very high crystal impedance to the amplifier input impedance.

Q What are four major advantages of piezoelectric transducers?

A (1) Small size and rugged construction, (2) self-generating (no power supply required), (3) negligible phase shift, and (4) dynamic response only, which allows for use in static, or zero, suppression of static pressure level.

Q What are four limitations of piezoelectric transducers?

A (1) Sensitive to temperature changes, (2) high impedance output requiring complex electronic signal conditioning system, (3) long cables generate noise and spurious signals, and (4) cannot measure static pressures.

Q Describe an electrical pressure transducer most often used in industrial processes where long transmission distances make pneumatic pressure transmission expensive and ambient weather conditions cause transmission problems.

A Process pressures (gage, absolute, vacuum, and compound vacuum and pressure) are effectively measured and transmitted electrically to a central process control center using the force-balance electrical pressure transmitter (Fig. 4-25). Process pressure is applied to a mechanical pressure element (Bourdon tube or bellows), which deflects. This deflection is transferred to an input spring which exerts a force on the force-balance beam and changes the air gap between two pieces of ferrite in a detector assembly. A detector assembly is in the input section of a transistorized oscillator circuit whose inductance changes as the detector air gap changes. The oscillator acts as a variable resistor and modulates the current in the transmitter output between 4 and 20 ma d-c for full-scale pressure input. The power supply is in the receiver. A portion of the 4- to 20-ma current output is fed back to a magnet unit, producing a balancing force on the other end of the force beam that is equal and opposite to the input force. The transducer mechanism is weatherproof or explosionproof housed. The output signal is enough to be fed directly into most readout devices and controllers.

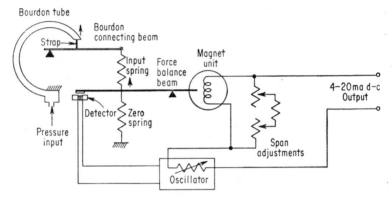

Fig. 4-25. Force-balance electrical pressure transmitter.

Q What are typical performance specifications for a force-balance electrical pressure transmitter?

A (1) Pressure ranges from 0 to 10 in. of water, to as high as 0 to 10,000 psig, with accuracies of ±½ per cent. (2) Frequency response from d-c to 15 cps. (3) Outputs of 4 to 20 ma d-c, 100 to 500 mv, 0.25 to 1.25 volts, and 2.5 to 12.5 volts.

Q Name four advantages of a force-balance electrical pressure transducer.

A (1) Accurate, (2) most suitable for industrial process conditions, (3) high output, and (4) wide pressure and vacuum ranges.

Q What are three limitations of force-balance electrical pressure transducers?

A (1) Large size, (2) low frequency response, and (3) sensitive to high ambient temperatures (above 160°F).

Q What is the most commonly used instrument for measuring industrial process vacuums in the ranges from 0 to 100 mm of mercury to 0 to 760 mm of mercury?

A A dual spring and bellows absolute pressure, mechanical or electrical transducer as an indicator, recorder, or controller. See Fig. 4-11 for details.

Q What is meant by the term *high-vacuum measurement?*
A High-vacuum measurement is the determination of gas pressures in the range from 10 mm of mercury to below 2×10^{-12} absolute (about one-billionth of atmospheric pressure divided by one million).

Q List seven examples of high-vacuum measurement in process applications.
A (1) Dehydration in drug processing, (2) purification in food processes, (3) distillation processes in the chemical industry, (4) evaporation of metals and metallic salts in certain metal production and optical coatings, (5) impregnation of capacitors, transformer windings, and textiles, (6) outer space simulating chambers, and (7) vacuum melting pressures.

Q How are industrial high-vacuum measuring instruments classified?
A By the principle of measurement: (1) thermal-conductivity vacuum gages and (2) ionization vacuum gages.

Q Describe two types of thermal vacuum gages and how they work.
A Pirani and thermocouple vacuum gages measure the total pressure of condensable vapors and permanent gases in a vacuum system. They operate on the principle that energy dissipated from a heated surface has a temperature proportional to the pressure of the surrounding gas. Thermal conductivity varies for different gases. These gages can be calibrated for any gas and vapor in a vacuum system. Thermal gages are used in the vacuum range between 1 and 1,000 microns (one-thousandth of a millimeter of mercury is equal to 1 micron). The Pirani gage (Fig. 4-26) operates on the principle that heat loss from a filament of resist-

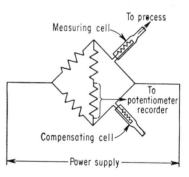

Fig. 4-26. Pirani gage.

ance wire carrying a constant electric current depends on the gaseous pressure surrounding the filament. In the range from 1 micron to 0.5 mm of mercury, this heat loss varies with changes in ambient pressure. A vacuum system measuring element is an open-ended steel tube which houses the coil of resistance wire. A second closed-end metal tube houses a resistance coil sealed in a vacuum that is far below 1 micron of mercury. This tube acts as a temperature compensating gage to balance out any false pressure indications from temperature changes. These two tubes are connected in a Wheatstone bridge circuit, together with two legs of equal fixed resistance. Current flows through the resistance coil in the measuring tube when constant power is applied to the bridge circuit. The resistance of the coil varies with its temperature. Since the temperature is governed by the heat loss from the wire, and the heat loss is proportional to the pressure, the resistance in this leg of the bridge circuit is proportional to the pressure.

The Wheatstone bridge circuit is balanced when the resistances of all legs are equal. A change in resistance in one leg unbalances the bridge, thus causing a current to flow through the bridge output terminals. Since two of the bridge's legs comprise equal fixed resistances while the other two legs comprise the measuring and compensating gages, any unbalance of the bridge circuit must be affected by the measuring or compensating gages. The compensating gage changes resistance with temperature changes only. Then any change in ambient temperature is compensated and the bridge output current is directly proportional to the vacuum measurement. The output current is read out on any millivolt or microampere measuring device (indicator, recorder, controller). Pirani gages generally have two scales; the higher is nonlinear, the lower is linear.

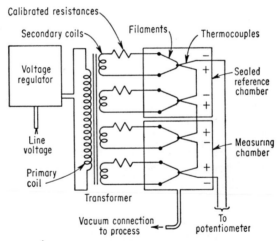

Fig. 4-27. Thermocouple gage.

Thermocouple gages (Fig. 4-27) use one to four filaments which are uniformly and continuously heated. Two of the four filaments in the measuring chamber are exposed to the vacuum under measurement. The other two are sealed in a reference chamber at a pressure of 1 micron. A small thermocouple is attached to each filament and connected so that the two in the reference chamber and the two in the measuring chamber are in series. Two sets of thermocouples are connected so that their emf's oppose each other. The temperature of the heated junctions varies with the amount of heat conducted away from the junctions by the gas in the chambers. Since the gas in the measuring chamber varies with its pressure, or vacuum, and the gas in the reference chamber varies only with a change in ambient temperature, the temperature of the thermocouple junctions varies with the vacuum in the measuring chamber. Output millivoltage from the two measuring chamber thermocouples is nonlinear and can be read out on an indicating, recording, or controlling potentiometer scale or chart, calibrated in pressure (microns).

Q What are the advantages and limitations of Pirani gages?
A Pirani gages (having two scales) provide better readability in the micron range than thermocouple gages, and readings are more accurate. They are sensitive, yet rugged for industrial use, especially when used as leak detectors. But Pirani gages are more susceptible to zero drift than thermal gages.

Q What are the advantages and limitations of thermocouple gages?
A They are simple, rugged, inexpensive, and less susceptible to zero drift than Pirani gages. But thermal gages are less sensitive and have only one scale; thus they are somewhat less accurate.

Q Describe three ionization vacuum gages and how they operate to measure vacuum in the ranges (1) 10 to 10^{-3} mm of mercury, (2) 0.1 to 10^{-7} mm of mercury, and (3) 10^{-3} to 2×10^{-12} mm of mercury.
A Ionization gages work on the principle that, when gas molecules collide with electrons, ions are formed. This formation of ions varies linearly with the gas pressure at pressures below 10^{-3} mm of mercury. Measurement of this ion current can be calibrated in units of gas pressure or vacuum.

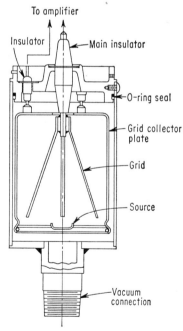

Fig. 4-28. Alphatron ionization gage.

(1) An alpha-particle ionization gage (Fig. 4-28) measures vacuum in the range 10 to 10^{-3} mm of mercury. A radioactive isotope sealed

in a metal vacuum capsule along with a grid and collector plate is the source of alpha particles (electrons). An isotope source is inserted at one end of an ionization chamber and the vacuum system is connected at the other end. When gas under vacuum is applied to the ionization chamber, the alpha particles bombard the gas molecules, causing a loss of positively charged ions which collect on the grid structure. This is called ionization. When the ions collect on the grid structure they become negatively charged, then flow through the grid electrode. This is called the ionization current. Current flow increases as the number of ions increase. The ion number increases with gas pressure increase in the ionization chamber. But the ionization current is extremely low and must be amplified before readout on a milliampere or millivolt measuring circuit. Readout is usually obtained with recording potentiometers calibrated to any of three ranges, between 10 mm and 1 micron of mercury, to accuracies of $\pm\frac{1}{4}$ per cent of the range.

(2) Cold-cathode ionization gages, sometimes called *Philips* or *discharge* gages, measure vacuums in the range of 0.1 to 10^{-7} mm of mercury (Fig. 4-29). Cold-cathode gages work on the principle of meas-

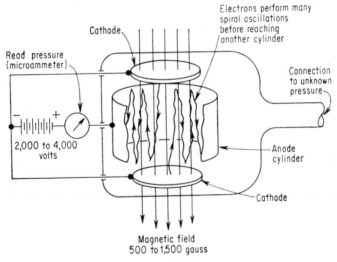

Fig. 4-29. Cold-cathode ionization gage.

uring an ion current produced by a high-voltage discharge. The sensing tube consists of a copper envelope, which houses a center loop electrode and steel pole pieces, surrounded by an external permanent magnet. When a high-voltage discharge is generated in the cathode, electrons flow in a spiral path across the magnetic field to an anode. Electrons collide on the way with the gas molecules in the tube. This spiral action increases the possibility of collision and sustains the flow discharge at lower pressures. The resulting ionization current is measured on a microampere measuring circuit and read out on a nonlinear scale or chart calibrated for vacuum. Often the indicator has three or four scales for covering a broad vacuum range.

(3) Hot-filament ionization gages cover the vacuum range from 10^{-3} to 2×10^{-12} mm of mercury (Fig. 4-30). The electrons emitted from a heated filament in the sensing glass tube are accelerated toward a positively charged cylindrical grid. Some electrons pass into the space between the grid and a negatively charged collector, then collide with gas molecules from the vacuum system, thus producing positive ions. Positive ions then collect on a negative collector. With a constant filament heater voltage applied and a constant emission current, the number of positive ions formed is proportional to pressure in the range below 10^{-3} mm of mercury.

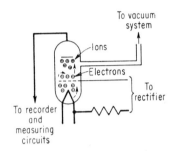

Fig. 4-30. Hot-filament ionization gage.

Extremely low ion current flow from the collector is amplified. Readout is on a microammeter or millivolt recorder in units of vacuum on a linear scale or chart. This is the most accurate gage for pressures below 10^{-3} mm of mercury.

Q What are the advantages and limitations of alpha-particle ionization gages?

A (1) Broad linear range, (2) total pressure indication, (3) instantaneous response to pressure changes, (4) emission stability, (5) long life, (6) immune to burnout in pressure surges, and (7) rugged. But it will not operate in the lower pressure ranges of the cold-cathode or hot-filament gages and its output current is extremely small.

Q What are the advantages and limitations of cold-cathode gages?
A (1) Very low pressure range, (2) high output current (may not require a preamplifier), (3) rugged and easily cleaned sensing tubes, (4) no filaments to burn out, (5) does not subject the gas to thermal abuse, and (6) adaptable to leak detecting jobs. But because of the high charge discharge they must be cleaned often and their accuracy is about 10 per cent.

Q   What are the advantages and disadvantages of hot-filament ionization gages?

A   Hot-filament gages operate over extremely low pressure ranges, with a linear scale calibration over a broad range. Their sensing elements are easily degassed. But since air pressures higher than a few microns cause deterioration of hot filaments, hot-filament gages cannot be used above 0.5 micron, and pressure surges cause filament burnout. Safety circuits are often used to prevent this. Hot filaments are susceptible to deterioration from certain gases.

SUGGESTED READING

Recommended Practices, sold by Instrument Society of America, 530 William Penn Place, Pittsburgh, Pa.

    ISA—RP 2.1, *Manometer Tables*, 31 pages

    ISA—RP 11.1, *Mercury Handling*, 7 pages

Books

    Hernandez, J. S.: *Introduction to Transducers for Instrumentation*, Statham Instruments, Inc., Los Angeles, Calif., 1958.

    Elonka, Steve, and Julian Bernstein: *Standard Industrial Electronics Questions and Answers*, vols. I and II, McGraw-Hill Book Company, Inc., New York, to be published in 1964.

    Elonka, Steve, and Joseph F. Robinson: *Standard Plant Operator's Questions and Answers*, vols. I and II, McGraw-Hill Book Company, Inc., New York, 1959.

    Elonka, Steve, and Quaid W. Minich: *Standard Refrigeration and Air Conditioning Questions and Answers*, McGraw-Hill Book Company, Inc., New York, 1961.

    Elonka, Steve: *Plant Operator's Manual*, McGraw-Hill Book Company, Inc., New York, 1956.

5

LEVEL MEASURING SYSTEMS

Q What is level?
A Level is the height of a liquid or solid contained in a vessel above a reference or datum line. Measuring the level helps you determine the volume or weight of liquid or solids in a vessel.

Q Define the units of level.
A Level is expressed directly in units of liquid or solid height (inches or feet). It can be calibrated to express volume (cubic inches or cubic feet), weight (pounds and tons), and capacity (gallons and barrels). To convert to gallons, divide volume in cubic inches by 231.

Q What level ranges are common in plant and process work?
A Level measurements are often limited by vessel height. Ranges from as low as 1 in. of water to several hundred feet are measured with accuracies within 1/32 in. in the lower ranges.

Q For what process and plant uses are level measurements important?
A In the operation of continuous, semicontinuous, and batch processes and plant equipment: (1) to determine and control quantity of material in physical or chemical processes, (2) to maintain control in capacity tanks used to supply a steady flow through a process, and (3) to determine continuously the quantity of contents of storage tanks for operational and cost accounting purposes. Level measurement and control is used in chemical, petroleum, paper, food, textile, water treatment, and waste treatment industries. Also in operation of power plant machinery. The trend in continuous processing is toward smaller storage capacity. When proper level measurement and control is correctly applied, vessel size and storage inventories may be reduced, and process efficiency increased.

Q Name the major categories of liquid level measuring methods and how they are classified.
A Liquid level can be measured using (1) direct, and (2) inferential methods. Direct methods include (*a*) visual indicators, (*b*) floats, and

117

(*c*) electrical conductivity liquid level measuring instruments. Inferential methods include (*a*) displacement types, (*b*) hydrostatic pressure types, (*c*) electrical capacitance, and (*d*) radiation types.

Q   Describe a visual liquid level indicator and its application.

A   The gage glass (Fig. 5-1) is a simple glass tube attached at both ends to a vessel containing liquid. Since liquid seeks its own level, the liquid remains at the same level in both the vessel and the glass tube. Liquid level is read along a calibrated scale attached to the gage glass. Gage glasses reinforced with a forged metal housing and protected with mica withstand boiler pressures up to 3,200 psi, temperatures up to 1000°F. Special variations are used for low-temperature, corrosive, and viscous liquid applications. Remote viewing is often done with mirrors and television.

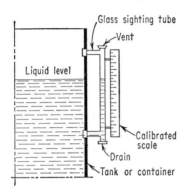

Fig. 5-1. Visual liquid level indicator.

Q   Describe a simple float level gage. How does it work?

A   The float level gage (Fig. 5-2) detects the position of a liquid surface inside a vessel. The principle is that of a buoyant member (the float) floating on the liquid's surface, which changes position as the liquid level varies. Float movement can be converted by mechanical linkage to indicate or to operate (1) switches (for detection), (2) solenoid valves (for control), (3) mechanical valves, (4) pneumatic transmitters, (5) pulleys and cables, or (6) electrical transmitters. A simple ball-float indicator has a hollow metal ball attached to a rod, which is fastened to a rotary shaft. The shaft operates an indicating pointer across a scale calibrated for inches of liquid level. The level

Fig. 5-2. Simple float level method.

range is independent of vessel shape and size. The rod's angle of rotation is limited to ±30° from the horizontal reference. The level range depends only on the connecting rod's length (usually from 0 to 24 in. length). Float diameters up to 12 in. are used.

Q   Name the most common use for ball-float level gages.

A   For detecting and indicating levels in open tanks, sumps, and reservoirs, and to control flow in or out of these vessels over a narrow range.

Q What type of ball-float devices are used for level measurement in vessels where pressures are greater than atmosphere, or under vacuum conditions?

A (1) A mechanical linked ball-float device is often placed inside the vessel, with its connecting rod extend-
ing outside through a pressuretight stuffing box. It works like the ball-float gage just described. (2) A cage-type float-operated level gage is often used to measure level in tanks under vacuum or pressure. In Fig. 5-3 the float cage is mounted on the outside vessel wall. The lower connection is from the cast metal cage's bottom into the liquid, and the upper connection is into the vapor. As the level in the tank changes, the level in the cage changes an equal amount. The metal ball float in the cage rises or falls with

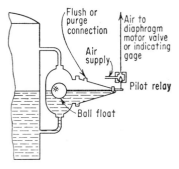

Fig. 5-3. Level indicators for closed vessels.

the liquid surface. The float's movement is transmitted through a packed rotary shaft, to move a valve stem or to operate a pneumatic pilot relay. The maximum range is limited to 15 in. by practical cage size.

Q Name four advantages of using float-cage-type level gages.

A (1) Measures levels in tanks under pressure or vacuum, (2) can measure interface level between two different liquids (using weighted float), (3) measures corrosive liquid levels (when properly purged), especially when the ball float cannot be inserted in a vessel, and (4) useful for remote indication by pneumatic transmission.

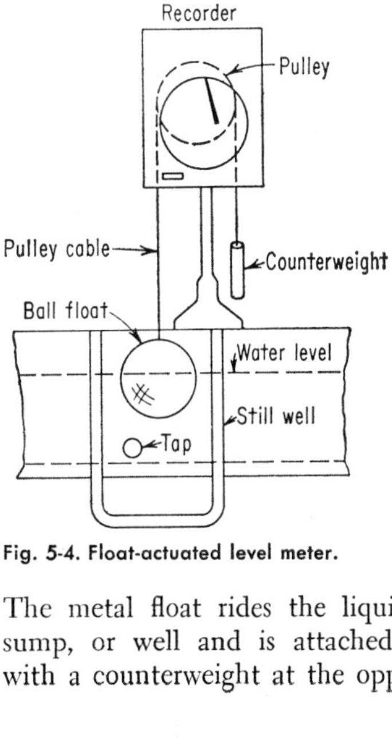

Q Describe a cable-and-pulley float-actuated level gage.

A The float level gage (Fig. 5-4) is used mostly to operate level recorders.

Fig. 5-4. Float-actuated level meter.

The metal float rides the liquid's surface in an open tank, reservoir, sump, or well and is attached to a pulley by a stainless-steel cable with a counterweight at the opposite end. A cam on the shaft carrying the pulley rotates as the float's vertical movement causes the pulley to rotate. A cam follower works the pen or pointer of the level recorder or indicator. The pulley, cam, and cam follower are inside a housing on the back of an instrument case. The same float can mechanically drive a counterbalanced, calibrated tape past a fixed reference point in a sighting glass. Or a noncalibrated tape or cable can drive a dial indicator or counter calibrated in units of height. Remote indication can be done with pneumatic or electric transmission systems. Level ranges from 0 to 10 ft for float and pulley types, and from 0 to 100 ft or more with calibrated tapes. Accuracies are $\pm\frac{1}{8}$ in. The calibrated-tape type of liquid level gage is used mostly in large bulk storage tanks and in automatic tank gaging systems.

Q   Name four advantages of float-actuated level systems.
A   (1) Level easily checked with dip stick, (2) no purges needed, (3) accessible float easy to clean, and (4) readings can be transmitted to a central data collecting point.

Q   What are the four limitations of float-actuated level systems?
A   (1) Narrow range of operation (except for calibrated-tape type), (2) float must be cleaned often, (3) fast-flowing liquids or surface agitation cause errors, and (4) solids in liquid alter float buoyancy characteristics.

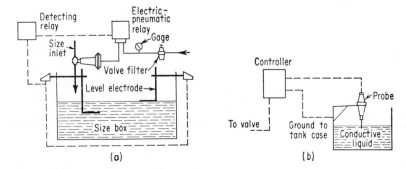

Fig. 5-5. Electrical conductivity indicates surface level.

Q   Describe a direct level detecting system which makes use of electrical conductivity.
A   Figure 5-5 shows a system which uses a liquid's ability to conduct an electric current. Liquid completes a circuit through a detecting relay or controller, a metal electrode, and the grounded metal wall of the vessel. As long as the liquid is in contact with the electrode, current flows

through the circuit. When the level drops below the electrode's end, the circuit is disconnected. Because the detecting relay distinguishes between these two conditions, it makes or breaks electrical contacts to operate a control valve, light a signal, or sound an alarm. Only one electrode is needed for smooth, nonfoaming liquids. But where turbulence or foaming is common, two electrodes are placed at nearly the same level (separated by a short vertical height) to maintain contact with the liquid surface. One electrode actuates the circuit to fill the tank (opening an inlet valve) and the other closes the inlet valve. There is no restriction to level range. But electric detecting relays operate best with liquids having resistivities from 20,000 to 20,000,000 ohm-cm. The interface level between a conductive liquid and a nonconductive liquid can be detected by an electrode system.

Q   What are four advantages of electrical conductivity level systems?
A   (1) Simplicity, (2) inexpensive, (3) flexible, and (4) unlimited range.

Q   What are the limitations of electrical conductivity level systems?
A   No indication or record, and cannot be used on liquids which are (1) nonconductive, (2) electrically viscous (build up deposits on electrodes which short-circuit to the tank wall), and (3) chemically corrosive to stainless steel.

Q   Name three processes which use electrode level systems.
A   (1) Paper (size-box levels), (2) textile (size box), (3) glass (special glass tank level system).

Q   Describe a displacement-type liquid level gage and how it works.
A   These gages operate on Archimedes' principle, which states that a body wholly or partially submerged in a liquid is buoyed up by a force equal to the liquid's weight that is displaced by the body. This force can be measured in terms of liquid level. Figure 5-6 shows a tubular-displacement float and torque-tube assembly. The displacer housing is connected at bottom and top to the vessel's side. Then liquid can enter and surround the displacer, indicate liquid level, and cause a pneumatic signal to be transmitted to an indicator controller or final con-

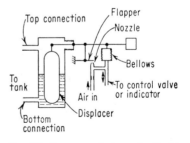

Fig. 5-6. Buoyancy displacer for liquid level.

trol element. The displacer housing is often mounted on the tank's top. The displacer is fastened to one end of a support rod, while the rod's other end is held by a pivot bearing. The torque tube is placed at 90° to the support rod and attached to it at the pivot point. The torque tube has a pressuretight inner-end fitting and a flanged member bolted to form a pressure seal with its housing. The rotary shaft inside the torque tube is attached to the inner-end fitting. The rotary shaft's other end can be attached to a pointer but is usually attached to a pneumatic transmitting unit (pilot relay).

When there is no liquid in the displacer housing, the entire displacer weight exerts a downward force on the support rod's free end. This causes a turning movement in the torque tube and the rotary shaft within it. Liquid rising around the displacer buoys it up by a force equal to the weight of liquid it displaces. That decreases the torque tube and rotary shaft turning movement proportional to the level. This movement is converted into a pneumatic signal through a pneumatic pilot relay or force-balance transmitter for either transmission or control. Displacers and housings are made from steel, Monel, and stainless steels. Displacer sizes range from 14 in. up to as long as 180 in.

Q Can displacement level gages be used for measuring the interface level between two immiscible (nonmixing) liquids of different specific gravities?
A Yes. The displacer level gage is most often used for interface levels between different liquids, liquids and gases, and water and another liquid. Displacer design is generally weighted or made longer than regular length for interface uses.

Q What are the advantages and limitations of displacement level gages?
A The range of level measurement is broadened; accuracy and sensitivity are excellent. This gage withstands higher pressures and temperatures than float types. But it must be cleaned often to prevent solids buildup or corrosion of the displacer. The gage must have a specific gravity adjustment. This is the most popular type of nonindicating liquid level controller for semicontinuous and batch process applications.

Q Hydrostatic liquid level measuring systems are the most widely used in continuous process applications. How are they classified?
A They infer the liquid level in a vessel from a pressure-head measurement, where the head is the weight of liquid above a reference line. Height of level H is equal to the pressure due to hydrostatic head P divided by the density of liquid D, $H = P/D$, irrespective of liquid volume. Pressure measuring methods used for liquid level gages in open vessels are classified as (1) pressure gage, (2) diaphragm box, and (3) meter-body type. In closed vessels the meter-body differential pressure type is used.

Q How are pressure gages used to measure liquid level?

A See Fig. 5-7. In the basic pressure gage method, liquid in an open vessel is connected from the vessel's minimum operating level to any of the elastic static pressure measuring elements described in Chap. 4, "Pressure and Vacuum Measuring Systems." Pressure is directly proportional to the head (height) of liquid in the open vessel. The pressure actuating element is mechanically linked to an indicator pointer, recorder, pen transmitter, or controller. A scale or chart is calibrated in level units. The actuating element should have a

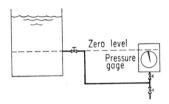

Fig. 5-7. Static pressure method in open vessel.

range equivalent to the static head of liquid in the vessel and should be installed at the same horizontal level as the minimum operating level. Ranges of level from 0 to 0.1 in., to unlimited maximum, can be measured with mechanical or electrical static pressure elements. Corrosive, dirty, or viscous liquids require a sealing liquid and pot, diaphragm, or bellows or a purge system. Any of the electrical pressure transducers described in Chap. 4 are also applicable to this liquid level measuring method.

Q What are the advantages and limitations of pressure gage level methods?

A This method is simple and inexpensive for clear liquids. Electrical flush diaphragm pressure transducers can be used for almost any type of liquids regardless of dirt, viscosity, sediment, or certain corrosive characteristics. This method is limited because the desired location in a vessel is often impossible. When the vessel's side cannot be pierced, the horizontal center line of the mechanical pressure actuating element should be installed at the same height as the minimum operating level of the vessel if practical. Dirty, corrosive, and viscous liquids require seal or purge systems that are hard to maintain.

Q Describe diaphragm boxes used for liquid level measurements.

A Diaphragm boxes measure liquid level when inserted in an open vessel and connected to a pressure gage. A flexible Neoprene diaphragm seals the liquid from the air inside the tubing that goes to the pressure sensing element in the instrument. Variations in the static pressure exerted by the liquid head produce corresponding variations in the pressure of the air trapped in the upper portion of the bronze box and gage line. There are two types of diaphragm boxes.

Figure 5-8 shows the open-type box which is immersed directly in the liquid at the minimum level. It is used for liquids (1) that will not corrode the bronze box or its copper tubing, (2) that contain suspended solids. Liquid enters openings in the bottom of the box under the diaphragm.

Figure 5-9 shows a closed-type box, mounted outside a vessel connected through a tap to the liquid near minimum (zero) level. Corrosive or viscous liquid levels can be measured using a seal pot with oil to protect

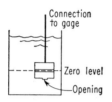

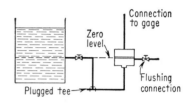

Fig. 5-8. Open diaphragm box method.

Fig. 5-9. Closed diaphragm box method.

a closed-type diaphragm box. Minimum range is 1 ft of water; maximum is as high as 50 ft of water. The closed-type box can be mounted as far as 50 ft from the vessel. It can be flushed to prevent trapped sediment and solids from collecting, which cause false level readings.

Q   What are the advantages and limitations of the diaphragm-box level system?

A   When a diaphragm box is used for level measurement in open vessels, the pressure instrument need not be placed at the same horizontal level as the minimum tank level. The instrument is inexpensive, easy to clean, simple, and easily flushed when used with liquids with entrained sediment and solids. But it is limited in level range also to liquid temperatures below 150°F. Besides, its dynamic response is slow.

Q   Describe an air purge, or "bubble," liquid level measuring system.

A   The measuring system in Fig. 5-10 uses a pressure element connected to an air line immersed in liquid at its minimum level in an open vessel. Air at constant volume and pressure is applied to the air line so that bubbles of air escape slowly through the open end at the vessel's bottom. Pressure in the air line is then equal to the back pressure exerted by the head of liquid. The pressure element which measures this static pressure is calibrated directly into liquid level units. Level ranges from a minimum of 0 to 5 in. of water, to an upper limit dependent on the air supply pressure used to balance the liquid head.

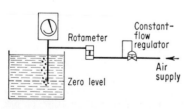

Fig. 5-10. Air purge for liquid level system.

Q   What components are needed for an air purge level system?

A   Constant air supply needs an air compressor, air filter, pressure reducing valve, sight-feed bubbler, rotameter, regulating needle valve, and shutoff valves. The bubble tube's submerged end is closed. Bubbles are emitted through a series of carefully designed circular and V-notched holes, cut around the tube's side. The air line and bubble tube pass through a standpipe in the open air vessel's top. Where agitator blades make such an arrangement impossible, the air pressure line can be tapped into the vessel's side at the minimum level. The pressure gage need not be installed at the same level. Not only air, but inert gases, water, and other liquids or combination of air and water can be used for purging.

Q   What precautions must you take when measuring widely varying liquid levels using an air purge system?

A   Where level varies widely, air consumption will be much greater at lower levels. Increased air flow will cause a measuring lag and inaccurate chart readings. A differential pressure regulator connected across the reducing valve or regulator will cause the air to flow at a uniform rate, regardless of liquid head, thus overcoming any measuring lag.

Q   What are the advantages and limitations of the purge level method?

A   Since the purge fluid actually purges the system, this method is ideal for (1) corrosive fluids, especially where no adequate seals are available, (2) viscous liquids, (3) liquids with entrained or suspended solids, and (4) liquids which will precipitate solids when cooled. Installation is much easier and unrestricted since the measuring element need not be placed at the same level as the minimum liquid level. But range limitations are imposed by the pressure of the purge supply line and the range of the measuring element used. Another limitation may be the need of an air supply.

Q   Can differential pressure measuring elements (mercury manometers, bellows meter, differential converters) be used for liquid level measurements in open tanks?

A   Yes. The high-pressure tap of the differential pressure element is connected to the vessel at the minimum level point. The low-pressure tap is left open to the atmosphere. Purge systems may be used for level ranges from 0 to 2 in. of water, to as high as 0 to 800 in. of water.

Q   Describe the most common method of measuring liquid levels in closed vessels under pressure or vacuum conditions.

A   The static pressure method (Fig. 5-11) is commonly used for measuring level in closed vessels, under pressure or vacuum. Here, pressure above the liquid is added to the liquid head and must be compensated. Differential pressure instruments (mercury manometers, bellows meters, differential converters, and transmitters described in Chap. 3) are needed. Connections from the differential pressure instrument are made to taps in the vessel at maximum and minimum levels. Between the instrument and maximum level tap is a constant reference leg. This is filled with liquid until its head is equivalent to the liquid's head in the vessel at maximum level. An instrument measures the difference in pressures at the two taps. At each tap, the total pressure detected equals the head pressure plus the pressure above the liquid. Since the pressure above the liquid is identical in both cases, it cancels out. Therefore, the differential pressure measured by the instrument is that produced only by the

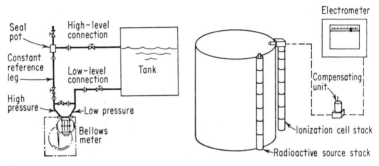

Fig. 5-11. Static pressure method for closed vessels.

Fig. 5-12. Radioactive source used to measure liquid level.

liquid's head in the vessel and is independent of the pressure or vacuum within the vessel. Differential pressure elements are effective in the range from 0 to 2 in. of water to as high as 0 to 800 in. of water level, at pressures as high as 2,500 psi. Use suppression adjustments when it is impractical to install an outer or constant reference leg. To avoid measuring lags, place the measuring element close to the vessel.

Q How is interface level measured with differential pressure elements?
A Interface level between two immiscible liquids of differing specific gravities can be measured by differential pressure elements if the less dense liquid always covers the upper tap. If the level is not clearly defined, the element will measure an average position of the interface.

Q What three methods of level measurements use radioactive sources?
A These level measuring methods are based on the principle that the number of gamma rays, which are produced by the source penetrating a layer of liquid, change as the thickness of the layer changes. As the layer's thickness increases, the number of gamma rays penetrating it decreases. Radiation (gamma rays) passes through the containing vessel

and is detected by a Geiger counter or ionization cells. The output current of the cells is calibrated in terms of liquid level. Figure 5-12 shows a typical arrangement. Here a stack of radioactive source is mounted outside the vessel, across a chord of the vessel from a stack of gas ionization cells. These cells detect and count the number of gamma rays and convert this number into proportional output current. Ionization cell output is amplified in a preamplifier and read out by an electrometer recorder, whose chart is calibrated in liquid level units. A compensating cell cancels out radiation needed to penetrate the vessel walls. As the level rises, the positive current generated by the measuring cells decreases, while the negative current from the compensating cell remains constant. As the level rises, there is a net increase in negative current.

The electrometer amplifier's readout instrument reads upscale for an increasing negative current, thus providing a conventional upscale reading scale and chart for increasing level. In another method, several radioactive sources are enclosed in thermowells. Intensity of radiation varies inversely with the depth of liquid. Radiation is measured by a Geiger counter whose output is amplified and read out on a recording potentiometer in units of liquid level. The third method of measuring level is a float which carries a radioactive source which rides on the liquid surface between vertical guides. For controlling liquid level at a specific point, the radioactive source is mounted inside the vessel at that point. The detector is mounted outside the vessel at the same point. As the level changes around the source, the change in penetration activates control action. The range of level measurements with these systems is limited to 2 ft with a fixed source and 15 ft in a float installation. Other methods are limited by the height of the radioactive source stack. These systems must be calibrated for each specific installation.

Q   Name the advantages and limitations of radioactive level methods.
A   Protection of personnel from overexposure to radioactive radiation must be taken. But level instruments using radioactive sources solve difficult level problems where (1) physical connections from inside to outside of tank are prohibited, (2) cleaning is difficult, (3) entrained solids give faulty readings, (4) corrosive, foamy, viscous liquids are used, and (5) sanitary conditions must be maintained.

Q   What is the best way to measure level when the liquid (1) is corrosive, (2) has suspended solids, (3) is viscous and solidifies at room temperature, (4) is volatile, (5) is explosive, (6) is sanitary, and (7) tends to foam?
A   For (1) use liquid, diaphragm, or bellows seals or purge systems to protect the static or differential pressure instruments. Use floats, displacers, and electrodes of corrosion-resistant materials. Use radioactive

source systems as they do not contact the liquid. For (2) if there is no trouble when agitated, but a problem when stagnant, use sediment traps, diaphragm seals, or purges. For (3) apply heat by steam coils around the measuring element and connecting piping, or use liquid seals, or ball-float devices. For (4) if volatile liquids such as light hydrocarbons and lacquers vaporize in connecting piping and meter bodies, arrange the piping to eliminate vapor pockets, or use liquid seals. For (5) use extreme care to avoid leaks and seals in connecting lines. For (6) use sanitary liquid or stainless-steel seal. For (7) keep the connecting piping completely filled with liquid.

Q   How do you determine (1) volume of liquid in a vessel having a uniform cross-sectional area, (2) weight of liquid in this vessel?
A   (1) If level measurement is to determine the volume of liquid in a vessel, then measuring the level height is best because the volume measured is independent of liquid density, which can vary with liquid temperature changes. Volume V is equal to cross-sectional area A of vessel, multiplied by height H of the level ($V = A \times H$). If measurement of hydrostatic head pressure must be used, the volume V in the vessel at a given level is equal to the cross-sectional area A of the vessel multiplied by pressure P due to hydrostatic head. Divide both by the density D of the liquid [$V = (A \times P)/D$].

   (2) If measuring the level to determine the weight of liquid in the vessel, measure the pressure due to hydrostatic head because head is independent of liquid density. Here weight W equals the cross-sectional area A multiplied by the pressure P due to hydrostatic head ($W = A \times P$).

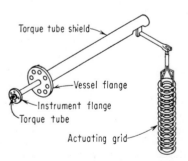

Fig. 5-13. Grid unit measures solids level.

If direct height measurement is used, weight W is equal to area A times density D times height H ($W = A \times D \times H$).

Q   Give three methods of measuring the level of dry solids in a vessel continuously.
A   (1) Grid unit. (2) Gamma-ray gage (described in detail under Radioactive Liquid Level Gages). Its application is similar for measuring the level of both solids and liquids. (3) Weigh the vessel.

Q   Describe a grid unit used for measuring solids level.
A   A grid response unit (Fig. 5-13) consists of thin metal rings connected by rods to form a vertical cylindrical-shaped member. The grid

Labels in figure: Torque tube shield; Vessel flange; Instrument flange; Torque tube; Actuating grid is designed specifically for each application and vessel and is installed partially immersed in the moving solids bed. Then, as the level rises or falls, the forces on the grid increase or decrease in proportion to the level. These forces are transmitted through a torque tube to a pneumatic pilot relay for transmission to a readout instrument or controller whose chart and scale are graduated in level units. The range depends on the grid's length. A grid unit can withstand temperatures to 1800°F and pressures to 2,000 psi.

Q Where are grid level units used?
A Grid units are used for measuring the level of moving granular solids in storage bins, continuous contact coking units, and petrochemical processing units such as hypersorption and hyperforming vessels.

Q How can the level of solids be determined by weighing the vessel? Name several weighing methods.
A When the cross-sectional area of a uniform vessel is known, the level of solids can be found very accurately by continuously measuring the weight of the entire vessel and subtracting the weight of the empty vessel (see Chap. 11). Level H is then equal to weight W, divided by the product of cross-sectional area A times solids density D $[H = W/(A \times D)]$. The most practical method of weighing large vessels is to install load cells (strain gage transducers) under the four corners of the vessel supporting members connected electrically in a Wheatstone bridge circuit. Variations in weight are read out continuously on a recorder. Smaller vessels are weighed on industrial scales or crane scales. Pneumatic weighing systems are also used for vessel weighing.

Q Name five methods detecting solids level at a fixed point in a vessel.
A (1) Spring-backed metal diaphragm, (2) probe deflection, (3) electrical contact, (4) rotating paddle, and (5) electric capacitance. These devices are used mostly for actuating alarms and indicator lights in solids handling and storage.

SUGGESTED READING

Books
    Elonka, Steve, and Joseph F. Robinson: *Standard Plant Operator's Questions and Answers*, vols. I and II, McGraw-Hill Book Company, Inc., New York, 1959.
    Elonka, Steve, and Julian Bernstein: *Standard Industrial Electronics Questions and Answers*, vols. I and II, McGraw-Hill Book Company, Inc., New York, to be published in 1964.

6

ANALYSIS MEASURING SYSTEMS

Q Define briefly the broad field of measuring systems used for product analysis.

A Proper analytical control ensures product quality throughout all phases of process control. Usually the starting materials are monitored for the content of the desired component, because the final yield of the product will be based on this value. Besides the starting materials, the materials at each stage of the process are also monitored for checking product quality during that part of the operation. Then the end product is again monitored to ensure its quality. Analysis instruments show materials in terms of their ingredients (components) in the stream, as well as their concentrations. They develop signals indicating the material's composition. These signals, tied into the control of such process conditions as temperature, pressure, and flow, give prompt correction of deviations from product specifications. Measurement and control of process conditions also assure plant stability, and thus a better product. The varying composition of the feed streams, the increased costs of plant equipment, raw materials, and labor, and the higher prices received for premium products, all make an optimum product necessary. Analysis instruments help in achieving a better product at reduced costs.

Q How are the fundamental product analysis methods classified?

A A large variety of measuring techniques are used in analysis instruments. Each determines some basic property of a sample in the process stream. Instruments used are classified as (1) specific or nonspecific, and (2) continuous or discontinuous. Product quality analyzers are also classified by the property of the product which is sensed by the instrument measuring system. Each subclass has several variations: (1) Radiant energy properties: (*a*) absorption spectrometry (visible, ultraviolet, infrared, and X ray), (*b*) refraction and dispersion, (*c*) nuclear magnetic resonance, (*d*) electron paramagnetic resonance, and (*e*) ionizing radiation. (2) Electrical properties: (*a*) dielectric constant, (*b*) magnetic susceptibility, (*c*) conductimetry, (*d*) electrolysis, (*e*) electrolytic con-

130

ductivity, (f) electromotive force (pH), (g) voltammetry, and (h) polarography. (3) Mechanical properties: (a) viscometry, (b) specific gravity, (c) velocity of sound, (d) absorption of sound. (4) Thermal properties: (a) thermal conductivity, (b) transition temperatures, (c) heats or reaction. (5) Chromatography (vapor fractometry). (6) Mass spectrometry. In *continuous* instrumentation, a continuous-flowing sample is diverted from the stream and introduced into the analyzing instrument, which measures its property (usually) instantaneously, and then sends it back to the stream or discards it. In *discontinuous* instrumentation a fixed volume sample is taken from the stream, introduced into the analyzing instrument, and held stationary while an indication is made available for it. Continuous output signals lend themselves to conventional on-off and proportional control systems, while discontinuous outputs are suited to sample data time-sharing controls. *Specific analysis* instruments respond only to changes in concentration of the component the instrument is designed to measure. While *nonspecific* instruments respond mostly to the concentration of the component of interest, they also indicate other components. The specificity of measurement can be improved by removing interfering components by changing the phase (liquid, gas, or solid) of the sample. Nonspecific instruments are not too successful for analyzing products with more than two key components.

Q What are the chief uses of chemical composition analysis?
A For (1) raw material analysis, (2) product quality control, (3) process control primary criteria, (4) waste disposal, (5) yield improvement, (6) inventory measurement, and (7) safety.

Q Name five major process and plant applications for chemical analysis instrumentation using different techniques.
A (1) Petroleum and chemical process streams, (2) combustible and furnace gases, (3) sulfur gases in air pollution studies, (4) water and industrial waste treatment, and (5) chemical composition of slurries and solids.

Q What are the most common methods used for process stream analysis in the petroleum and chemical industries?
A (1) Chromatography; (2) mass spectrometry; (3) radiant energy properties of the stream; these are photometric types and can be subdivided into (a) colorimetry, (b) infrared (nondispersive and dispersive types), (c) ultraviolet (dual and single beams), and (d) refractometry; (4) also by these miscellaneous methods: (a) fractional distillation, (b) ionization (alpha) (beta), (c) dielectric constant, (d) polarography, and (e) nuclear magnetic resonance.

Q   Describe the gas chromatography method of analysis.

A   Chromatography (Fig. 6-1) is a method for analyzing chemically the percentage of constituents in a gas, vapor, liquid, or suspension. It is a measure of the identity of the components in a mixture. A constant stream of sample gas, flowing directly from the process, passes through

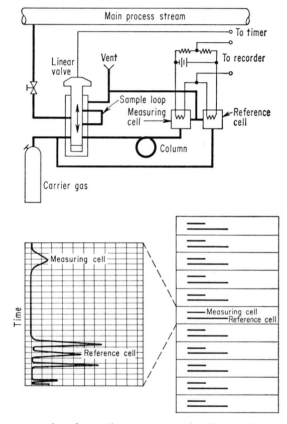

Fig. 6-1. Chromatograph analyzer with continuous record and bar graph.

the instrument's linear sampling valve, which periodically transfers a precisely measured sample into a stream of inert-carrier gas, usually helium. This gas flushes the sample through the chromatographic column, which is a coiled tube of copper, aluminum, or stainless steel, ⅛ to ½ in. in diameter and from 8 to 50 ft long, filled with absorptive or adsorptive granules. These granules reduce the speed of the sample mixture, retaining the heavier components longer than the lighter ones.

By the time the sample leaves the column, the gas mixture is separated into its component parts. As each of the components passes through the measuring cell, a thermistor senses its thermal conductivity. At the same time, a second thermistor in the reference cell measures pure carrier gas. Two matched thermistors are part of a Wheatstone bridge circuit which is connected to a strip chart recorder. The result is shown either as a continuous record of the entire mixture or as a bar graph of important components, made from the chart record (Fig. 6-1). A new sample is automatically introduced into the carrier stream at the end of each cycle. The accuracy of chromatographic analysis depends on precise temperature control of sample gas, carrier gas, and column. Temperatures can be controlled within 0.2°C at any setting between 40 and 110°C. The accuracy of the record is $\frac{1}{2}$ to 2 per cent of full scale. Readings on individual components down to 1 per cent concentration can be expanded to full scale. Detection is limited to about 100 parts per million, depending on the exact application. Regulated power supply and matched thermistors in the measuring and reference cells provide stability of 0.2 per cent of full scale. Laboratory and plant models monitor the chemical composition of any process stream consisting of a mixture of gases, or liquids that can be vaporized. The instrument is used mostly for the analysis of process streams that contain oxygen, nitrogen, chlorine, carbon monoxide, sulfur dioxide, or any hydrocarbon (saturated or unsaturated, aromatic or halogenated).

Q Name three systems used for vapor-phase chromatography.
A Three systems of vapor-phase chromatography (frontal, displacement, and elution) all use a carrier gas to force the sample through a packed column. The elution system (separation, or purification, of materials by washing with carrier gas) offers the greatest overall advantages in vapor-phase adsorption chromatography. Two variations of this system are (1) gas-solid adsorption chromatography, in which the sample adsorbed components are selectively desorbed and eluted by a carrier or stripper gas, depending on their vapor pressures; and (2) gas-liquid partition chromatography. Here the gas-sample components are dissolved by the liquid coating of the inert column packing material and therefore eluted selectively by the carrier gas according to their liquid partition coefficients.

Q What is the mass spectrometry method of analyzing liquid and gaseous samples and what does it do?
A Chemical analysis by mass separation is based upon (1) the complex molecules which form a chemical compound produce ionized molecules and molecular fragments after colliding with high-velocity electrons, and

(2) fragment masses obtained for a pure compound occur in a sequence, and in peaks which constitute a fragmentation pattern characteristic for that compound. So, using the principle of mass separation, the instrument measures and records the relative abundance of the masses in the range from 1 to 300. This instrument quickly and precisely determines the chemical composition of materials in a gaseous state, in many cases those in liquid or solid form also.

Q   Where is the mass spectrometer used?
A   In a wide range of chemical analysis. For routine hydrocarbon process control, determination of impurities, and end-point product analysis. In nuclear work the mass spectrometer simplifies and expedites the solution of many problems in gas analysis. In petroleum refining, it analyzes light hydrocarbon streams such as overheads and bottoms of depropanizers and debutanizers. Analysis by this method helps set up distillation columns for optimum operation. It indicates the best feed tray location and reflux ratios, thus reducing the pumping costs and improving efficiency. In the rubber and chemical industries it is used for controlling product quality. In research, microchemical analysis is possible which normally would require special technique and costly operations. It is also used in the manufacture of rare gases for proving the analysis of gases supplied to customers.

Q   Explain the principle and operation of the mass spectrometer.
A   See Fig. 6-2. The sample to be analyzed enters the spectrometer as natural gas molecules. An ionization chamber at low pressure receives gas molecules through a small opening, which maintains constant flow into the spectrometer tube. Here a high vacuum is retained by continuous pumping. Some of the gas molecules of each constituent are converted to positively charged ions after colliding with electrons emitted by the heated filament in the ionization chamber. Neutral molecules not affected by the electric field are withdrawn by an exhaust pump. But the ionized molecules are accelerated by high voltage and focused into a beam which passes through the narrow collimating slit into a region within the spectrometer tube where no electric field exists. In the spectrometer tube, the ion beam is deflected by the varying magnetic field. This causes ions of specific mass to follow orbital paths of certain radii. With the magnetic field at a certain known intensity, ions with a certain mass will follow a definite path through the magnetic field and pass through a narrow collector slit. They reach the collector plate and produce a measurable electric current. This current is amplified and read out on the chart of a null-balance potentiometer or oscillograph. As the magnetic field intensity is varied by changing the current through the magnet, the mass spectrum is scanned. By correlating changes in magnet current with

the recorder chart movement, the time divisions of the recorder chart indicate the mass numbers being measured.

A precollector circuit automatically adjusts the sensitivity and speed of the recorder for optimum recording of each mass peak. The precollector circuit has a precollector slit which comprises a fine wire electrode. This electrode collects a few of the ions (of the mass number under measurement) passing through the collector slit just before they reach

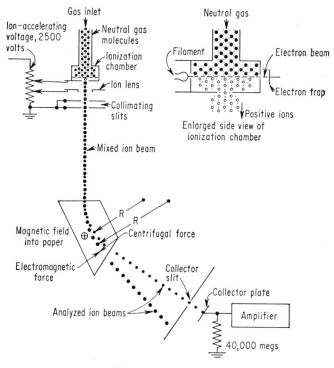

Fig. 6-2. Mass spectrometer principle schematic.

the collector plate. Current from this electrode thus constitutes a preliminary measurement of the abundance of the mass which is about to be measured. Electric circuits inform the spectrometer of the mass measurement about to be made, and the recorder is automatically adjusted accordingly. Mass range of 1 to 300 is obtained with automatic magnetic scanning. Higher mass numbers to 400 can be measured by adjusting the accelerating voltage. This instrument will detect leakage (of any material that can be vaporized) too small for other methods. The threshold of detecting impurities in raw materials or plant stream is so low that as little as 1/1,000 mole per cent can be detected.

Q   What is colorimetry? Where is it used?

A   Colorimetry is an optical method of chemical analysis. It is used to analyze gases, vapors, liquids, solutions, slurries, and solids for dyestuffs, pigments, color indicators, and other substances whose reflectance, or transmittance, in visible light is characterized by any dispersion vs. wavelength; to record a colorimetric analysis; and often to control the color of a product. Color plays a critical role in the manufacture of pigments, paints, dyestuffs, foods, plastics, synthetic fibers, coated fabrics, pharmaceuticals, and many other industrial and consumer products. Products manufactured in batch-type processes can have their color controlled by periodically checking grab samples on laboratory-type colorimeters. Others, continuously processed, can have rapid and continuous color measurement by instruments. Colorimeters are used for continuous processes today, but the problem is the complexity of color science and the difficulty of making accurate and reproducible color measurements.

Q   Describe the colorimetry method of analysis.

A   Colorimetry (Fig. 6-3) compares light transmission of various colors (produced with monochromatic filters) through a sample and a white standard. Light from an integrating sphere may be passed alternately through the sample and the standard. A light chopper is used to read the comparative transmission of the light with a photomultiplier tube. The system can be balanced to the nonpulsating output of the photomultiplier by reducing the light reaching the standard. The sketch shows a photoelectric colorimeter using two similar

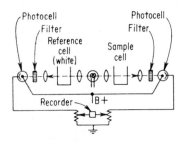

Fig. 6-3. Colorimeter compares colors by light transmission.

photocells. Light passes through the sample to one cell; then part of the same light is passed to the reference cell. Cell outputs are then compared with the recorder circuit, balanced, and recorded as relative transmission. The strength of the color is determined by measuring the amount of light reflected or transmitted at the wavelengths of peak absorption, compared with an absolute or standard white. The samples measured can be liquid placed in cells, painted panels (wet or dry), and woven fabrics. The amount of the sample varies widely and its preparation may require considerable study. The probable error is ±0.2 per cent. The human eye limits the sensitivity of this method.

Q Explain how absorption spectroscopy makes use of the absorption characteristics of molecules to perform chemical analysis.

A The technique of absorption spectroscopy involves passing electromagnetic radiation of different wavelengths through a chemical substance and measuring the radiation absorbed or transmitted to determine the material's identity, concentration, and molecular structure. Electromagnetic radiation commonly used is (1) ultraviolet (0.2 to 0.4 micron, or thousandth of a millimeter wavelength), (2) visible (0.4 to 0.7 micron), and (3) infrared (0.7 to 200 microns, but most useful from 2.5 to 15 microns). Absorption methods are valuable in chemical analysis because matter absorbs radiation very selectively with respect to wavelength. This action occurs since all molecules are made up of atoms connected by electromagnetic bonds. These atoms are in continuous motion, vibrating and rotating around their center of gravity. Valence electrons in the outer orbits of the atoms contribute to the bonding forces as well. Atoms of each molecule vibrate at a definite frequency with respect to each other. This frequency is specific to its molecular structure and to that of no other molecule.

If radiation of a given frequency, or wavelength, strikes a compound which has the same vibration frequency, this radiant energy is absorbed by the molecule, increasing its natural vibration. But if radiation of some other frequency strikes the compound, it passes through the molecule without change in radiant energy. Since the molecular vibrational frequencies of substances have the same range of values as the frequency of infrared radiation, infrared can be used to characterize molecular structure. But electromagnetic energy involved in electron bonding is of a much higher order than infrared's resonant vibration with the movements of atoms. It corresponds to the shorter, higher-frequency radiations of ultraviolet. When molecules absorb ultraviolet and visible radiations, they undergo energy shifts in the valence bond electrons which are specific to the molecule and are thus useful in characterizing it. Infrared, ultraviolet, and visible radiation when used for chemical analysis determine what compound is present and also how much.

Q What is infrared analysis and how is it used in industry?

A Process stream analysis by infrared absorption is based on two fundamental facts. All organic and inorganic substances have characteristic absorption spectra in the infrared region of the spectrum. When infrared radiation passes through a substance, certain wavelengths of energy are absorbed in proportion to the concentrations of the various components of that substance. Thus evaluation of the type and amount of energy absorbed provides a measure of the concentration of a component of a process stream made up of several substances. The chemical and petroleum industries use these methods of analysis widely. Infrared methods are outstanding for their ability to respond to a great variety of substances and to a specific substance in a complex mixture. The term *infrared* describes electromagnetic radiation whose wavelength is longer than visible light and shorter than radio waves; that is, wavelengths between 0.7 and 200 microns, but useful range from 2.5 to 15 microns. These instruments are used for separation control (distillation, absorption, stripping), synthesis control (where variations in catalyst activity, reaction temperature, or feed composition exist), solvent recovery, control of furnace atmospheres, blending of fuels, and determining the concentration of one specific component in various chemical mixtures.

Q Explain the principle of infrared analysis.

A Infrared instruments measure the characteristic vibration of a chemical sample by passing infrared radiation through it and recording which wavelengths have been absorbed and to what extent. Since the amount of energy absorbed is a function of the number of molecules present in the sample, the infrared analyzer provides both a qualitative and a quantitative answer. The recorded infrared spectrum is a plot of the sample transmittance vs. the wavelength of radiation. This is a measurement of the fundamental property of the sample and is used to characterize the sample and determine the concentration of the specific components for which the test has been conducted.

Q Describe a typical infrared analyzer.

A See Fig. 6-4. Infrared analyzers are usually classified as (1) dispersive and (2) nondispersive types. The difference is that, in the dispersive type, the desired wavelength, or wavelengths, are selected by a dispersive element, such as a prism or a diffraction grating, which diffracts radiation through various angles for different wavelengths. Each wavelength forms an image at a different location in an optical system, and proper placement of a narrow slit-shaped aperture selects the desired one. The sketch shows a dispersive type using a single beam. Nondispersive analyzers achieve wavelength selection by optical filtering.

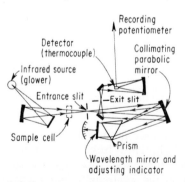

Fig. 6-4. Dispersive-type infrared analyzer.

All available nondispersive analyzers are of a type called self-filtering; a gaseous sample of the component being detected is sealed in a container within the analyzer to serve as a filter. Nondispersive analyzers further fall into two sub-classes: (1) those with a nonselective detector responsive to all infrared wavelengths (radiation thermocouple) and (2) those with a selective detector (capacitor microphone filled with a particular infrared-absorbing gas).

In the dispersive type (see the sketch) radiation from the glower is focused by mirrors onto a sample cell, then passed through the entrance slit to the collimating parabolic mirror which reflects onto the prism. Radiation dispersed by the prism is reflected by moving the wavelength mirror back through the prism and the parabolic mirror, then eventually through the exit slit and mirrors to the thermocouple. The intensity of the narrow frequency band selected by the wavelength mirror is then measured. As the spectrum is scanned, the recorder plots the radiation intensity vs. the wavelength on a strip chart. This type of instrument is used for analysis of organic materials in solid, liquid, or vapor state in the range from 2 to 40 microns, depending on the prism material. The infrared analyzer, in general, is limited to applications involving homologous (having the same relative structure) series of compounds, with the exception that the first couple of members in the series are usually fairly distinctive. Monoatomic gases and diatomic molecules in which the two items are identical do not absorb infrared radiation. Thus He, H_2, O_2, etc., cannot be determined by infrared. Accuracy claimed for these instruments is ± 1 per cent of full scale.

Q Explain the nondispersive types of instruments.

A The infrared analyzer (Fig. 6-5) is the nonselective or negative type. Where spectrometers use monochromatic radiation, these analyzers use all radiation from about 1 to 15 microns. Two general types are (1) nonselective, with two steady beams, and (2) selective, which uses chopped radiation. The nonselective type (sketch) passes radiation through two lines, one containing sample S and filter F, the other containing sample S and compensator cell C. The filter con-

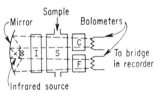

Fig. 6-5. Nondispersive-type infrared analyzer.

tains 100 per cent of the component analyzed for, and a compensator for other gases in the mixture not analyzed for. Interference cell I is used sometimes to desensitize the interfering gas. Comparison of radiation received by the bolometers is indicative of the per cent of gas for which analysis is made if the various cells are properly sensitized.

These instruments are used for continuous plant stream analysis. Examples are methane in illuminating gas, acetone in air, isobutane in normal butane, and other hydrocarbons, as well as sulfur dioxide, water vapor in low concentrations, carbon dioxide and monoxide, etc. Infrared analysis methods are much more sensitive than most instruments measuring physical properties (refractive index, thermal conductivity, specific gravity, sound velocity) but are not so sensitive as ultraviolet or electrolytic analyzers. Infrared analyzers measure 0 to 50 per cent ethylene to ±0.5 per cent in varying mixtures containing methane, ethane, acetylene, propane, ethyl chloride, and hydrogen chloride. A strip chart recording potentiometer is commonly used, with either 1- or 2-sec full-scale pen travel, for reading out bolometer outputs in the bridge measuring circuit. The range is 10 mv, calibrated accuracy ±¼ per cent, and sensitivity $\frac{1}{32}$ per cent; chart speed is 6 in. per min. A speed changer in the instrument permits the entire spectrum to be scanned in either 15 sec or 1 min.

Q What is the ultraviolet method of process analysis? Where is it used?
A Ultraviolet and visible spectrometry (Fig. 6-6) are based on the

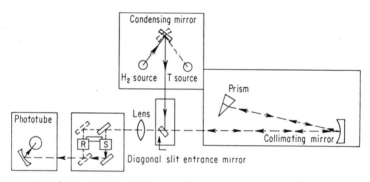

Fig. 6-6. Optical system for ultraviolet spectrophotometer.

selective absorption of electromagnetic waves in the 0.2- to 0.7-micron region by various substances. Uses are for the continuous automatic analysis of many process streams of either liquid or gaseous material. A recording potentiometer and a few modifications provide continuous analysis and automatic periodic analyses of as many as three plant streams with one instrument. But all such process streams must be subject to analysis at the same wavelength. Compounds which absorb ultraviolet energy are those known as a "chromosporic," or color-absorbing group. In general, ethylene and carbonyl structures and molecules which include the benzene ring in their structure, such as benzene, toluene, and xylene, all absorb in the ultraviolet region. Conjugated diolefins, such as butadiene and chlorophyll, and some of the vitamins are further examples of substances which absorb ultraviolet and visible wavelengths. Chemical analysis by ultraviolet spectrometry is a very valuable asset to the chemical plant and the pharmaceutical industry.

In the sketch, the optical system uses a quartz prism for dispersion. Light from the source is focused by a condensing mirror and directed to a monochromator diagonal mirror. This mirror directs the light through the entrance slit and into the monochromator to the collimating mirror. Light falling on the collimating mirror is reflected to the prism, where it undergoes refraction. The back surface of the prism is aluminized so that light refracted at the first surface is reflected back through the prism, undergoing further refraction as it emerges from the prism. The desired wavelength of light is selected by rotating the wavelength control, which positions the prism. The spectrum is directed back to the collimator, which centers the chosen wavelength on the exit slit of the monochromator. Light is directed alternately through the sample and reference paths by the vibrating mirror. All the optical elements are common to both the sample and the reference paths. A change in the source or in any mirror or lens will cause an equal change in both the sample and the reference paths. For this reason, while a change will affect system energy, it will not affect the relationship between the sample and the reference.

For rapid, routine use, the programmed slit ensures enough resolution to perform accurate qualitative and quantitative analyses. The micrometer slit adjustment is adjustable from 0.01 to 2.0 mm. Resolution in the ultraviolet range is better than 1.2 millimicrons, and in the visible range better than 4.0 millimicrons. Stability of the 100 per cent line of the ultraviolet system is better than ±2.0 per cent from 220 to 700 millimicrons. Reproducibility is better than ±1.0 per cent T while photometric repeatability is better than 0.5 per cent T. While ultraviolet analyzers are used most widely for gases and liquids, they are also used on some solids. Present designs can be applied to (1) measuring broad or very narrow ranges of concentration, (2) operating at visible and near-visible wavelengths only, or at these and ultraviolet wavelengths down to the limit where oxygen begins to absorb, and (3) analyzing with broad (continuous) or narrow (monochromatic) bands of radiation; all with a variety of sampling and electronic arrangements.

Q When do you select an ultraviolet chemical analyzer?
A When either might be used, an ultraviolet analyzer is usually preferred over an infrared unit. Most ultraviolet analyzers are simpler in design, need less maintenance, and have higher sensitivity than infrared instruments. The better ultraviolet units detect concentration changes (sensitivity) as small as a few parts per billion and are restricted mostly by variations in concentration of unsuspected contaminants. Analyzers

normally have a linear response to changes in gas density so that large fluctuations of temperature and pressure appear as errors in measured concentration. But this problem is less severe with liquid samples. Ultraviolet analyzers (like others) are useful only when a change in process stream composition produces a comparable change in the sample's radiation absorption properties. Then the unit responds as if only one component at a time is varying. These analyzers can handle not only a variety of multicomponent samples, but simple two-component (binary) samples to which a refractometer usually is applied. For some binary samples, an ultraviolet analyzer offers up to 1,000 times higher sensitivity than a refractometer.

Q   Explain the refractometer method of process control.

A   A refractometer measures the difference in refractive index between a liquid standard and a flowing liquid sample obtained directly from a process line. Because refractive index is a unique value for any given liquid, this measurement provides a direct indication of composition changes in binary (composed of two elements) mixtures. Some of these instruments can be used with clear liquids such as light oils and with highly viscous and semitransparent substances such as catsup, jellies, jams, and other food products. Of course, the turbidity must not be too great to prevent satisfactory operation. In some cases, filtering is needed to eliminate excess solid material. Used for continuously examining a flowing sample from a process stream, it measures the difference in refractive index between the sample and a reference standard liquid, and provides a signal for recording or control. These signals can be used to control such variables as the concentration of relative amounts of two components in a binary mixture, boiling points of distillates, and degrees of hydrogenation.

Continuous flow refractometry is widely used in refinery operation in blending and fractionization. Two types of refractometers are: (1) The differential refractometer, in which a light beam is transmitted through a two-section cell which refracts it at an angle. These refractometers, operating under optimum conditions, are accurate to 2×10^{-6} units of refractive index difference between two liquids. (2) The critical-angle refractometer, in which one light incident on the surface of the solution changes sharply from reflected to transmitted light at a critical angle. Figure 6-7 shows an automatic refractometer.

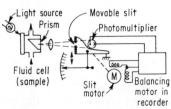

Fig. 6-7. Automatic refractometer system.

Monochromatic light enters the sample cell along the face of the prism and is refracted through the prism on a path depending on the refractive index of the sample. A slit interposed in front of a photomultiplier tube is driven to the position of the emergent beam by a balancing motor operated from the tube output. The slit position is multiplied and recorded as refractive index. Limiting sensitivity ranges from 0.00001 to 0.000002 in refractory index, depending on the design of the unit. A refractometer should be the first-choice analyzer when the sample to be analyzed is a simple binary mixture such as alcohol in water. Density measuring analyzers are used when the range of compositions is broad or when the range is narrow, down to about 0.4 per cent.

Q Give a brief description of the fractional distillation process.

A A common method of separating two or more volatile liquids is by distillation in a fractionating column. This is simply a tall vertical (low- or high-temperature) column with a number of horizontal chambers in which liquids are alternately vaporized and condensed. Higher-boiling components remain in the lower sections while the low-boiling ones rise to the top. This allows each product (depending on its boiling point) to be drawn off from the horizontal chamber that corresponds to its boiling point. Liquid (feed) to be distilled flows into the column's center at a controlled rate. A heat exchanger using steam supplies heat to the column's bottom. Steam needed for the process is controlled to maintain the vapor's temperature entering the bottom of the column. The level of the condensed liquid in the column's bottom is maintained by controlling the flow of product drawoff. Operating conditions of the column are maintained by controlling the flow of cooling water to the overhead product column. The accumulated product in controlled amount is then returned to the top tower as reflux. Controlling the flow of the overhead product drawoff maintains the level desired in the accumulator.

Q What is dielectric constant? How is it used in instrumentation?

A When a capacitor (consisting of two conductors) is separated by a nonconducting material, the material is known as a dielectric. But the electric field established between the conductors permeates the dielectric material to a certain extent. Intensity of such a field depends on the dielectric constant of the material placed between the electrode plates. Capacitance also is affected by the area of the plates and distance between them. Thus we see that capacitance is a function of dielectric constant. Measurement is in units of farads or their subdivisions, known as microfarads and micromicrofarads. Capacitance is used to determine the compositions of binary systems where each component has a dissimilar dielectric constant. Correlation is found from a calibration curve of dielectric constant vs. composition. You can use capacitance to determine a component having a high dielectric constant if it is in a multicomponent system with other components having extremely low dielectric constant. An example is finding the percentage of water in organic materials, such as paper. We know that water has a dielectric constant of 80, while that of most organic materials is between 0 and 10. Variations in moisture content in paper produce definite changes in the capacitance, which is hardly affected by pH, temperature variations, chemical changes, etc.

In Fig. 6-8 electrodes in the head of the unit come in contact with sheet paper. Because this head is an electrical capacitor, it uses the paper

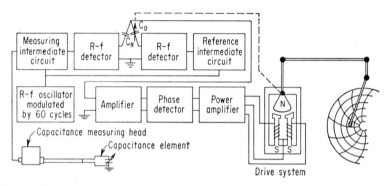

Fig. 6-8. Continuous capacitance measuring system.

as part of its measuring circuit. Electrical capacitance is proportional to the dielectric constant of the paper in the capacitor's electrical field. Because water has such a high dielectric constant when compared with other materials, minute amounts of water are detected by its effect on measured capacitance. The paper's surface condition in this case is no problem because the electric field penetrates the paper sheet. These instruments detect down to 0.05 per cent water in paper sheeting. Sensitivity varies with different materials. As a material's dielectric constant lowers, the detection of moisture increases in sensitivity (see Fig. 7-8). Because moisture content of paper is so important, this instrument is widely used to monitor all types of paper, from the lightest tissue to heavy kraft papers. They are also used to monitor the water content of acetone-acetaldehyde mixtures, water in ammonia, and acetic acid in acetic anhydride. Levels of materials are also indicated by these instruments, in closed nonobservable systems where other indicators cannot be used. Examples are corrosive liquids, liquids under high temperature and pressure, and dry solids such as grain, salt, and borax. See Chap. 7, under discussion of electrical capacitance.

Q How is ionization (radioactivity) used to analyze liquids and gases?

A Radiological analyzers (Fig. 6-9) are based on the principle that ionization and other effects are caused in a liquid or gas when bombarded with energy from a radioactive source. Material being bombarded absorbs part of the energy. Measuring this absorption indicates the composition of the sample material, especially if it is a binary mixture. Higher sensitivity in gas analysis is obtained in practice by directly measuring the ionization effect. Ionization measurement in liquids is not practicable, and absorption is found by measuring transmission. For

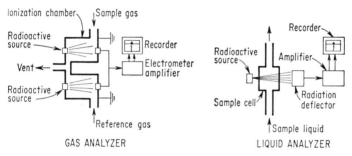

Fig. 6-9. Dual-beam radiation analyzer (gas) and absorption measuring liquid analyzer.

analysis, the radioactive sources emitting alpha, beta, or gamma rays may be used. Alpha and beta radiation consists of high-energy charged particles which interact with the sample matter. Interaction occurs as electrostatic forces between the particles and the electrons surround the nuclei of the material being analyzed. All three of these radiations have the same result: absorption of energy accompanied by ionization of the sample material. Current flowing in the ionization chamber in Fig. 6-9 depends on (1) type and intensity of radiation source, (2) ion recombination rate, (3) potentials on the electrodes, and (4) ionization cross sections of the gases. Current becomes a function only of ionization cross section if the first three of these factors are held or assumed constant at suitable values. In Fig. 6-10, the gas composition within an ionization chamber used for measuring nuclear radiation has a marked effect on the ion current. This current can then be used for analyzing certain binary or pseudobinary gas mixtures. The ionization method is used for determining argon in ammonia plant circulating gases, after removing the ammonia and hydrogen. Different gases give widely varying ion currents, but mixtures must be calibrated to give predictable results.

The gas analyzer shown uses two temperature-controlled ionization chambers, with the sample passing through one. The other contains a reference gas, such as nitrogen. A strontium 90 source (pure beta emitter) for each cell ionizes the gas. Measurement of ionization current is made by placing a pair of insulated electrodes in the gas and applying an accelerating voltage large enough to collect ions on them before the ions recombine. The ion current is amplified and recorded on a strip chart as per cent of the constituent measured. Accuracy is ±1 per cent absolute on 0.5 per cent argon. This instrument is claimed to be both sensitive and accurate, although nonspecific. Liquid is analyzed by measuring the absorption of radiation passing through a sample of the liquid. Only beta or gamma radiation sources are useful for measuring concentration or density because alpha radiation becomes completely absorbed in an extremely thin layer of liquid.

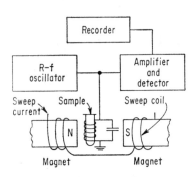

Fig. 6-10. **Nuclear magnetic resonance spectroscopy.**

Q   How do you select the type of radiation to be used?
A   Choice of radiation type depends on accuracy, sample condition, and availability. Use beta radiation where high accuracy is needed and where a side-stream sample may be taken from the main product stream. Use gamma radiation for applications needing less accuracy. Because of its high penetrating power, the measurement of process stream density can be made in any normal plant piping, in processing vessels, or in storage tanks. This eliminates the need for taking a side-stream sample. Radiation passing through the liquid sample is detected with ionization chambers, scintillation counters, and Geiger-Müller counters. But for plant-type instruments, ionization chambers are the most rugged, reliable, and stable detector. Ionization chambers allow much higher intensities from the sample, stronger sources, and thus small statistical variations in output.

> CAUTION: Exposure to or ingestion of radioactive material by operating personnel makes ionizing radiation instrumentation hazardous in the plant. Be sure to follow AEC safety standards when using these instruments.

Q How is nuclear magnetic resonance used as an industrial analytical tool?

A Nuclear magnetic resonance (Fig. 6-10) is used to make simple nondestructive tests specific to a particular nuclear species in either liquids or solids. This technique has been used in product identification in the petroleum and chemical industries and moisture determination for food processing. Besides these isotopic identifications, nuclear magnetic resonance studies can be related to a wide variety of physical phenomena, giving information on bond energies, crystal structure, diffusion rates, phase transitions, surface phenomena, chemical group identification, and interactions between nuclei and electrons. Chief uses are identifying products and determining moisture content. Basically, nuclear magnetic resonance identifies a sample within seconds or minutes by determining the nuclear species within the sample. It does this by subjecting the sample simultaneously to a high-frequency magnetic field from an r-f (radio-frequency) oscillator and a d-c magnetic field so that, when nuclear resonance occurs, the relation of the r-f oscillation frequency to the d-c magnetic field strength is the pulse signal, which is detected and amplified, then recorded on a strip chart. The resulting record pattern uniquely identifies the nuclear species. Nuclear spin in elements having odd atomic numbers causes radio-frequency absorption in a uniform magnetic field. When the sample contains more than one nuclear species the product can be identified by the relation of each species in a spectrum. Information appears intermittently, leading to control by sampled-data systems. Data obtained from a nuclear magnetic resonance spectrometer take various forms: (1) an accurate count of the gross number of a particular species in a sample and (2) records which yield, with proper interpretation, subtle information relating to molecular structure. One application is that of high-resolution nuclear magnetic resonance to monitor periodically the yield of a reaction (such as aromatization) by observing the spectra. A more common use is the accurate and speedy measurement of water, especially in granular solids, where other physical methods have severe limitation, because hydrogen has the highest sensitivity of any nuclear species to detection by nuclear magnetic resonance. This method has an accurate measurement of moisture in solids, even those containing hydrogen. Accuracy is within 0.1 per cent or better.

Q Explain how polarography is used for making chemical analyses.

A Analysis by means of polarography (Fig. 6-11) can be applied to almost all types of substances in electrolytic solution which are subject to electrolytic reduction and oxidation. This includes all metals and makes it especially useful for the rapid determination of copper, zinc, lead, iron, and nickel in brass and similar alloys; copper, nickel, cobalt, manganese, and chromium in steel; aluminum, zinc, manganese, and lead in magnesium alloys. It is also used for determining trace materials in ores, alloys, and scrap and is very valuable in checking and controlling high-purity zinc alloys used in die casting, where traces of lead, cadmium, and copper of only a few thousandths of a per cent can seriously weaken the alloy. Polarography is useful for analysis in applications such as electroplating, where the plating solution can be checked and controlled; lubricating oils, where the amount of metal pickup through bearing wear can be tested; and in the preparation of many commercial chemicals, where the presence and amount of impurities can be ascertained. Other applications are in the fields of organic chemistry, biology, petroleum refining, etc.

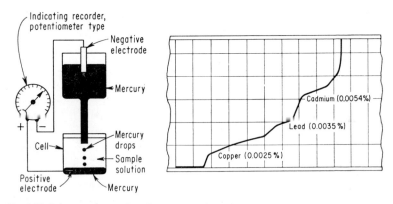

Fig. 6-11. Polarograph uses dropping mercury electrode.

Both qualitative and quantitative analyses of either aqueous or non-aqueous solutions can be made. Because of the extreme sensitivity of the equipment, quantities of a constituent as low as a few ten-thousandths of a per cent can be determined. As the sketch shows, analyses are made by putting the material to be analyzed in solution. Then a gradually increasing voltage is applied across the dropping-mercury electrode and the pool of mercury at the cell's bottom which contains the solution to be analyzed. As the voltage increases, the current through the solution does not increase in proportion but rather rises in a series of steps, as shown in a polarogram. Each of these steps indicates the presence of a certain element and their height represents the amount of the element present. The curve shown is called a polarogram and is representative of a quantitative and qualitative analysis of the solution in terms of the identity of the elements present and their amount.

A few drops of mercury added to the sample constitute one electrode of the cell. Mercury from the reservoir dropping through the capillary acts as the other electrode of the cell. Then the capillary feeds mercury drops into the cell at the rate of one every 2 to 4 sec. This causes a direct current with an oscillatory component to flow through the cell. The value of this current is dependent mostly on two factors: (1) the emf (electromotive force) impressed on the cell and (2) the electrolytic nature of the solution. After the material to be analyzed is placed in the cell, the dropping-mercury electrode is started and the motor-driven resistor drum (which varies the voltage applied to the cell) is started. Thus the voltage across the cell starts at zero and gradually rises to the value desired (usually under 4.5 volts). Current through the cell is at first barely perceptible and rises slightly in rough proportion to the voltage rise. When the applied voltage reaches a certain value, certain ions from the material in solution are attracted to the mercury electrode (where they deposit their electrical charge), thus causing a sharp rise in current. As voltage continues to increase, the speed with which ions are attracted to the electrode increases to a point where the solution can no longer supply them more rapidly. At this point, the current limit is reached and the polarogram curve levels off and remains so until a voltage is reached at which the ions of another constituent of the solution discharge, whereupon the entire process is repeated. This sequence continues, depending on the number of elements in the solution.

A polarogram is a current vs. voltage curve. At different points along the voltage axis, the presence of steps shows evidence of certain elements, while the height of the step indicates the concentration of the element in the sample. Current from the analyzing cell is passed through a resistor so that a voltage (result of the IR drop across the resistor) will be developed across it. This voltage will vary synchronously with the current variations through the cell and can thus be used as input to a recorder measuring circuit. Because the recorder chart is driven by a constant-speed synchronous motor, as well as the polarographic bridge which varies the voltage to the analyzing cell, the chart displacement is a linear function of the voltage applied to the cell. As a result, the recorded curve is current vs. voltage and is suitable for direct analytical chemical interpretation. This instrument measures down to ten-thousandths of 1 per cent. It is used for element analysis as well as large concentrations.

Q What are the most important methods for analyzing combustible and furnace gases?
A (1) Thermoconductivity, (2) paramagnetic analyzers, and (3) combustible gas detectors.

Q Explain the thermal conductivity method of analyzing gases.
A Because all gases and vapors conduct and transfer heat (thermal

conductivity) in various degrees, this characteristic is used to determine the concentrations of the various gases. Thermal conductivity units (Fig. 6-12) are used to measure and control percentage of purity, or of contamination of one gas with another, as nitrogen (or argon) in oxygen, oxygen in nitrogen, nitrogen in argon, oxygen in enriched air, and oxygen in hydrogen. They are commonly used for flue-gas analysis and efficiency, production of fertilizers, dyes, drugs, and explosives. Here are refinements of these instruments: (1) double-cell, single-pass; (2) double-cell, double-pass; (3) four-cell conductivity-convection; (4) four-cell, single- or double-pass, etc. In the thermal conductivity method the gas mixture to be measured and a background gas are analyzed. In the basic application the mixture consists of the gas to be measured and one other gas (binary mixture), the net thermal conductivity varying directly as the percentage of unknown gas.

There are two cases in which a mixture of gases may be considered as one background gas. In one, the mixture is composed of gases with thermal conductivities nearly identical but differing widely enough from that of the gas being measured to permit analysis within the limits of accuracy. In the second, the background gas consists of a mixture of gases with different thermal conductivities. Here all but one of the background gases maintain a constant or nearly constant ratio of concentration to each other, depending on the accuracy needs. The percentage of gas to be measured then increases or decreases as the background gas increases or decreases. Under these conditions, the net thermal conductivity can again be used to measure the percentage of gas in question.

The instrument shown has two electrically self-heated, identical, glass-covered resistors mounted in separate chambers (see Fig. 6-12) in the analyzing cell block. These resistors form two legs of a Wheatstone bridge circuit. To make the measurement, the electrically heated resistor is surrounded by the sample gas and an equilibrium temperature is established. If the composition of the gas and, therefore, its thermal conductivity changes, the resistor temperature and resistance change. A reference gas with known thermal conductivity diffuses into one chamber (reference cell) and the sample gas diffuses into the other chamber (measuring cell). The amount of heat absorbed by the reference gas remains constant because the cell block temperature is held constant.

The resistance value of the reference cell resistor remains constant to provide a standard against which that of the measuring cell resistor is compared. The sample gas diffusing into the measuring cell absorbs heat from the measuring resistor in a direct ratio to its thermal conductivity. Thus any difference in the thermal conductivity of the two gases changes the resistance and therefore the voltage balance of the Wheatstone bridge circuit. The resultant output voltage is transmitted to the recorder where it is detected, amplified, and impressed on the pen drive motor. This motor operates a slide-wire to rebalance the bridge circuit. A cam, also rotated by the motor, operates the indicator and/or a pen to show the net thermal conductivity directly as a per cent by volume measurement of the sample gas. The range of the analyzer in Fig. 6-12 is 0.5 per cent minimum to 0.100 per cent. Accuracy is ±0.25 per cent of the gas involved to and including 0 to 15 per cent range, ±2 per cent of scale for ranges above 0 to 15 per cent.

Q Describe the paramagnetic method of oxygen analysis.

A This principle of measurement (Fig. 6-13) is based on the fact that

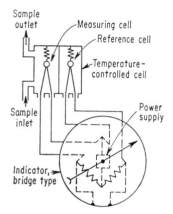

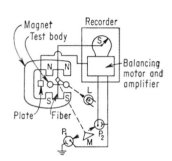

Fig. 6-12. Thermal conductivity gas analysis system.

Fig. 6-13. Paramagnetic analyzer is based on magnetic susceptibility.

oxygen exhibits a positive susceptibility in a magnetic field (much higher than other common gases) so that the field force tends to concentrate where oxygen is present. Instruments based on this principle are used to control the quality of carbon oxidation from products fired in tunnel kilns, etc. Chemical plants, refineries, power plants, air and gas plants, the metallurgical field, and the food and beverage industry all use these instruments. The sketch shows the magnetic susceptibility, nonuniform-field-type instrument. In a nonuniform magnetic field, a light test body tends to be pushed from the field if O_2 (oxygen) is present. Displacement increases with O_2 concentration and can be converted to a signal for a recorder. Here a plate with fixed d-c potential draws the charged test body back to the zero position when a balanced bridge applies the proper charge. The balanced bridge operates from the light beam on photocells P_1 or P_2 as the test body position changes. Bridge balance is therefore a measure of the O_2 concentration. The range of this instrument is from a few parts per million O_2 to 100 per cent. Accuracy is 1 per cent for ranges over 1 per cent O_2. Use for analyzing oxygen-gas mixtures only.

Q   Describe a combustible gas analysis system.

A   Combustible gas analysis systems (Fig. 6-14) are used for both safety and process control. Units are made for (1) continuous checking of one point, and (2) periodic sampling of many points. Some instruments use a Wheatstone resistance bridge detector; others detect gas through temperature changes of a platinum wire. These instruments are used by refineries, chemical plants, sewage works, gas and oil pumping stations, solvent recovery operations, power plants, jet engine test cells, pipeline operators, and manufacturers using combustible gases, etc. Uses range from the detection of leaks and similar safety functions to process control by means of controlled drying and vapor recovery. Whether a mixture of combustible gas or vapor and air may be flammable depends on its concentration. The explosive range includes all concentrations in which a flash will occur or a flame will travel. The lowest percentage at which this happens is the lower explosive limit and the highest percentage is the upper explosive limit. Any confined mixture that is ignited between these limits will explode. Mixtures above the upper explosive limit are too rich to support combustion; those below the lower explosive limit are too lean to explode. All concentrations above the lower explosive limit are dangerous because air which surrounds us is the diluent and is always available.

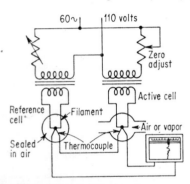

Fig. 6-14. Combustible gas detector circuit with recorder.

Figure 6-14 shows a thermocouple-type filament arrangement. This unit utilizes the temperature increase of a heated platinum filament (as measured by a thermocouple) when exposed to a combustible gas or vapor-air mixture as compared with the temperature of a similarly heated filament and thermocouple sealed in air. Thermocouples are connected in series opposing; so the differential emf is applied to a recording null-balance potentiometer. With no combustibles surrounding the exposed filament in the active cell, the emf's from both thermocouples are equal so they cancel out and the potentiometer indicates zero. When a combustible gas or vapor is admitted to the analyzing chamber, it burns and the temperature of the filament increases, thereby increasing the emf from the thermocouple bonded to it. This instrument indicates the resultant differential emf, which is in proportion to the concentrations of combustible gas or vapors present. Thus the potentiometer can be calibrated in terms of per cent of the lower explosive limit of the gas or vapor for which the analyzer is intended. For continuous measurements, a remote analyzing cell, mounted at the source of measurement, sends an electric signal back to the potentiometer measuring circuit. The chart is calibrated from 0 to the lower explosive limit of a specific gas or vapor with the lower explosive limit considered 100 per cent of scale, while points below are expressed in percentages.

Q   Name three methods of analyzing for sulfur gases in air-pollution studies.
A   (1) Reaction product (H_2S), (2) electrolytic conductance (SO_2), and (3) radiation.

Q   Explain the chemical reaction method of gas analysis.
A   The concentration of hydrogen sulfide (H_2S) is one gas that must be known since it is poisonous. It is essential to measure its concentration in the natural gas industry, in catalytic chemical processes, and in atmospheric pollution control work. In natural gas transmission lines, H_2S concentration is held below 0.25 grain per 100 cu ft (equivalent to 4 ppm) to limit corrosion. The measuring system (Fig. 6-15) automatically records H_2S concentrations in streams of gas or air. The sensing element is fabric tape impregnated with lead acetate, through which a metered flow of the sample is passed for a preset time interval. The H_2S reacts quantitatively with the lead acetate, forming a brown lead sulfide stain. The intensity of the stain is directly related to the amount of

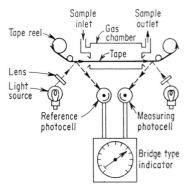

Fig. 6-15. Chemical reaction method of gas analysis.

H_2S presented to the tape. This instrument measures H_2S only and is unaffected by other constituents such as organic sulfur or unsaturated hydrocarbons.

Gas is admitted from a sample line at about 2 psig and passes through a flow regulator and rotameter. Gas is then bubbled through a 5 per cent solution of acetic acid in a temperature-controlled humidifier, and through a passage in an aluminum plate thermostatically controlled at 50°C. The sample then flows to the measuring cell and through a sensitized cotton tape stretched above the cell. Finally it flows into a suction vent line. The lead acetate impregnated tape converts the hydrogen sulfide in the gas sample, regardless of concentration, to brown lead sulfide. Reflectance of the tape area subjected to the gas flow is compared photometrically with the reflectance of the clean tape. Two 6-volt lamps, optical filters, and photovoltaic-type reference and measuring cells produce an electrical signal proportional to the difference between the sample and the reference for the recorder. Photocells are connected in a balanced bridge circuit which maintains the linearity in the current-illumination relationship. The sensitized tape is positioned and clamped in the analyzer by means of a tape motor which operates through a timer. Fifteen-minute cycles are usually used. This analyzer is also used to monitor stack gases from metallurgical operations or for the effluent gases from chemical processes before they discharge to the atmosphere. It can guard against accumulation of toxic concentrations of H_2S in working areas of refineries and chemical plants. Range is 0 to 0.5 grain of H_2S per 100 cu ft. Other full-scale ranges from 0.05 to 25 grains H_2S per 100 cu ft (1 to 500 ppm) can be obtained by adjustments.

Q   How is sulfur dioxide (SO_2) in the air detected?

A   In Fig. 6-16, a sample of air containing SO_2 is fed into an absorption tower where it is absorbed in sulfuric acid and hydrogen peroxide. The electric conductivity of the solution before absorption is measured by cell C_1 and after absorption by cell C_2. Any increase in conductivity of the solution is caused by SO_2 being converted to sulfate and is recorded on a Wheatstone bridge recorder as per cent SO_2. The spent solution accumulates in a reservoir and is measured periodically by cell C_3 for totalization (integration) of SO_2. Range of measurement is 0 to 5 ppm to accuracies of better than 0.1 ppm. This system is especially useful for air-pollution determinations of low SO_2 concentrations in the air.

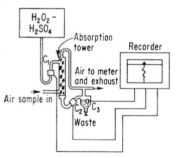

Fig. 6-16. SO_2 detection in air-pollution studies.

Q   Describe briefly a radiation monitor system for airborne particles.

A   This instrument (Fig. 6-17) is used for measuring concentrations of airborne radioactive particles in and around a nuclear facility, or any installation using radioactive materials or processes. Air from the source to be monitored is drawn through a slowly moving filter paper. Dust particles collected on the filter paper are continuously monitored for the presence of radioactive particles by means of a photomultiplier crystal detector. Signals from the detector are converted to a d-c voltage, then transmitted to a recorder. If the signal from the detector exceeds the value for which the alarm is set, visual and audible alarm signals are energized. The unit has a connection for a remote indicating alarm. A

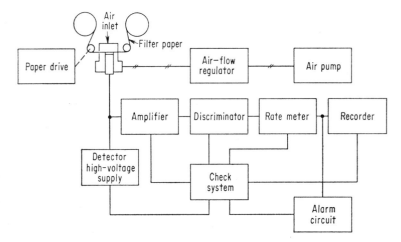

Fig. 6-17. Radiation monitor.

single-pen strip chart potentiometer continuously records airborne alpha, beta, or gamma radiation. The unit is used for reactor fuel processing, or hot laboratory installations, operating at a gamma background high as 10 milliroentgens per hour. Calibrated with Na 24, the unit has a sensitivity range of 8×10^{-10} to 8×10^{-7} microcuries per cubic centimeter.

Q What are the most common analysis methods for water and industrial waste treatment?

A Water and industrial waste are analyzed by their electrical properties: (1) electromotive force (pH), (2) electrolytic conductivity, and (3) oxidation-reduction potential (redox). Dissolved oxygen and turbidity methods are also used.

Q What is the meaning of pH in water chemistry? Why is its measurement important?

A The pH is a measurement of the acidity or alkalinity of a solution. It is defined as the negative logarithm (reciprocal) of hydrogen-ion concentration in a solution. On a scale it is a number between 0 and 14, indicating the degree of acidity or alkalinity. The pH scale resembles a thermometer or hydrometer scale. Just as a thermometer measures intensity of heat and a hydrometer the density of a solution, the pH scale indicates intensity of acidity or alkalinity. The midpoint of the pH scale is 7 and a solution with this pH is neutral. Numbers below 7 denote acidity, those above alkalinity. Since pH is a logarithmic function, solutions having a pH of 6.0, 5.0, and 4.0 are 10, 100, and 1,000 times more acid than one with a pH of 7.0. Now let's apply this to water chemistry. In addition to molecules of H_2O, pure water contains separated parts of molecules called hydrogen ions (H+) and hydroxyl ions (OH−). The amount of dissociation is constant at any given temperature. At 25°C the product of the H+ and OH− concentration is 1×10^{-14}. When hydrogen concentration changes, the hydroxyl-ion concentration changes in proportion and always in the opposite direction. If the H+ ions decrease, the OH− ions increase enough so the product of the two concentrations at 25°C remains 1×10^{-14}. The exponent −14 is the basis of the pH scale, a method of expressing hydrogen-ion concentration in terms of a negative logarithm to the base 10. The acid or alkaline nature of a solution depends on whether hydrogen or hydroxyl ions predominate. The ionic theory is that salts, acids, and bases are torn apart by water molecules to form positively or negatively charged fragments called ions. When acids are mixed with water, hydrogen ion is one result of the breakup. In a mixture of bases and water, hydroxyl ions result. Hydrogen ions make a solution acid; hydroxyl ions tend to make it alkaline. When the solution contains one OH ion for every H ion, the acid effect of one balances the alkaline effect of the other. The result is a neutral solution with a pH of 7.0.

Process stream pH measurement has become as standard as the measurement of process flow rate, pressure, and temperature. Many industries benefit from pH control. Water and industrial waste treatment plants and plants requiring cooling tower and boiler feedwater monitoring find pH control invaluable. Process industries use pH to monitor and control emulsification, electrolysis, and acid waste neutralization process, recovery of metals, acid processes, chemical treatment, etc. Also, in many plants pH control means better product quality and more efficient operation, saving time, labor, and raw materials.

Q Describe an instrument for measuring pH continuously.

A Figure 6-18 shows that measurement of pH requires immersion of a glass electrode and a reference electrode in the process liquid. The glass electrode detects the presence of hydrogen ions, producing an electrical potential proportional to the hydrogen-ion concentration. The reference electrode completes the circuit, furnishing a stable reference potential for accurate pH measurement. The difference in potential between the reference electrode and the glass electrode is directly proportional to the solution pH. The graph in Fig. 6-18 relates millivolts potential (difference in potential between reference and glass electrodes) to solution pH, a relationship which is the basis of accurate, reproducible pH measurement. The pH-millivolt relationship varies for varying solution temperatures. A temperature compensator is immersed in the process

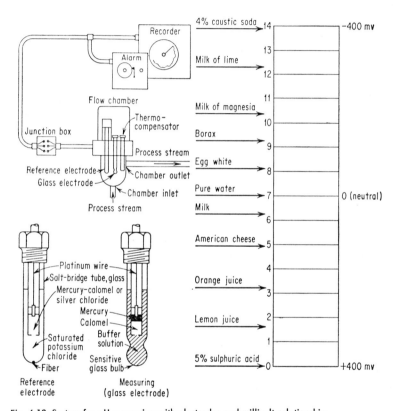

Fig. 6-18. System for pH measuring with electrodes and millivolt relationship.

liquid to compensate automatically for solution temperature variations. The two electrodes (glass and reference) and temperature compensator are placed in a process stream by mounting within a stainless-steel flow chamber which is installed directly in the stream, or by mounting in electrode glands which are installed in the stream piping. The flow chamber houses all needed electrodes, while each electrode gland holds only one electrode. For pH measurements in open vessels, the electrodes are mounted within an immersion chamber, or submersion assembly. Signal voltage developed at the glass electrode is fed to an indicating pH meter, which is a high-impedance voltmeter calibrated in pH units. A recording or controlling potentiometer is used to record and control process pH continuously. It measures over ranges from 2 to 14 pH, within an accuracy of ±0.02 pH.

Q   How is electrolytic conductivity used in the analysis of process streams, feedwater, and chemical composition of gases?

A   Electrolytic conductivity is a measure of the chemical concentration of solutions. Electrolytic, or solution, conductivity is a measure of the ability of a solution to carry an electric current, defined as specific conductance, and is measured in mhos (1/resistance, ohms). So it is basically a measurement of solution resistance. By measuring the solution conductivity, (1) steam purity is maintained by withholding entrained solids, (2) boiler feedwater is controlled to the required purity, (3) caustic scrubbing towers are rejuvenated, (4) solvents are recovered, (5) chemical purity is maintained, (6) sulfur dioxide, carbon dioxide, and other contaminants in gas and air are determined, (7) plant wastes are controlled, and (8) irrigation water treatment is controlled. Figure 6-19

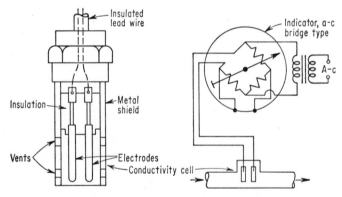

Fig. 6-19. Electrolytic conductivity system uses conductivity cell and Wheatstone bridge.

shows the conductivity cell and the basic measuring circuit. The primary sensing device (conductivity cell) has two platinum electrodes set in a stainless-steel housing for connection in process piping. These electrodes, when immersed in the process solution or water stream, measure its conductivity by sensing resistance and changes in solution resistance. Electrodes form one leg (the variable) in an a-c Wheatstone bridge circuit. Resistors R_1, R_2, R_3, and R_4 are fixed in the other legs, and R_5 is the rebalancing slide-wire. As the solution conductivity changes, resistance changes, thus unbalancing the bridge. An amplifier senses unbalance and causes the balancing motor to turn, moving the R_5 slider to a new position to balance the circuit. At the same time, the recording pen attached to the R_5 slider records the new conductivity figure. For measuring conductivity of gases, only those which ionize in water can be detected and measured.

For gases, analysis is based on the increased conductivity of distilled water after a gas ionizes in it. The measuring principle utilizes the differential measurement of conductivity before and after a gas sample ionizes in distilled water. Conductivity is measured by two sets of electrodes arranged in an a-c bridge circuit. Distilled water passes continuously through the reference electrodes, then goes to the mixing chamber. After the gas sample and water are mixed, the liquor passes over the active electrodes. The difference in conductivity between the reference and active electrodes is proportional to the amount of gas ionized in the sample. When the analyzer is for sample concentration in the low range of 0.50 ppm, or if the sample is relatively pure air, a water-recirculating system is used. For this service, the instrument has a distilled water reservoir, ion-exchange chamber, flowmeters, analyzing cell, and a special dual-purpose pump to draw the sample and recirculate the water. When the equipment is used for process control or where the sample concentration is relatively high, a constant supply of distilled water is needed. The recirculating system is best, since this eliminates the need for water supply and drains, and keeps the analyzer a self-contained unit. In the electroconductivity analyzer, the sample is admitted at a constant rate. If not under pressure, the sample is drawn in by a suction pump or by a water aspirator. When needed, a pyrolyzing furnace is used to break the gas down into components that will ionize in water. The sample is mixed with distilled water in a fixed ratio and then passed into the analyzing cell. The difference in conductivity between the distilled water and the mixture is recorded in terms of parts per million or percentage concentration of a gas or vapor.

For cyclic analysis of gases or vapors from as many as a dozen locations, some analyzers have a commutating valve. This motor-driven rotary valve admits samples from the different points in sequence. It also purges the common tubes between samplings. Sampling points are checked regularly and the various concentrations are recorded on a multiple-point strip chart instrument. Both circular and strip chart recorders are used. The purity of carbon dioxide in nitrogen is indicated full-scale at 50 ppm; hydrogen sulfide concentrations full-scale at 2 per cent H_2S in air; nitrous oxide fumes full-scale at 100 ppm N_2O fumes; sulfur dioxide content full-scale deflection at 5 ppm; etc.

Q Explain the redox (oxidation-reduction potential) method of measurement for process control.

A This method of analysis is based on the concept that certain compounds in solution exhibit a potential which is due to their tendency to react on the basis of oxidation and reduction of certain elements or ions. An ion, or element, which gains in its positive charge is oxidized; or one that loses in its charge is reduced. An element which is oxidized is called a reducing agent because it causes the other element to be reduced. The element being reduced is called an oxidizing agent. Redox (Fig. 6-20)

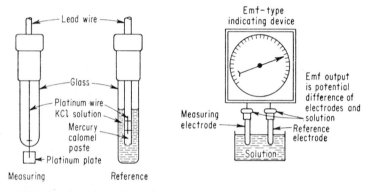

Fig. 6-20. Redox electrodes and recorder.

is used widely in extracting bromine from sea water, where oxidation potential guides the process at several stages. An example is the steaming-out towers where bromine is removed from HBr by adding chlorine. Here measuring electrodes are placed in the effluent lines from each of two towers. Measurement of oxidation potential is then used to throttle the addition of chlorine. The method is based on the fact that, in many chemical reactions, a given ion in solution undergoes oxidation or reduction, either completely or partially. Controlling the process depends on how accurately the reagents are controlled. Electrometric equipment is used to measure the potential developed because of the relative amounts of oxidant and reductant in the solution. Putting it another way, in redox reactions, negatively charged electrons are transferred between reactants, e.g., a ferrous ion loses an electron and becomes ferric (is oxidized or gains increased positive charge). Such a reaction may not involve the presence of oxygen. Reduction is the reverse. Here the inert metal electrode vs. calomel reference electrode (cf. pH measurement) will develop potential showing the balance of oxidized vs. reduced ions in solution. Remember that redox potential is influenced by both temperature and pH. These factors must be controlled where they are not sufficiently stable.

Limitations of this method are: (1) True redox potential is not measurable in solutions where reaction products are precipitated or where highly complex molecules are formed. (2) Results will be incorrect if the platinum electrodes tend to catalyze appreciable side reactions. But using a gold electrode in place of platinum may avoid this problem. (3) Some solutions tend to evolve reactive gases, such as H_2 or SO_2. Besides, many oxidation-reduction systems react rapidly with oxygen from the air. When measuring such solutions, use special provisions to protect them from gas exchange, which gives erroneous readings. Oxidation-reduction potentials may be expressed in terms of either of two measured potentials, Eh or rH. Eh is more commonly used; it is the potential an unattackable metal electrode assumes in a solution relative to that of the normal hydrogen electrode. The reference electrode is usually a calomel instead of a hydrogen electrode, Eh being calculated by adding the calomel electrode potential to the measured voltage.

Q How would you analyze for dissolved oxygen in a solution? Explain why this analysis is important.

A Analyzing accurately the dissolved oxygen concentrations in high-purity water is very important, especially in: (1) Boiler feedwater of high-pressure steam power plants. Here efficiency of oxygen removal by chemical scavenging treatment for the prevention of boiler tube and auxiliary equipment corrosion is critical. (2) Checking deaerator efficiency in steam power plants. (3) Detecting sources of oxygen leakage in feedwater systems. (4) Monitoring dissolved oxygen concentrations of water streams in nuclear power plants. Figure 6-21 indicates the method based on the reaction of dissolved oxygen with nitric oxide. This results in ionized products which increase the conductance of the sample. Increase in conductance is directly related to the concentration of dissolved oxygen in the sample. Measuring the change in conductance gives a measurement of the quantity of dissolved oxygen. A sample, at an adjusted flow rate and pressure, enters the resin column, which removes metallic cations present and replaces them with hydrogen ions. Outflow from the resin column flows to the reference cell where conductivity is measured. From here the sample flows into the reaction column. Nitric oxide flows from its cylinder through an Ascarite cartridge and scrubber; these remove traces of acidic nitrogen compounds which would give false oxygen readings. Nitric oxide then flows into the reaction column where it joins the sample, and the chemical reaction takes place. The sample then flows into the analysis cell where the conductivity is measured. The analyzer output is the difference in conductivity between the sample in the reference and analysis cells. A temperature compensating network corrects the differential conductivity measurement for any temperature variation of the sample within the range given in the specifications. The corrected differential conductivity value is quantitatively proportional to the amount of dissolved oxygen in the sample. The d-c readout signal can be fed to a recording null-balance potentiometer, for continuous recording of oxygen content. This unit is based upon a rapid and irre-

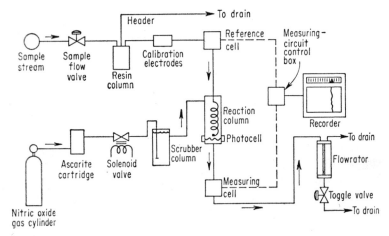

Fig. 6-21. Dissolved oxygen analyzer.

versible chemical reaction which is specific for dissolved oxygen ($O_2 + 5NO + 2H_2O \rightarrow 4HNO_2$). Minute traces of oxygen, as low as 1 part per billion, are detected. Measurement accuracy is to ± 5 per cent of the reading. It takes about 2 min for 90 per cent of response from the time the sample enters the analyzer.

Q   What is turbidity? Why is liquid turbidity measured?
A   Turbidity is a measure of the clarity of liquids or gases. It is a critical measurement in the clarification of beverages, chemical solutions, water supplies, domestic and industrial wastes, and mineral slurries. A turbidimeter is used to evaluate the operation of filters, clarifiers, and settling basins. In the removal of suspended solids from solutions, tur- bidimeter recordings serve as a basis for adjusting feed rates of coagu- lants and other filter aids. They are also used for scheduling filter backwashing, cleaning, or diverting operations. Another use is for moni- toring the effluents from sewage and industrial waste treatment plants. Turbidity helps detect rust and oil contamination of boiler feedwater and evaluate surface water supplies for industrial and domestic use. Tur-

bidity is defined as the ratio of the amount of scattered light to the amount of transmitted light when a light beam is directed into a solution. Thus if a solution is free of suspended solids, all the light will be transmitted and not scattered; turbidity will be zero. As the concentration of suspended solids increases, more light will be scattered and the light ratio or turbidity will increase in proportion.

Q How do you determine the chemical composition of solids and slurries?

A Chemical analysis of solids and slurries is based on the radiant energy properties of the compound. Analysis is made by (1) emission spectrometry, (2) X-ray spectrometry (fluorescence and diffraction), (3) flame photometry, and (4) radio-frequency (r-f) spectrography.

Q Explain how emission spectroscopy is used for metallurgical process control.

A Emission spectroscopy (Fig. 6-22) is a valuable control procedure in metallurgical manufacturing processes. This instrument produces compositional information within a few minutes between drawing the sample and getting answers. Variations in composition are detected and corrections made without slowing the production process. The basics of emission spectroscopy are simple: When an element is subjected to an arc, spark, or flame of enough energy, a fraction of that energy is absorbed by the atoms or ions, then released as radiant energy. This radiant energy occurs at fixed frequencies, depending on the characteristics of the atoms and ions which make up the compound. Because frequencies emitted by various elements differ, measurable element frequency characteristics can be sorted out and identified with optical instruments. Such frequency characteristics are referred to as lines, and expressed in terms of wavelength.

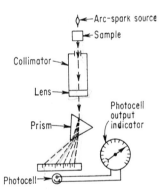

Fig. 6-22. Emission spectrochemical instrument.

As the sketch shows, an excitation source generates a spark. The sample in the spark's discharge zone emits radiant energy which is characteristic of the elements in the sample. Total radiant energy is focused through the primary slit onto a prism. This prism separates the emitted energy into appropriate frequencies, each of which goes through its associated secondary slit and is then reflected to a phototube (cell). The phototube output charges an integrating capacitor which selects and records the accumulated charge. The recorded charge for each element is a function of the concentration of that element. In spectrographs, a camera and photographic film are used in place of the photoelectric receivers. Here the blackness of the spectrum lines is measured to deduce concentrations. All metallic, and most semimetallic elements, emit lines within the spectrum range of 2,000 to 9,000 angstroms when excited in conventional arcs or sparks. Most nonmetallic elements require special equipment for their excitation and measurement. Three broad types of optical assemblies are used in industrial spectroscopy: (1) special spectrometers for flames, (2) grating and prism spectrographs, and (3) large-grating polychromators. Emission spectrometry can identify trace elements down to a billionth of a gram. Accuracy depends on the quality of optics used.

Q   How is X-ray spectrometry used for analyzing product composition?
A   X rays identify and quantitatively measure individual constituents of a compound. Acceptance of X ray as an analytical technique came first with X-ray diffraction spectroscopy, then with X-ray fluorescence. X-ray absorption is widely used for measuring density, thickness, and level but is not gaining as an analytical method. A truly analytical tool must selectively measure one or more individual constituents of a substance in the presence of varying amounts of the remaining constituents. X-ray diffraction and X-ray fluorescence do these. X-ray diffraction distinguishes and measures substances on the basis of a crystalline structure. X-ray fluorescence does it by sensing atomic compositions. X-ray fluorescence analysis is used widely in analyzing the basic products of the metals industries and in detecting small concentrations of metals in products of the powder or fluid process industries. X-ray diffraction remains a laboratory technique. In X-ray diffraction technique (Fig. 6-23a) the

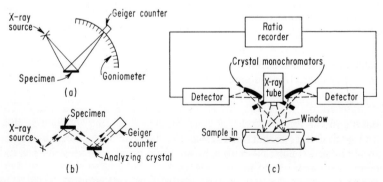

Fig. 6-23. X-ray diffraction fluorescence spectrometer and continuous analyzer.

X-ray beam striking the sample gives off a cone of secondary rays. The intensity of the rays at different radii varies with atomic structure. The rays can be photographed to give characteristic concentric-ring patterns. For recording, a cross section of the diffraction cone is scanned by a Geiger counter moving along an arc. This technique is used mostly in atomic structure study and in identification of materials by comparison with known patterns. Because crystal structure is shown, it can be used, for example, in distinguishing between rutile and anatase phases of titanium dioxide. Range is unlimited as no two materials show identical patterns. Accuracy is high. The X-ray fluorescence method (Fig. 6-23b) causes some elements to give off characteristic individual radiations. These are collimated, and analyzed by a crystal which, by its position, reflects individual radiations at specific angles. Intensities are measured by Geiger-counter goniometer. This technique differs from X-ray diffraction in that it gives results characteristic of elements present in the sample, rather than atomic structure. The technique is suitable for metals, alloys, minerals, chemicals, mixtures, and compounds. Accuracy is high.

The X-ray fluorescence continuous analyzer (Fig. 6-23c) has X rays falling on the sample to produce characteristic radiations which are picked up by curved crystal monochromators. One for reference diffracts only scattered radiation of a chosen wavelength, the other a wavelength characteristic of the element being analyzed. Diffracted beams fall on separate Geiger counters whose output is ratioed and recorded as concentration. Use is for various analyses such as metals in ores, in plating solutions, in catalysts, etc. Range when used for elements is applicable on atomic number 19 (K) and higher. Accuracy is highly selective.

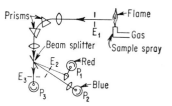

Fig. 6-24. Flame photometry for analysis of metals.

Q Explain flame photometry and how it is used in product analysis.

A In flame photometry (Fig. 6-24) the spectral emissions from a solution sprayed into a flame source are analyzed. The big advantage is that the instrumentation needed is much less expensive and less complex than for spectrography. Flame photometry is used widely for metals which can be prepared in a solution. It has also been used for nonmetals. Solid samples cannot be analyzed. This is mostly a laboratory instrument for rapid analysis for sodium, potassium, lithium, and other metals in mixtures. The test is good for trace elements also. About 50 elements can be determined by this method.

As the sketch shows, the powdered sample in solution is sprayed into the gas flame, giving off a characteristic light which passes through entrance slit E_1, through an optical system of prisms and lenses, to the beam splitter where part goes to movable exit slit E_2, and the remainder goes to standardizing cell p_3. Red- and blue-sensitive cells measure the intensity of characteristic lines with the air of movable slit E_2. Usually an oxyhydrogen or oxyacetylene flame is used for hotter excitation than that produced in a simple bunsen burner. Time is less than 2 min per element. Range is Na, K, Li, Ca, Sr, and other metals; 3 to 1,000 ppm, depending on metal. Accuracy is 1 to 2 per cent.

SUGGESTED READING

Recommended Practices, sold by Instrument Society of America, 530 William Penn Place, Pittsburgh, Pa.

    ISA—RP 25.1, *Materials for Instruments in Radiation Service*

Reprints sold by *Control Engineering* magazine, costing $1 or less

    Analysis Instrumentation

Reprints sold by *Power* magazine, costing $1 or less

    Air Pollution, 48 pages

    Water Treatment, 56 pages

Books

    Coates, Vincent J., Henry J. Noebels, and Irving S. Fagerson: *Gas Chromatography*, Academic Press, Inc., New York, 1957.

    Siggia, Sidney: *Continuous Analysis of Chemical Process Systems*, John Wiley & Sons, Inc., New York, 1959.

    Stout, Melville B.: *Electrical Measurements*, Rubicon Division, Minneapolis-Honeywell Regulator Company, Philadelphia, Pa., 1959.

    Elonka, Steve, and Julian Bernstein: *Standard Industrial Electronics Questions and Answers*, vols. I and II, McGraw-Hill Book Company, Inc., New York, to be published in 1964.

    Elonka, Steve, and Joseph F. Robinson: *Standard Plant Operator's Questions and Answers*, vols. I and II, McGraw-Hill Book Company, Inc., New York, 1959.

    Elonka, Steve, and Quaid W. Minich: *Standard Refrigeration and Air Conditioning Questions and Answers*, McGraw-Hill Book Company, Inc., New York, 1961.

    Elonka, Steve: *Plant Operator's Manual*, McGraw-Hill Book Company, Inc., New York, 1956.

7

PHYSICAL AND ELECTRICAL
MEASURING SYSTEMS

Q Why must moisture content of air and gas be measured?

A Moisture content of air or gas (air is a gas) is an important variable and must be known to be controlled. The percentage of permissible water vapor in a gas usually depends on its use or on conditions making its moisture content a critical factor. Examples are air conditioning for human comfort and for controlling product quality, such as foods, textiles, paper, and tobacco; and drying operations, as when a product is put into a drying chamber for a definite moisture content. Heat-treating of metals, such as the moisture control of protective atmosphere, is critical. Free water forming in pipelines of gas transmission lines is a hazard causing freezing and corrosion. When producing gases such as oxygen and ammonia, moisture content is critical. Recording and measuring moisture content of gas can both minimize the dangers of corrosion and freezing, as well as improve production efficiency.

Pure dry air is a mixture of about 4 parts of nitrogen to 1 of oxygen, plus small amounts of rare gases, such as argon. The air around us also contains moisture in varying amounts. Air to be conditioned might therefore be called a mixture of air and steam.

Q How is the moisture content of air or gas usually measured?

A The per cent relative humidity indicates the actual weight of water vapor contained in 1 cu ft of the sample, divided by the weight of water vapor that this same volume would hold if saturated at the same temperature. Because it is seldom practical to make this measurement, psychrometry is used instead. Instruments used for these measurements come in three types: (1) wet- and dry-bulb thermometer, (2) wet- and dry-bulb resistance thermometer, and (3) wet- and dry-bulb thermocouple.

Q What is wet-bulb temperature and how is it measured?

A To measure an air temperature lower than that of a dry bulb, a

167

thermometer bulb, or thermocouple, or resistance thermometer bulb from which water is constantly evaporating is needed. The bulb is covered with a wetted gauze or wick and placed in the air stream to be measured. Some of the water in the gauze will evaporate, taking heat from the remaining water. The water temperature will thus drop. The amount of this temperature drop depends on the dryness and temperature of the air. The wet-bulb temperature of the space will be lower than the dry-bulb temperature because water evaporates from the surface of the bulb, lowering its temperature. The less moisture in the air, the greater is the cooling effect. To find relative humidity, a graph known as a psychrometric chart is referred to for the answer. For example, if the dry-bulb temperature is 90°F and the wet-bulb temperature is 75°F, as shown by point A on the chart in Fig. 7-1, the relative humidity is

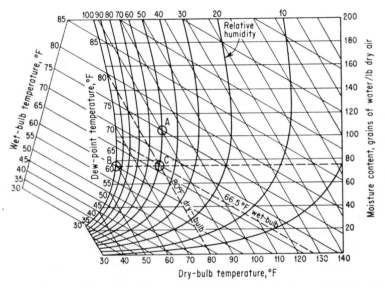

Fig. 7-1. Psychrometer chart. A psychrometric chart can be used with wet- and dry-bulb measurements to give relative humidity, dew point, and grains of moisture per pound of dry air. (*Copyrighted by Minneapolis-Honeywell.*)

50 per cent. See *Standard Plant Operator's Questions and Answers* and *Standard Refrigeration and Air Conditioning Questions and Answers* for detailed information on humidity.

Q Describe a wet- and dry-bulb psychrometer.

A A sling psychrometer (Fig. 7-2) has a wet and a dry bulb, each one on the end of a mercury-in-glass thermometer. The wet bulb is covered with a wick or gauze, which is wetted with clean water of room temperature. The operator holds the swivel-mounted handle and swings it around to give the proper air movement against the wet bulb. This whirling operation is repeated after each reading until two readings of the wet

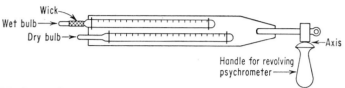

Fig. 7-2. Sling psychrometer.

bulb agree. There must be no moisture contacting the dry bulb during these operations and readings must be taken immediately after each whirling. Another type of wet- and dry-bulb psychrometer has a water reservoir into which the wick extends. Water level is maintained by (1) continuous flow and overflow, (2) float-operated valve, or (3) constant-level bottle feed. A porous ceramic sleeve or a sintered-metal porous sleeve is often used instead of the cloth wick. Air circulation must be at least 15 fps to assure proper humidity measurement. Where natural circulation is too low, a suction fan and psychrometer box are used to assure enough air movement past the sensing element. The big advantage of a wet- and dry-bulb thermometer is that it is more accurate than a hygrometer. It is also easier to maintain.

The disadvantage is that its readings must be interpreted by using a chart or table to convert them into needed information. Bulbs must also be maintained and kept clean or information isn't accurate.

Q Describe recording wet- and dry-bulb systems.

A As Fig. 7-3 shows, this instrument also has a wet- and dry-bulb assembly over which the air to be measured flows. The two measuring elements can be filled thermal systems, thermocouples, or resistance thermometers (see Chap 2).

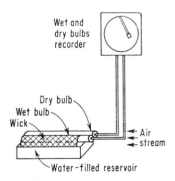

Fig. 7-3. Wet- and dry-bulb thermometer elements.

Filled thermometers read wet-and dry-bulb temperatures separately with two pens, but thermocouples or resistance thermometers read the temperature difference between wet bulb and dry bulb. Filled thermal systems are connected to a two-pen thermometer. The thermocouple instrument uses a differential thermocouple potentiometer circuit. The resistance thermometers are connected to a Wheatstone bridge circuit. Both instruments have a relative humidity range of 5 to 100 per cent. Both have a temperature range of 30 to 212°F on the wet bulb. Either circuit is ideal for using the instrument as part of a central control panel. Resistance thermometer bulbs can be as far as 1,600 ft from the instrument without losing accuracy. A distance up to 2,500 ft is practical with the thermocouple type. The difference between two circuits is that a thermocouple is a voltage-producing element. The small voltage produced in response to heat is compared in the instrument against a known voltage. The difference between these two voltages is then converted by the instrument into a reading of temperature. Minimum measuring span of thermocouples is 150°F. Because known voltage in the instrument must be kept constant, the potentiometer circuit needs both a standard cell and standardizing rheostat. A resistance thermometer bulb produces no voltage of its own. Its measurements are based on the principle that electrical resistance of conductors varies with changes in temperature. The bulb is connected as one arm of the instrument's measuring bridge; its resistance to current flow is converted into a reading of temperature. Minimum measuring span of resistance thermometers is 20°F.

Q   What is a hygrometer? Explain how these instruments measure moisture content of air or gas.

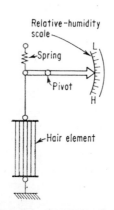

Fig. 7-4. Hygrometer, hair element.

A   If a material absorbs moisture readily, we say it is hygroscopic. Human hair, wood, salt, and other materials can be called hygroscopic and are used for the sensing element of a hygrometer. In Fig. 7-4, a strand of human hair is used as the primary element. One end of the strand is fixed, while the other end is connected through a mechanical linkage to an instrument pen or pointer. Because of its hygroscopic quality, the hair expands with an increase in relative humidity. This allows a spring to move the pen or pointer upscale. A decrease in relative humidity causes the hair to contract, forcing the pen or pointer downscale. A hair hygrometer gives an accurate, direct reading of per cent relative humidity once it is properly calibrated. It is often used with a temperature pen in a single portable instrument. Uses are checking relative humidity in textile mills, food processing plants, etc. It also comes as an electric controller for operating fans, spray nozzles, dampers, or dehumidifiers. These instruments are usually reliable between 15 and 90 per cent relative humidity. Check them at least four times a year for accuracy. Hair elements may have to be renewed, depending on environment. Membrane, wood, and salt-conductivity hygrometers are three others commonly used. Under changes in atmospheric humidity, these sensing elements also take up and give off moisture, thus changing in length as does human hair.

Q Describe an electric hygrometer.

A Here the accurate, direct-reading measurements of relative humidity depend on moisture-sensitive compounds which alter their electrical conductivity in relation to the amount of moisture absorbed. Both a moisture-sensing element and a potentiometer are used. The sensing element is a plastic form upon which two gold-leaf grids are stamped. The form is then coated with moisture-sensitive lithium chloride. Because this element converts relative humidity into electrical units, it is a transducer. Electrical resistance of the transducer changes when exposed to variations in humidity, which effects are sensed by the resistance measuring circuit. This electric hygrometer has a compensating circuit that is effective across the entire relative humidity range of 5 to 95 per cent, also between 40 and 120°F temperature limits, within accuracies of ±1 to 2 per cent of the reading. A transducer can be as far as 1,000 ft from the recorder if connected by a pair of shielded leads.

Q What is meant by the dew point of air or gas, and how is it measured?

A Dew point is the temperature at which water vapor in the gas will condense into liquid, or the temperature at which a mixture of air and water vapor is saturated. The name is derived from slowly cooling a polished surface until condensation takes place. The temperature of the surface when the first droplet appears is used as the dew point. Knowing this point permits rapid calculation of the gas's moisture content. On the psychrometric chart (Fig. 7-1) the dew-point temperature for air with a dry-bulb temperature of 80°F and a wet bulb of 66.5°F is found to be 60°F by extending a horizontal line left to the 100 per cent or saturation curve, point *B*. Horizontal line *BC* represents a constant moisture content line for the air. As the air's moisture content increases or decreases, the dew-point temperature also goes up or down. That is why this temperature serves as well as the combination of wet- and dry-bulb temperature to indicate the moisture content of air or any gas. We explained relative humidity before, but absolute humidity refers to the weight of water vapor per unit volume, pounds per cubic foot, or grams per centimeter. Two popular methods of measuring the dew point are the electric conductivity method and the mirror method.

Q Describe the electric conductivity method of measuring dew point.
A Double wire winding on the insulating tube (Fig. 7-5) is coated with hydroscopic conducting (lithium chloride) solution. Inside the tube is a resistance thermometer bulb. Low-voltage current supplied to the wires from a separate source heats the coating, thereby driving out the moisture until equilibrium is reached between moisture leaving and moisture returning. The temperature of the equilibrium point measured by the thermometer is related to the dew point of air at the bulb. The instrument's measuring circuit is a Wheatstone bridge. The chart reads directly in dew-point degrees Fahrenheit or centigrade, grains per cubic foot or per cent water vapor by volume. Use directly in air for dew points −50 to +142°F at ambient temperatures to 220°F. Accuracy is ±1°F. Higher temperature measurements can be made by cooling the sample. Element protecting tubes allow use at high pressures to 600 psi and in dirty or dusty atmospheres, such as in blast furnaces, heat-treatment furnaces, dryers, dehydrators, and storage spaces.

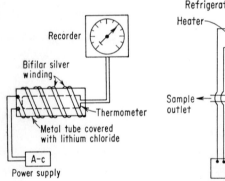

Fig. 7-5. Conductivity method of dew-point measurement.

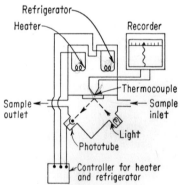

Fig. 7-6. Mirror method of dew-point measurement.

Q Describe the mirror method of measuring the dew point of air and other gases.
A Gas under test (Fig. 7-6) enters the gas chamber, where it comes in contact with a thin metallic mirror attached to a thermocouple. This mirror is refrigerated to −90°F, causing moisture from gas being tested to form on the surface. As this moisture fogs the mirror's surface, it is heated to a temperature which evaporates the dew. This temperature represents the dew point of gas being tested. A heater controlled elec-

tronically keeps the mirror at dew point at all times, regardless of changes in moisture content. A continuous record of this dew point is made by a thermocouple attached to the mirror and thus measuring the output voltage. The dew-point recorder must have enough positive pressure to cause flow through the gas chamber. Being insensitive in the range of $\frac{1}{8}$ to 1 cfm gas flow, a blower or aspirator is used. But 15 psi is the top pressure within the chamber. Because the basic operation of a dew-point recorder depends on the mirror's reflectivity, a fine glass-wool filter is placed in the gas inlet to keep dirt off the mirror's surface. The mirror is automatically flashed every hour to remove entrained condensables.

Q   Why is the measurement of moisture content of liquids and solids important? What measuring methods are used?

A   The quality of products like paper, yarn, foods, etc., depends largely on their moisture content during manufacture. Excessive moisture in sized yarn, for example, may cause mildew, while too little moisture causes brittleness. Overmoist paper, on the other hand, may crush, blacken, or mottle in the calender rolls. Moisture content of chemicals, sand, and even gravel must often be known. Instruments for measuring moisture content continuously, as well as for controlling the needed content of moisture, are of various types. Here we shall cover two of the more common types: (1) electrical resistance (conductivity) and (2) electrical capacitance.

Q   Describe the electrical resistance method of measuring moisture content.

A   Material measured for moisture content (Fig. 7-7) passes between a detector roll and a machine, or idler, roll that is electrically grounded. An electrical potential is thus impressed upon the detector roll, causing current flow between the detector roll and grounded machine, or idler, roll to vary proportionately. This happens because the electrical conductivity of the measured medium varies in relation to its moisture content. Material being tested then becomes a variable resistance placed in the measuring circuit. As the moisture content of the ma-

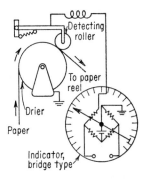

Fig. 7-7. Electrical resistance method of moisture measurement.

terial contacted by the detector roll varies, its electrical conductivity varies in proportion. This causes the instrument to indicate and record these changes continuously in terms of moisture content. Change in moisture content of the material causes change in resistance in one leg of the measuring circuit bridge, which unbalances the bridge. This small electrical unbalance is amplified and sent to the instrument, causing a slide-wire contact to be repositioned and thus rebalancing the instrument. Used widely in the textile and paper industries, this instrument can also be equipped to control moisture regain by regulating steam to the dryer rolls.

Q Describe the electrical capacitance method of moisture measurement.
A Meters of this type are known as (1) dielectric, (2) a-c impedance, (3) radio-frequency power loss, and (4) capacitance-type meters. The operating principle of the capacitance-type (Fig. 7-8) moisture-measuring

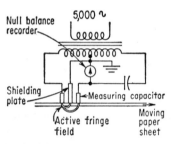

Fig. 7-8. Electrical capacitance method of moisture measurement.

meter depends on change taking place in the dielectric constant (specific inductive capacitance) of a material between its moist and dry conditions. The dielectric constant of many organic materials such as grain, cereal, and textile fibers is very low, in the order of 2.2 to 5.0 for dry samples. The dielectric constant of water is about 80, one of the highest. Adding a little water to a product having a dielectric constant of 2 or 3 causes a great change in the dielectric constant for a very slight increase in moisture content. These instruments are chiefly used with materials having moisture contents below 20 to 25 per cent. Measuring circuits used are (1) bridge circuits, (2) resonance methods, and (3) beat-frequency methods. Advantages of capacitance moisture meters are (1) additive agents usually used in processed products affect calibration very slightly, (2) the slightest change in moisture content of most materials makes a large change in dielectric constant, (3) materials need not contact the sampling electrodes for accurate readings, (4) the instrument is rugged and reliable, (5) they are safe because the applied radio-frequency voltage is low, and (6) they are ideal for continuous measurement and control because meter indications are instantaneous. For best results, remember: (1) The sample should have moisture well distributed. (2) Because the dielectric constant of most materials decreases as temperature increases, the meter will indicate low for temperatures above ambient. (3) Do not use on samples containing large percentages of additives in the form of electrolytes; dielectric losses caused by these additives make some meters less sensitive.

Q What are viscosity and consistency? Why are they important in process control?
A Viscosity of a fluid is an indication of its relative fluidity. It tells

how well the fluid will flow at a given temperature. Viscosity can also be described as a fluid's resistance to deformation under shear; it is expressed as

$$\text{Viscosity} = \frac{\text{shear stress}}{\text{rate of shear}}$$

To understand shear in the sense indicated here, picture two blocks of wood separated by a light lubricating oil. Then picture two similar blocks separated by molasses. Obviously, the blocks separated by lubricating oil will offer less resistance to sliding than those separated by molasses. The reason is that the light oil will shear more easily than the sticky molasses. Measurement and control of viscosity, as well as understanding its variation under pressure and temperature changes, are important in product control. Substances undergoing continuous deformation when subjected to a shear stress are said to exhibit fluid behavior. Resistance offered by the substance to this deformation is called consistency. Consistency control is often the means of reducing the quantity of valuable material lost in the process. An example of consistency can be given when mixing foods; overmixing dough results in a weak, sticky mass with loss of texture. But undermixing results in irregularities of fermentation, non-uniformity of ingredient, and a heavy, tough dough. Both conditions are bad. Today instruments control viscosity and consistency. Viscosimeters (also viscometers) are classified as (1) laboratory viscosimeters for measuring samples only and (2) continuous viscosimeters for continuous viscosity measurement. The latter types are (1) batch-continuous type and (2) continuous-flow type.

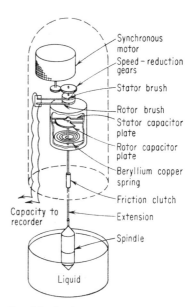

Fig. 7-9. Continuous rotary torque viscometer.

Q Describe a continuous measuring viscometer.

A Figure 7-9 shows a device which measures viscosity by sensing torque needed to rotate a spindle in a liquid. Continuous measurement of motor torque is directly related to continuous viscosity measurement and is recorded on a potentiometer recorder calibrated in centipoises. A synchronous motor drives a vertical spindle at constant speed through a beryllium copper spring. As the viscosity of the fluid in which the spindle is immersed increases, the viscous drag opposing rotation of the spindle will flex the spring to a new position where the spring's torque balances the viscous drag. Angular lag of the spindle behind the motor is proportional to viscosity. The angle is measured by capacitance change, resistance change, or a timed impulse, thus producing an electrical signal proportional to viscosity. Figure 7-9 shows details where capacitance change is created as the spring deflects a set of condenser plates attached to its free end in relation to plates at the fixed end. A measuring circuit in the recorder detects capacitance change and calibrates it directly in viscosity units (range is 0 to 100 and 0 to 50,000 cps). The viscometer housing is constantly purged with clean dry air or inert gas; it can be explosionproof and is suitable for open or closed vessels by flange connection. Advantages are (1) continuous measurement eliminates sampling, (2) easily cleaned and purged, (3) measures viscosity of agitated fluids, and (4) measures both Newtonian and non-Newtonian liquids.

Q Describe the pressure differential method of viscosity measurement.
A This method is widely used in a wide range of industrial liquid applications for continuous viscosity measurement. It measures the differential pressure drop (Fig. 7-10) through a friction tube, in ranges up to 3,000 centipoise. Liquid is pumped at a constant rate through a friction tube at viscous flow. Pressure drop across the tube ends is measured in terms of absolute viscosity by any differential measuring element described in Chap. 3. The most popular is the pneumatic force-balance type with remote recording and controlling functions. Its advantage is in simplicity and lack of maintenance and adjustment. This method is used widely for petroleum products, rubber, greases, and polymers.

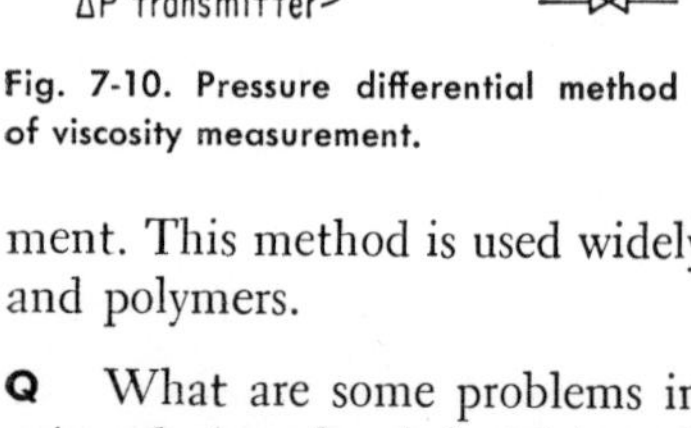

Fig. 7-10. Pressure differential method of viscosity measurement.

Q What are some problems in applying continuous consistency measuring devices for industrial use? How are these instruments classified?
A One problem is stratification and nonuniformity of the fluid stream. This makes it more accurate to handle the entire flow instead of a sample. Because there should be no separation or settling of solids from suspension, a sample taken from large tanks must be well agitated. If sampling from a pipeline, the diluent must be well mixed with the main stream to get accurate readings. Broad classification of these instruments depends

on the principles used; these are (1) apparent viscosity, both mechanical and hydraulic types, (2) drainage rate, (3) electrical resonance, and (4) optical methods.

Q Describe the drainage rate method of measuring consistency.

A This low-consistency regulator (Fig. 7-11) works on the principle of measuring the drain rate of water or other solvent from solids in suspension. At consistency ranges below 1.8 per cent, apparent viscosity methods are unreliable. But since the rate of change of head is high for the same

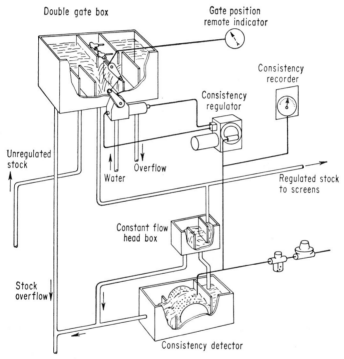

Fig. 7-11. Consistency-control system based on drainage rate.

increment of consistency change even below 1.8 per cent, the draining rate method is best applied as a low-consistency regulator in the range of 0.1 to 1.5 per cent. It is widely used to maintain the consistency of paper stock upstream of thickeners and fine screens. A continuous sample of regulated stock flows from a double-gate flow box to the consistency detector after passing through the constant-level box. Fibers form a mat on the rotating screen of the consistency detector, and the drainage rate of water at the upstream end of the detector box is regulated by the depth of the fibers. Measurement of the detector box level by head pressure provides the signal for consistency regulator control over the double gate position through the hydraulic cylinder. If the consistency drops below the desired percentage, the gate opens to allow greater stock flow, and closes proportionally on the water side.

Q   What is meant by apparent viscosity?

A   Consistency is inferred by using apparent viscosity methods to measure parameters in a fluid system affected by changes in viscosity and consistency. Mechanical types convert the fluid resistance to rotation of a motor-driven paddle or agitator, as measured by the torque needed to drive the agitator at constant speed. Often the power required to drive the agitator is measured and related to consistency. Consistency is found by hydraulic measurement of apparent viscosity. For constant flow through a friction cylinder, pressure differential varies with viscosity and consistency. Many schemes are used to measure the change in differential pressure.

Q   Explain the power-consumption system for consistency measurement.

A   See Fig. 7-12. Pulp-stock consistency in a stock chest or storage tank

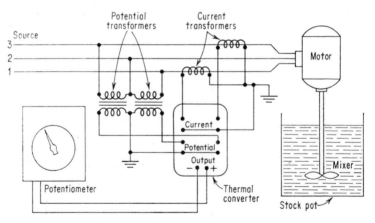

Fig. 7-12. Power-consumption system of consistency measurement.

is often controlled by measuring the power consumed in driving an agitator in the chest or tank. The agitator motor load changes with variations in the stock consistency. A thermal converter, as the primary sensing element, converts an a-c watt (power) input from the drive motor into a d-c watt output. This output is fed into the wattmeter measuring circuit of a potentiometer recording controller. A consistency controller regulates a pneumatic valve in the dilution line to maintain uniform consistency in the chest. This system is easy to install and maintain, but accuracy is limited by the effect of wear in motor and bearings. Also, an agitator assembly coupling which produces variations in power measurement at the thermal converter has no relation to consistency. Sensitivity is low, which means a large change in consistency is needed to give a small change in power output. Therefore, the system is usually applied to high-consistency ranges above 3 per cent.

Q Explain how consistency is measured with a hydraulic system using differential pressure.

A See Fig. 7-13. The principle is that, when all variables are kept constant, fluid to be measured flowing through a channel forms a hydraulic

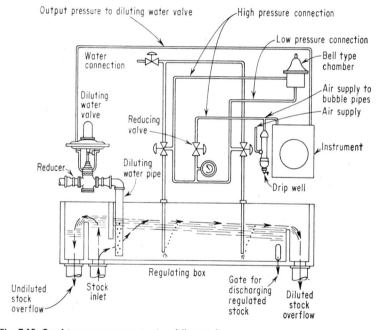

Fig. 7-13. Consistency measurement using differential pressure.

gradient directly proportional to consistency of the fluid. Consistency is thus controlled by measuring the slope and diluting the slurry as needed. The slope is kept at a predetermined level by diluting the slurry before it enters the channel. Slope is measured by submerging two air-bubble pipes into the fluid, one at each end of the channel, to the same distance from the level bottom. Measured volumes of air supplied to these pipes build up to equal the stock head above the bottom end of the pipe.

Escaping air bubbles through the slurry keep pressure constant. Transmitting differential pressure between these two points to an automatic instrument in turn controls the dilution valve. This instrument is claimed to have full-volume control and consistency regulation to within $\frac{1}{10}$ per cent when the slurry consistency is above 2 per cent; it is also sensitive to slight variations in consistency and provides accurate automatic control over a wide consistency range.

Q   What is an optical method of measuring consistency?

A   Various optical devices are made for measuring consistency. The instrument in Fig. 7-14 relates the absorption of radiant energy by

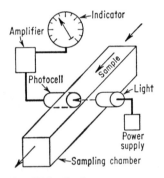

Fig. 7-14. Consistency measurement using optical method.

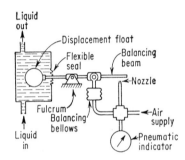

Fig. 7-15. Density meter, displacement-type.

particles suspended in water slurries to consistency. In this unit a continuous sample of fluid flows through a sampling chamber having glass side plates opposite each other. A shielded light placed at one glass plate is mounted on a sliding base. This permits moving the light closer to the chamber as it loses its intensity through use. On the opposite side is a photocell to receive the light transmitted through the fluid. The amount of light transmitted has a measurable relationship to consistency. The photocell actuates an amplifier whose output in microamperes is indicated and recorded. Measurement is very inaccurate when fluid or particles change slightly in color. Be sure to keep instrument carefully calibrated.

Q   What are density and specific gravity? Why measure these for industrial process control?

A   Density is defined as the weight (mass) of a given substance per unit volume. It is expressed in grams per cubic centimeter, pounds per cubic foot, and pounds per cubic inch or pounds per gallon. Water is a substance whose volume varies slightly with changes in temperature, causing its density to vary with its temperature. For example, at sea level, at 32°F or freezing, the density per cubic foot of water is 62.418 lb. Specific gravity, on the other hand, is the ratio of the unit weight of a substance to that of the same weight of water. For critical scientific work, double-distilled water at 4°C is used. In engineering the reference is usually to water at 60°F. Because the specific gravity of water is unity (1), oils and spirits are below, while aqueous solutions are above this figure. The specific gravity of oil, for example, is equal to the ratio of a unit quantity of oil to the weight of the same quantity of water, both oil and water being at the same temperature. Thus if the weight of 1 gal of oil at 60°F equals 7.986 lb and the weight of 1 gal of water at the same temperature is 8.328 lb, then 7.986/8.328 = 0.9589 specific gravity. Density and specific gravity are important to determine and control the concentration of a solution or mixture. They are often used for measuring product quality.

Q What units of measurement are used for indicating specific gravity?
A Industry uses a variety of units and scale calibrations, depending on the industry and on the fluid being measured. The API (American Petroleum Institute) scale used mostly by the petroleum industry is based on this formula: Degree hydrometer scale (at 60°F) = (141.5/ sp gr) − 131.4.

The Baumé scale is used mostly for acids, light and heavy liquids, glue, syrups, etc. One Baumé scale is used for liquids heavier than water, a second for those lighter than water. Balling is another scale used mostly to measure per cent wort in brewery products and also per cent by weight of dissolved solids or sugar liquors. Barkometer, Brix, Quevenne, Richter-Sikes-Tralles, and Twaddle are still other scales. But regardless of which one is used, the temperature, pressure, and nature of solution all affect a liquid's specific gravity. Hand hydrometers and indicating and recording instruments use all varieties of calibrations.

Q Describe the displacement meter used for measuring density.
A The liquid to be measured flows continuously through a displacement chamber (Fig. 7-15). A balance beam pivoted on a fulcrum extends into the displacement chamber through a flexible seal. One float is on the end of the beam, inside the chamber, while the other end extends over an air nozzle. As liquid flows through the chamber, an upward force acts on the balance beam. Upward action is caused by the volume of liquid displaced by the float. This upward force is balanced by a pneumatic system which transmits a signal that is proportional to the density of the liquid. The system shown can measure liquids of specific gravities of 0.5 and higher. A thermostatic heater is used for liquids when temperature isn't constant. One popular use of these meters is for liquid sugar density control. In the continuous production of liquid

sugar, precise density control is needed. The reason is that this product is usually marketed on the basis of a specified standard density. Control is most important on large volumes where a small change in solids content can cause large sugar loss.

Q   What is the liquid purge differential pressure method of measuring density?

A   A vertical process flow line carrying liquid to be measured has two taps in the side (Fig. 7-16), one above the other at different elevations,

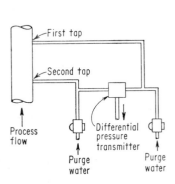

Fig. 7-16. Liquid purge differential pressure measurement of density.

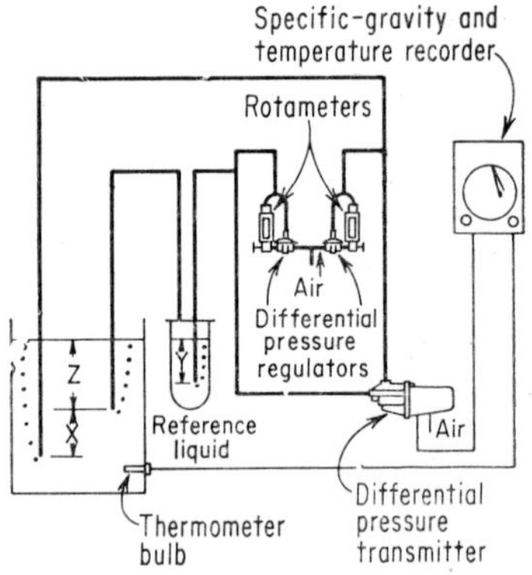

Fig. 7-17. Specific gravity measured by air purge system.

usually 10 in. apart. A pressure differential measuring device (such as that described in Chap. 3) hooked up to taps as shown is purged with a reference fluid such as water. This creates an automatically suppressed range that prevents the taps from plugging. The sample fluid and the water (reference fluid) provide the measured differential pressure in the two columns. Dilution is negligible because the purge rate is very small. The pulp and paper industry uses this system to measure and control the density of green liquor, heavy black liquor, clay or starch slurries, lime slurries, and lime-mud slurries.

Q   How is specific gravity measured by the air purge system?

A   This method is used for flotation, evaporation, mixing, solvent recovery, and other industrial operations involving the concentration of liquid solutions. Industries included are the production of sugar, chemicals, alcohol, beverages, paper, textiles, and others. Here air at the same pressure is purged through two dip tubes, both immersed in the liquid under test (Fig. 7-17). Air flow through the tubes is regulated by needle valves in the supply lines and is measured by the two rotameters. Any difference in air pressure between the tubes is caused by the difference of the depths of immersion, and difference in the specific gravities of the reference and measured liquids. Since the difference in tube depth is constant, any variation in differential pressure is due to changes in the liquid's specific gravity. Measurement of the pressure differential is made by a differential converter transmitter and is applied to a pressure gage or recorder actuated by a pneumatic receiver element. The force producing the specific gravity reading equals the difference in depth X between dip tubes in the measured liquid multiplied by the specific gravity of the liquid. Thus a portion of the chart is used to indicate level, and gravity measurement does not begin at the lowest point. To obtain a range on the instrument chart or scale, some suppression must be provided. Reference liquid produces this suppression. The depth Y of this liquid above the bottom of the dip tube is equal to the difference of immersion depths X of the two dip tubes in the measured liquid. Therefore, if the specific gravity of the measured liquid is lower than that of the reference liquid, the pressure in the low-pressure chamber of the differential converter will exceed that in the high-pressure chamber. Then no pressure will be transmitted to the indicating instrument. By using the reference liquid with a specific gravity equal to the lowest value which is to be measured, a wider range of specific gravity measurement is possible. As the vertical distance between the two dip tubes X is fixed, variations in Z have an equal effect on the immersion depth of both dip tubes. Differential pressure therefore remains unchanged. The sketch shows a specific gravity recorder with a temperature pen, the thermometer bulb being immersed in the measured liquid. This allows the user to calculate the temperature correction of the recorded specific gravity.

Q How is the boiling-point-rise system a measure of specific gravity?

A The boiling-point-elevation method (Fig. 7-18) compares the temperature of a boiling solution with the temperature of water boiled at the same pressure. Common use is in evaporators to determine the end point of evaporation. For a given solution, the relationship of concentration (density, Baumé, etc.) vs. boiling point at various pressures is well known. In an evaporator, the temperature of the outlet liquor from the first-effect evaporator is measured to determine its boiling point. The temperature of the vapors leaving the same evaporator is measured as

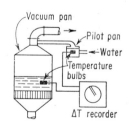

Fig. 7-18. Boiling-point measure of specific gravity.

compensation for pressure change in the vessel. Resistance thermometers or thermocouples are used to measure the temperatures and their differ-

... measured in a differential temperature measuring circuit. Temperature transmitters are preferable because of ease in installation and data
transmission.

Q Describe a flow-through-line method of continuous density measurement.

A Figure 7-19 shows a density sensing device for measuring the density
of liquids flowing in process lines. It converts this measurement into a

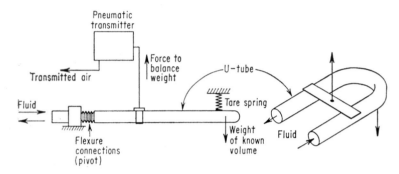

Fig. 7-19. Continuous density measurement.

proportional pneumatic output signal (3 to 15 psi). It is especially useful
for food industry applications and for other process liquids. It works on
the principle of measuring the weight of a fixed volume of liquid. Process
liquid flows from the process line to 2-in. inlet and outlet connections to
a U-tube primary element. The active portion of the U tube has constant
volume. The U tube has four fixed sections and two flexible sections. A
load arm joins two sides of the tube and is connected by a small cable to
the primary beam of a force-balance pneumatic transmitter. Inlet and
outlet connections of the U tube are anchored to the transmitter base,
allowing the tube to move upward or downward about its flexible sections
as the weight of the process liquid changes. The load arm is located at
the U tube's center of gravity so that any change in weight of the flow
liquid exerts an equal force on each half of the tube. Thus the entire
tube, up to the flexible sections, is raised or lowered in a horizontal
plane. The suppression system subjects the tube to an upward force equal
to the liquid weight and weight of the tube. Then the only significant
force produced by the unsuppressed weight of the liquid is due to a
change in the liquid's density. The density change moves the primary
beam, which acts as the flapper in a flapper-nozzle pneumatic transmitter.
That produces an output signal proportional to density for a pneumatic
receiver. A portion of this output pressure is fed back through a balancing
bellows to balance the primary beam. Pressure or temperature compensa-

tion can be added to the device. It measures densities from 0.250 to 3.050. Sensitivity is 0.0004, accuracy ±0.0009. Advantages include (1) no line restrictions, (2) simple, sanitary construction, (3) narrow span, extremely accurate and sensitive, and (4) easy installation and maintenance.

Q Name a method of continuous density measurement for difficult liquids.

A Radioactive materials encased in a safety housing are placed on the outside of a process line with a radiation detector on the opposite side. The amount of radiation through the pipe section and flowing process liquid picked up by the detector depends on the mass of the intercepting liquid. The detector converts the amount of radiation into an electrical signal which is amplified and read out on a recorder or indicator. Accuracies of ±0.001 with sensitivities of ±0.0001 specific gravity can be achieved. It is especially useful for density of acids, slurries, coal, cement, paper pulp, plastic, and minerals.

Q Why is weight measured and recorded in process applications?

A For (1) monitoring the amount of material supplied to, or removed from, particular processing areas, machines, or plants; (2) regulating the amount of material fed to treatment vats or tanks containing chemicals of a mixed concentration; (3) batching, blending, or transferring operations; (4) determining the production of a section; and (5) counting and inspecting.

Q What are the basic components of a weighing system?

A (1) Load receiving element (primary element); (2) an indicating, recording, and/or controlling means; and (3) a sensing or measuring and transmitting apparatus to couple the first two components mentioned. The load receiver may be a platter, scoop, platform, hopper, tank, hook, a section of conveyor, bag holder, etc. The uneven-balance scale (Fig. 7-20a) is the simplest form for weighing. The steel yard shown illustrates the principle of most weight-balanced industrial scales. An unknown

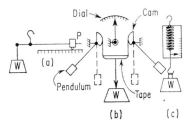

Fig. 7-20. Basic components of weighing systems.

weight on a short moment arm is balanced by a movable known poise (or known weights plus poise) on a long moment arm. This is the most widely used weighing method for industrial use; it includes manual and automatic types. Some have indications on a dial; others print the weight automatically. Figure 7-20c is a spring-balanced scale. Spring deflection within limits is directly proportional to load, so deflection can be used as a measure of the weight supported. The system is chiefly used for small commercial scales but is also used to balance a beam in automatic industrial scales. In the hydraulic (spring) balance scales the force produced by load is detected by a liquid-filled capsular element, transmitted to a spring-loaded pressure-sensitive element. This is used in crane-hook scales and other industrial applications. Figure 7-20b shows a pendulum-balanced scale. One or more pendulums balance, increasing loads as they move from the vertical (zero) to horizontal (maximum). Because the load balanced varies as the sine of the displacement angle, cams are used to give linear scale graduation. The cam may be on a pendulum or on a pointer. A metal tape transmits the motion. Common use is in both commercial and industrial scales, especially where dial indication of weight is desired. It is available in recording and printing types and with photoelectric cutoff. There is also a remote digital recording for this scale.

Q   How does the pneumatic weight transmitter work?

A   This type of transmitter (Fig. 7-21) senses weight pneumatically,

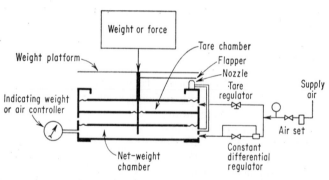

Fig. 7-21. Pneumatic weight transmitter.

then sends a proportional air signal (3 to 15 psi) to other standard pneumatic circuit components. These can be pneumatic receiving indicators, recorders, and controllers. The transmitter works on the pneumatic-balance principle. Here a diaphragm is supported by the exact pressure needed to counterbalance the measured weight. The measuring system is practically null balance, since the extent of diaphragm movement from zero to full load does not exceed 0.010 in. Transmitted air pressure bears a fixed relation to measured weight and is linear throughout the weighing range. A tare balance chamber and a tare load diaphragm can be provided on all models to counterbalance pneumatically any portion of the total weight.

Q How are strain gages used to measure weight?

A Strain gages measure weight, translating it into electrical signals. A column of steel designed to give the desired strain for a designed load is compressed or stretched by the load. This depends on the load applied in compression or tension. Strain gages attached to sides of a column are connected to form an electrical bridge. A given input voltage develops an output voltage proportional to the load (weight). An electronic measuring instrument can be used to position an indicator, recorder, or printing device, or to actuate an automatic control mechanism. See Figs. 4-16 and 4-17, strain gage pressure transducers, for more details.

Q How does the belt-meter system measure weight?

A For continuous weighing of a steady flow of loose material carried on a belt conveyor, the belt-meter system (Fig. 7-22) provides a large dial indication and chart record of the instantaneous weight of the material being conveyed. It also gives a counter reading of the accumulated ton-

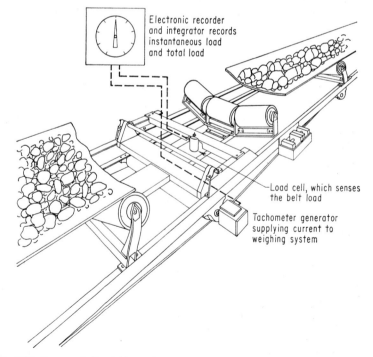

Electronic recorder and integrator records instantaneous load and total load

Load cell, which senses the belt load

Tachometer generator supplying current to weighing system

Fig. 7-22. Conveyor belt weighing system.

nage. This system measures (1) weight of material on a short section of the belt and (2) belt speed, then multiplies these two variables to obtain the pounds per hour being delivered. An industrial-type tachometer generator is driven by an idler operated by the return belt's underside. This produces a voltage proportional to the belt speed. Voltage is combined with the load cell output (strain-gage type sensitive to force) which measures the weight of material on the belt's section. The strain gage transmits to the recording instrument an output voltage proportional to the product of the weight and belt speed. The recorder is modified for this service and shows the instantaneous flow rate on a large circular scale. It makes a continuous record of it on a circular chart having 24-hr revolution chart timing. An integrator shows the total tonnage on a small counter mounted in the door's face. Readings are transmitted electrically, with no moving parts or mechanical linkages involved. By providing temperature compensation in the measuring circuit, the equipment need not be kept at a constant temperature.

Q Describe other scales used in industry.

A (1) Floor scales are for permanent installation, either on or below the floor. These self-contained units have built-in levers, usually installed in a pit. The load-receiving element is a platform, hopper, or tank. Scales range in capacity from 250 to several hundred thousand pounds. (2) A crane scale is a suspended unit. It weighs the load that is lifted or transported by a crane. These scales come in the graduated bar, beam, or dial types. An electronic-type crane scale has a weight recorder in the crane cab, a hook-and-load cell supporting the crane hook. A shielded cable connects the recorder and the load cell. Weighing is done by a strain gage. Hydraulic and electronic scale capacities go up to 60,000 lb. (3) Motor-truck scales are of large capacity, with a built-in scale which carries a moving load (truck driving on and off platform). The axle type weighs a single axle of a truck. Others weigh a full truck. Capacities range up to 50 tons. (4) Overhead scales have levers installed overhead which are suspended from the building or frame supported by a floor. The load-receiving element is either a platform at floor level, a hopper, or a tank, or a section of conveyer. These scales handle weights up to several hundred thousand pounds. (5) Batching scales are for weighing each ingredient for process separately. Here, a scale is used for each ingredient, especially for large permanent operation. Usually each scale is designed for a given material handled, as tonnages are very large and only slight changes are made in the formula. Weights can be held to within $\frac{1}{10}$ per cent. Usually a cutoff device stops the discharge feeder on each scale when the desired weight is reached. (6) Continuous weighing is for strip material like roofing paper or extruded rubber.

Here material passes directly over a roller on a balanced endless belt. The linear weight desired is usually preset by positioning a poise on a beam. A scale indicator shows the deviation from the desired weight. Accessories are used for recorders, remote indication, over and under signal lights, and controls.

Q   What are speed and stretch measurements? Why are they used?

A   All moving equipment must be controlled, or the speed measured in some way. For example, linear and angular acceleration is measured in elevators, engines, etc. Speed is also measured in steel, paper, textile, and other process industries. Stretch must also be known in paper and textile products where materials being processed either stretch or shrink. Since stretch measurement is closely related to speed measurement, two tachometer generators are used to measure the input speeds of the machine on which the stretch or shrinkage occurs. Speed is measured in feet per minute, feet per hour, miles per minute, or miles per hour.

Q   Describe the stroboscopic method of speed measurement.

A   For measuring rotational speed or other cyclic movement, stroboscopes can be used to "stop the motion." Speed of the stroboscope itself is then measured. Stroboscopes do not need to contact the rotating part. They come in various types, but all permit the moving object to be viewed once per cycle, with a shutter or flashing light. Speed range is unlimited and synchronization is perfect. Main use is in experimental work and trouble shooting.

Q   Describe an electric tachometer.

A   This instrument consists of a speed-sensing unit and an indicating

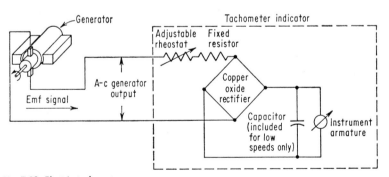

Fig. 7-23. Electric tachometer.

or recording device (Fig. 7-23). The sensing unit is mechanically connected by a flexible-shaft coupling, gears, or a chain drive to the machine whose speed is to be measured. It is a small electric generator, with d-c or a-c emf generated in direct proportion to its speed. Thus the value of this emf is indicative not only of the generator's rotational speed but also of the machine speed. When little current is drawn from the generator, its output voltage increase with increasing speeds is mostly linear. As the current drawn increases, the output voltage from the generator assumes more and more of a nonlinear character. So it is important that the speed-indicating device draw the minimum possible current from the generator. With an indicating instrument needing a low actuating milli-voltage, the load resistor for the generator can be of a relatively high ohmic value, thereby approaching an ideal no-current condition. The speed indicating or recording device may be either a millivoltmeter or a recording instrument to indicate and/or record the value of the output voltage from the tachometer generator and may be calibrated in rpm, fpm, or any other units. When this instrument is used, the generator load resistor is "tapped" to give a relatively low voltage drop of about 25 mv at maximum speed. The instrument is ideal for measuring rapidly fluctuating speeds. Since speed can be measured, it can also be controlled. Its use is widespread on paper and textile machines, conveyors, and printing presses.

Q How is stretch measured?

A Figure 7-24 shows schematically two generators connected to a voltage ratio bridge circuit. The recorder is calibrated directly in per cent stretch (or shrinkage). Any of the conventional forms of control can be used where appropriate regulation of the machine is possible to maintain a desired percentage of stretch. Actually, stretch measurement is a form of voltage ratio measurement. But there are some important differences. Stretch measurement is expressed in terms of percentage stretch or shrinkage, which

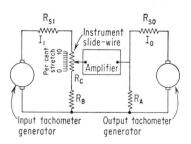

Fig. 7-24. Stretch measuring circuit.

is negative stretch, of a material such as paper, cloth, or wire as it passes through a process. Sensing elements, which provide a voltage input signal to the measuring system, are d-c tachometer generators. Alternating-current tachometer generators can't be used with this measuring system unless their output is converted to a linear d-c signal. Stretch and percentage stretch are defined as

$$\text{Stretch} = \frac{\text{output speed} - \text{input speed}}{\text{input speed}}$$

$$\text{Percentage stretch} = \frac{\text{output speed} - \text{input speed}}{\text{input speed}} \times 100$$

where input speed = linear speed of material entering the process
output speed = linear speed of material leaving the process

Q Explain the theory and function of stress and strain measurements.
A Strain-gage measurements, whether of pressure, load, torque, or displacement, are basically *force* measurements. Measured force operates against a restraining or force summing member such as a load column, load ring, cantilever beam, or spring. It then produces a proportional deflection or deformation which causes a change in resistance of the strain gage. When strain gages are arranged in a Wheatstone bridge circuit powered by a gage voltage supply, and electrical and mechanical zeros brought to coincidence by a bridge balance circuit, then the output voltage can be read out on a recording Wheatstone bridge, oscillograph, or magnetic tape system. Forces measured by strain-gage elements range from ounces to thousands of tons, microinches per inch of stress or strain, in many shapes, and for all types of materials. Stress, strain, and force measurements are made over static (d-c) and dynamic (cycles per second) ranges primarily in the design of structures, vehicles, missiles, rockets, and machines to determine structural strength data.

NOTE: See strain-gage general theory in Chap. 4 under electrical pressure transducers, Figs. 4-15a, 4-15b, 4-16, and 4-17.

Q Explain briefly some of the strain-gage measuring circuits used.
A The Wheatstone bridge (Fig. 7-25, sketch *a*) is one of the most common circuits used in process instrumentation. Its purpose is to determine an unknown resistance such as that of a resistance thermometer, in terms of three resistances. Known resistances M, N, and P are connected together with the unknown X. A galvanometer is connected across one diagonal and a source of direct (or alternating) current across the other. M and N are usually equal. But regardless, $X = P \times M/N$. Then if a known value for P can be chosen which will show no current flow through the galvanometer, X can be calculated. Such a circuit is usually used with some system for adjusting P automatically and continuously to give a null galvanometer deflection. Strain gages are usually connected so they unbalance a four-arm Wheatstone bridge circuit when resistance is changed by stress (sketch *b*). In sketch *c*, the difference in potential across the output terminals is a measure of strain. The reason is that the only source of unbalance is the change of resistance in the gage resulting from applying strain to the gage. This potential can be measured by a sensitive voltmeter.

One problem in strain gages is that wire is sensitive to temperature as well as to strain. Potential output is thus the combined result of strain and temperature. This is why this hookup is used only for dynamic measurements where slowly varying output caused by temperature changes can be ignored or corrected by instrumentation. Sketch *d* shows how a dummy gage is used in the circuit to cancel out the effect of temperature. This gage is mounted on an unstressed piece of the same material as the stressed member. Two gages hooked close together avoid temperature differences. Here, temperature has slight effect on the measurement of stress-induced strain because the resistance changes caused by tempera-

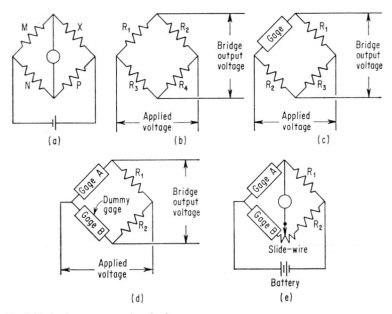

Fig. 7-25. Strain gage measuring circuits.

ture alone are the same for both bridge arms connected to these gages. Because measurement includes strain from thermally induced stresses in metal, it is a true measure of stress, even if stress is caused from temperature of force, load, or both. The purpose of the dummy gage here is to compensate for the unwanted effects of temperature. Two effects combine to determine the total thermal coefficient of the gage in any installation. Two effects are: (1) thermal coefficient of resistance of the gage, and (2) thermal expansion strains in the mounted material. Sketch *d* shows the circuit for measuring static strains or static components of a varying strain with d-c or a-c power. Sketch *e* uses d-c or battery power, with a slide-wire between fixed resistors to balance the bridge when starting a test. Unbalance is indicated with a light-spot galvanometer or a microammeter, or a millivoltmeter can replace the galvanometer for direct reading. But such systems measure only steady strain or strain changing only up to 1 cps. Dynamic strain measurements are recorded on oscillographs (frequency response direct current to 6,000 cps) and magnetic tape systems (direct current to 20,000 cps).

Q Explain the theory and principle of vibration and shock measurement.

A The ability of manufactured products, machines, aircraft and missile components and systems, vehicles and ships, and weapons systems to withstand extreme shocks and vibrations takes careful measurement of vibration and shock during their development and testing. Whenever there are unbalanced forces, changing pressures, or relative motion in any systems, vibration and shock are produced. Vibration is a continuing condition in which an oscillatory (repeated swinging) force exists at some frequency or combination of frequencies. Shock is a transient force-motion condition. To completely analyze vibration and shock, you must measure displacement, velocity, and acceleration. When a displacement transducer electrical output is differentiated, velocity is obtained; a double differentiation gives acceleration. On the other hand, if an acceleration transducer electrical output is integrated, velocity is the result; displacement results from a double integration. Displacement is measured in terms of linear distance (inches, feet) by linear potentiometers and linear variable differential transformer transducers. Velocity is the time rate of displacement (displacement per unit time). Velocity and acceleration are measured in terms of feet per second and feet per second per second. This shows linear acceleration as the time rate of change of linear velocity. Angular acceleration is the time rate of change of angular velocity (radians per second per second). Displacement transducers can measure to d-c or zero displacement, but velocity and acceleration transducers cannot measure to d-c or zero; they measure only moving objects (a-c). Velocity and acceleration vibratory transducers are classified in these types: (1) strain gage, (2) seismic mass, (3) piezoelectric, and (4) variable reluctance. Shock, although somewhat more difficult to analyze because it occurs in pulses or irregular intervals, still uses these types of transducers. Recording vibration and shock phenomena is done on dynamic recorders such as oscilloscopes, oscillographs, and magnetic tape systems. Accurate and significant results depend on very careful positioning and installation of the transducers and selection of signal conditioning equipment.

Q What is a piezoresistive strain gage?
A A strain measuring transducer whose active element is a semiconduc-

tor (germanium, silicon, iridium antimonide) which changes its electrical resistivity (resistance) with the application of stress (distributed force per unit area).

Q   What are the advantages of piezoresistive strain gages compared with wire element gages?

A   (1) High-voltage output (sensitivity) often eliminating amplifiers, (2) infinite resolution, (3) freedom from hysteresis, (4) excellent performance when exposed to high temperatures (up to 1000°F), (5) rugged, and (6) easy to compensate for temperature change. Semiconductor strain gages are relatively new in their use as transducers. Complete information on performance, conformance, configuration, and environmental capability will be available after broader application.

Q   Describe a seismic mass velocity transducer used for vibration measurements.

A   This type of transducer measures linear, sinusoidal, or random velocities, especially in vibration systems (Fig. 7-26). Here a voltage is

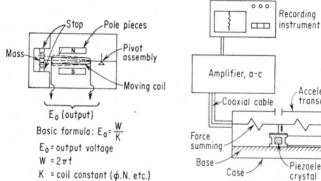

Basic formula: $E_0 = \dfrac{W}{K}$

E_0 = output voltage

$W = 2\pi f$

K = coil constant (ϕ.N. etc.)

Fig. 7-26. Velocity transducer.

Fig. 7-27. Accelerometer measuring system.

generated by the motion of the small coil in a magnetic field. The electrical output signal produced is proportional to the velocity of the coil. This transducer has a seismic mass suspended by springs within a supporting case with a means of damping its swing. Output current, which is proportional to instantaneous velocity, is generated when magnetic lines of force are cut by the coil of wire moving relative to the magnet. Vibrations whose frequency response range varies from 0 to 5,000 cps are measured with this transducer. Its output may need amplification for most readout devices.

Q Explain how the piezoelectric accelerometer transducer is used for vibration and shock measurements.

A An electrical potential is produced in some crystals when elastically deformed along specific planes of stress. For this reason a piezoelectric transducer converts a displacement that is proportional to random vibration into an electrical signal. An electrical output is produced only when the crystal transducer is in motion. Piezoelectrically active crystals are quartz, tourmaline, ammonium dihydrogen phosphate (ADP), barium, titanate, and Rochelle salts. Natural quartz and synthetic crystals (Rochelle salts) are two widely used groups of piezoelectric crystals. Natural crystals have low leakage; thus when used with an electrometer or very high impedance input (cathode follower), they allow measurement of slowly varying phenomena. These can be used with lower-frequency variations, higher temperature, and under shock and vibration conditions. Synthetic crystals have a much higher output for a given stress, strain, or pressure. But they won't stand as high a mechanical strain. Figure 7-27 is a block diagram of a measuring system. Piezoelectric vibration transducers packaged in compact cases are used widely for dynamic measurements in ballistic weapons system testing, underwater blasts, shock tube work, rocket blasts, internal-combustion and jet engines, structural vibrations, etc., on ranges from ±0.5 to ±200 g's (measurement of force of gravity acceleration).

Q What is involved in the measurement of electrical variables?

A Electricity has neither weight nor shape. It is invisible, and cannot be measured by conventional scales, rulers, pressure gages, thermometers, or flowmeters. Yet all precise electrical knowledge depends on measurement. Ohm stated that the magnitude of the current flowing in a circuit depends directly on electrical force or pressure and inversely on a property of the circuit known as the resistance. Today, we measure these units of electricity in the size of amperes, volts, and ohms. These three electrical units have been so chosen that 1 volt pressure impressed upon a circuit of 1 ohm resistance will cause a current of 1 ampere to flow. Relation between volts, amperes, and ohms may be shown by the expression: amperes = volts/ohms; that is, the current flowing in a circuit is equal to the volts impressed on the circuit divided by the resistance of that circuit. The three units are represented by symbols, namely, volts by E, current by I, and ohms by R. Therefore, in symbols the expression for the current is $I = E/R$. This formula may be transposed so it reads $R = E/I$, which means the resistance of a circuit is equal to the volts divided by the current. It then follows that $E = R \times I$; the voltage impressed upon a circuit is equal to the product of the resistance of the circuit times the current. We have standards of resistance, current, electromotive force, etc. The National Bureau of Standards maintains the basic standards in this country, and these values are very specific. Determining the value of direct current is the first and basic step in electrical measurements. Usually a permanent-magnet moving-coil combination does the job. Direct current is used in many types of instruments and their recorders. The same fundamental instrument may be used for a-c measurement by adding a few refinements. There are various ways to measure current resistance. Probably the most obvious is an ammeter and voltmeter. A wattmeter measures power (watts) being consumed in an electric circuit; $W = E \times I$. This is fairly simple with direct current but more complicated with alternating current. Electrical power is the rate at which electrical energy is used. Its unit of measurement, the watt, implies a time factor. Hence the term watt includes the implied meaning *per hour*. Electrical energy is the total use of electricity over a period of time. It is the product of rate of use of power (watts) multiplied by the number of time units, usually in hours. Frequency indicates cycles per seconds. Knowing the exact frequency in instrumentation is very important when using motors and transformers. Cycle simply means that current flows in one direction, stops, reverses itself, and flows in the opposite direction, making one complete cycle, usually 60 per second. Selecting the proper full-scale range of any electrical instrument is important. Accuracy is greatly affected by temperature. Most instrument makers guarantee their instruments to be within normal accuracy for a temperature change of $\pm 10°C$. The normally accepted ambient is 25°C or 77°F.

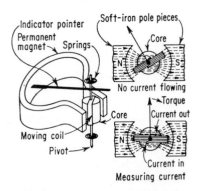

Fig. 7-28. Permanent-magnet moving-coil voltmeter.

Q   How is direct current measured?
A   Figure 7-28 shows the permanent-magnet moving-coil combination usually used. It is a permanent-magnet moving-coil ammeter (and voltmeter). This device, measuring direct current only, is called a D'Arsonval instrument because it resembles the galvanometer. A coil of wire, with pointer attached, placed in a magnetic field is connected across the potential to be measured. When the current flows, the magnetic field produced by the coil reacts with the field of the permanent magnet to cause rotation against a calibrated spring. The spring opposes the torque and carries the current in and out of the coil. The moving coil is wound on an aluminum frame to

damp the coil and thus bring the pointer to rest quickly. As the moving coil twists, a voltage is induced in the frame, thus causing a current flow in the frame. Because a magnetic field is produced opposing the coil's movement, the coil stops. To prevent an outside source of magnetism from upsetting the readings, a shield of soft iron or other high-permeability material is used as a case. Ranges are very high (amperes) to very low (microamperes). This ammeter will also measure voltages if used with a series resistance.

Q How is alternating current measured?

A The same basic instrument for measuring direct current will measure alternating current by adding a thermocouple or rectifier. This thermocouple-type unit is a permanent magnet tied into a thermocouple. But a heater strip is welded to the thermocouple. Current passing through the heater strip raises the strip temperature, which in turn shows up as a d-c voltage in the thermocouple. This voltage is fed to the instrument. Calibration can be in terms of current flowing in the a-c circuit. These instruments measure high frequency, from 10,000 cycles up into radio frequency (up around 1.6 megacycles). The only limit to current handled is the size of heater used. This same permanent-magnet moving-coil instrument is also used with a rectifier. Here the instrument is connected directly across the output terminals of a disk-type rectifier. Alternating-current voltage can be measured if proper resistance is hooked in series with the rectifier. This hookup is used when power taken by the measuring instrument itself is an important factor. The rectifier unit combination is useful in communication circuits where the instrument current must be kept to a minimum.

Q Where does the potentiometer fit into the measurement picture?

A The potentiometer (Fig. 7-29) is used to compare voltages. The

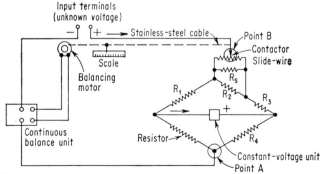

Fig. 7-29. Potentiometric circuit.

standard for the comparison is referred to as a standard cell (in this diagram, a constant-voltage zener diode reference) because it provides an accurate basis for the measurement. This cell can be used directly for measuring voltages also. Measurements of current and voltage can be made in a working circuit, or used for the calibration of ammeters and voltmeters. For calibration work, it becomes the standard for indicating meters for current, voltage, and power, making it very important for electrical measurements. The circuit shown in the sketch is a null-balance potentiometer. The unknown voltage is measured against the standard balancing feedback voltage at point B. Voltage can be fed back across a slide-wire, capacitor, or strain-gage device. Any difference between the two voltages between points A and B is amplified by the continuous balance unit, which energizes the balancing motor to move the contactor point B until the difference in voltage is reduced to zero. From this you can see that a potentiometer measures an unknown potential difference by balancing that difference (wholly or partly) against a known potential difference. In most potentiometers the final reading of emf is made in terms of position along the slide-wire. Exactness of measurement depends on the slide-wire characteristics. One feature of the potentiometer method is that no current is drawn from the source being measured when the balance is attained. Thus the determination of the emf of a source is independent of its resistance. These instruments are used for comparison of standard cells, measurement of voltages, measurement of current, calibration of a voltmeter and ammeter, and measurement of temperature by thermocouples.

Q How are alternating voltage and current measured and recorded?
A Thermal converters, such as those used for power measurement, are also used to measure alternating current and voltage, converting this measurement into a d-c millivolt output for a recording self-balancing potentiometer calibrated directly in a-c potential or current (see Fig. 7-30). The converter is connected directly across the a-c potential source, or to a potential transformer. For alternating current, the converter is connected directly to a current source, or through a current transformer. A self-balancing potentiometer measuring circuit compares the converted d-c millivolt output with a precise standard potential and records the unbalance signal. Several measurements from widely separated points can be transmitted (20 to 50 miles) over telephone lines to a centrally located multiple point recorder. Figure 7-30 (center) shows a schematic of the thermal converter. Instead of using differential thermocouples as in the load measuring converter this type uses a thermocouple with a single heater circuit. Voltage or current flow through the heating element raises its temperature, which is sensed by the thermocouple whose output is

d-c millivolts. Thermocouple cold junctions are compensated so that, as the ambient temperature and the effect of the heating element change

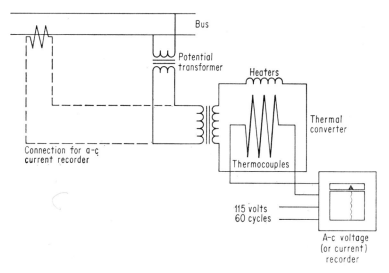

Fig. 7-30. Alternating voltage and current measurements.

with shifts in input voltage or current calibration, accuracy is maintained. This is called a single-element converter, whose d-c output is proportional to the input quantity squared. Alternating voltage and current recorders are used by power systems operators to supervise voltage schedules and monitor feeder voltages and current fluctuations.

Q How is power measured using the current-heating effect?

A Figure 7-31 shows how power is measured by a two-element Lincoln thermal converter. This device resembles the a-c thermal converter, but its output is proportional to power consumed by a load and can be telemetered for long distances. Potential leads, connected across the line, are connected to the primary of a transformer. Leads from a current transformer are connected into a bridge circuit so that current

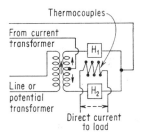

Fig. 7-31. Power measurement by thermal converter (two-element).

in one side of the bridge is added to the current induced in the transformer. Current in the other side is opposed by the transformer current.

Thus heat from heaters H_1 and H_2 will be different, depending on the load, and their average, determined by the series thermocouples, will be proportional to the load. Two-element converters are used by measuring three-phase three-wire power but can also be used with single-element units to measure three-phase four-wire systems where only two phases are measured, or for measuring reactive power (var) using a phase shifting transformer. The combination of watt and reactive volt-amperes (var) will provide a result equal to volt-amperes (kva = $\sqrt{kw^2 + kvar^2}$).

Q   How is energy consumption measured?

A   Energy consumption is measured with the induction watthour meter

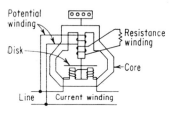

(Fig. 7-32). This is the most common type of a-c device for integrating watt consumption over a period of time. The meter shown has a potential winding P on an iron core, with current windings C. The armature is an aluminum disk with a shaft behind the core. The interaction of flux produced by the three poles with the induced eddy currents in the disk causes rotation proportional to

Fig. 7-32. Induction watthour meter.

the power. Adjustment of phase relations is obtained with a compensating winding and external resistance R. Revolutions counted by the register represent watthours.

SUGGESTED READING

Write to manufacturers of physical and electrical measuring systems for literature

Books

Harris and Crede: *Shock and Vibration Handbook,* McGraw-Hill Book Company, Inc., New York, 1961.

Lion, Kurt S.: *Instrumentation for Scientific Research,* McGraw-Hill Book Company, Inc., New York, 1959.

Elonka, Steve, and Julian Bernstein: *Standard Industrial Electronics Questions and Answers,* vols. I and II, McGraw-Hill Book Company, Inc., New York, to be published in 1964.

Elonka, Steve, and Joseph F. Robinson: *Standard Plant Operator's Questions and Answers,* vols. I and II, McGraw-Hill Book Company, Inc., New York, 1959.

Elonka, Steve, and Quaid W. Minich: *Standard Refrigeration and Air Conditioning Questions and Answers,* McGraw-Hill Book Company, Inc., New York, 1961.

Elonka, Steve: *Plant Operator's Manual,* McGraw-Hill Book Company, Inc., New York, 1956.

8

READOUT AND DISPLAY SYSTEMS

Q What are readout and display systems?
A You must observe and record the physical parameters and process variables measured by the measuring systems described thus far. Readout and display systems do these jobs for you. Indicating and recording mechanisms may be actuated (1) directly from the measuring system through a lever and linkage system, as are thermometer and pressure gage instruments, or (2) indirectly by a servo-operated system where the printer or recording pen is motor-driven. In a servo-operated system, a feedback (rebalancing) signal is produced to drive a pointer or pen. It rebalances the measuring circuit when an error exists between the measured variable signal and a signal representing the position of the balancing system.

Q Name and classify the major components of a readout system.
A (1) Display, which includes the indicating means (pointer, lights, or index), chart, and chart drive mechanism. (2) Operating mechanism (direct-connected and servo-operated), which is the link between the indicating and recording mechanism and measuring circuit. (3) Measuring circuits, the means of measuring process variables and physical parameters, many of which have already been described.

Q Why do we need an indicating means? What are its components?
A Most indicating means have an accurately graduated, easily readable, calibrated scale along which a pointer is positioned to define an exact value of the measured variable. An indicator is made up of parts for producing and controlling either the motion of a pointer along a stationary scale or the motion of a scale with relation to a fixed reference. With digital indicating means, the display is easily read; arabic numerals represent the instantaneous value of the input signal.

Q Name seven types of movable-pointer fixed-scale indicating display means.
A See Fig. 8-1: (1) straight, (2) arc, (3) vertical straight, (4) vertical

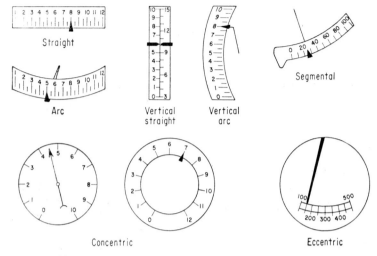

Fig. 8-1. Movable-pointer fixed-scale indicating display means.

arc, (5) segmental, (6) concentric, and (7) eccentric. These are metal scales, 3 to 12 in. long, white or black face with black or white graduations and numbers. Pointers are sharp and thin, triangular or arrow shaped, or blunt, black or brightly colored, in various sizes. Scales have fewer but wider graduations, and large numbers for distant observation. For close, accurate reading, an index line is scribed on and scales have many fine graduations.

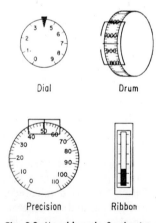

Dial   Drum

Precision   Ribbon

Fig. 8-2. Movable-scale fixed-pointer indicating display means.

Q Explain the four types of movable-scale fixed-pointer displays in Fig. 8-2.

A (1) Dial, (2) drum, (3) precision indicator, and (4) ribbon, or painted strip. Types 1 and 3 are flat metal disks, with a maximum rotation of 340°, and up to 29 in. in diameter. Disk scales have up to 200 divisions, precision indicator scales up to 600. Drum scales (type 2) rotate edgewise vertically or horizontally. All have a fixed pointer or hairline index. In type 4, a two-color painted metal ribbon moves in a vertical plane in front of a viewing window; it is used for a level indicator.

Q Name two types of digital indicators and a special indicating display means.

A See Fig. 8-3. (1) Drum counter, displays numeral digits on adjacent drums in a horizontal line through the window. (2) Electronic digital indicator, displays lighted plastic numerals in adjacent windows with

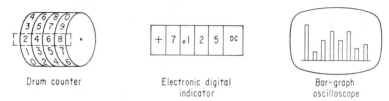

Drum counter   Electronic digital   Bar-graph
indicator   oscilloscope

Fig. 8-3. Digital and special indicating display means.

decimal points, symbols, and signs. (3) Bar graph, displays up to 20 points as a broad vertical bar, proportional to the amplitude of the input signal on a cathode-ray oscilloscope face (like a television tube).

Q What is the purpose of the recording means and what are its major components?

A The chief purpose of the recording means is to provide an accurate, readable record of the measured variable on a chart from which amplitude, dynamic response, and time can be read. Other information, such as date, clock time, operations marker (machinery on, off), and record number, is sometimes recorded. Often one or more measured variables are plotted on the axis against another measured variable (other than time) on the chart drive axis. A recording system consists of (1) recording chart (paper, plastic-coated paper, photographic paper) with calibrated graduation, reference lines, and no marking; (2) recording device (pen and ink, heated stylus, mirror and light source); and (3) chart drive system. Indicating pointers and scales are often combined with the recording means.

Q Name six reasons for using chart records.

A (1) Provide the operator of a process with an operating guide or trend record, (2) furnish a process performance record, (3) provide a legal or archival record of satisfactory operation, (4) give management data for process economics and efficiency figures, (5) provide product quality checks, and (6) produce an instantaneous record of many variables related to a process or product during design and development.

Q Illustrate and classify the two basic chart types.

A Recording charts are classified as either (1) circular (Fig. 8-4) or

(2) strip (Fig. 8-5). Circular charts are usually 7¼, 10, or 12 in. in diameter, with calibrated widths from 3¼ to 4⅝ in. and time markings

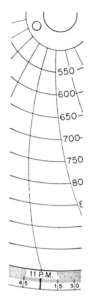

for 1-, 8-, 12-, and 24-hr revolution. Calibrated graduations are printed for a great variety of ranges (Fig. 8-5). Strip charts come in widths of 2, 3, 4, 6, 8, and 12 in. for most industrial recorders, and in a variety of lengths up to 500 ft long. Charts have holes punched at regular intervals along both edges which fit guide pins in the drive for driving the chart. Range and time calibrations are often printed. Some charts have a heat-sensitive plastic or an electrical-sensitive coating. Others used in photographic oscillographs are light-sensitive to incandescent or ultraviolet light. All data and reference records are photographed on the chart at the time of the recording. Both strip and circular charts are sometimes multirange and divided into segments (Fig. 8-5b).

Fig. 8-4. Circular chart section.

Q   What are four advantages of circular chart records?

A   (1) Charts are flat and easy to handle and file; (2) they provide the entire record of a process for rapid review; (3) they use simple measuring and recording mechanisms to produce an arc motion; and (4) the mechanism is easy to calibrate, and it is easy to change the range. But circular charts are limited in calibrated space and recording time. Often graduations are circular rather than rectangular.

Q   Name five advantages of strip chart records.

A   (1) Chart is graduated in rectilinear coordinates, (2) long recording times (127-ft chart at 2 in. per hr travel provides continuous recording for 31 days), (3) wide chart (12 in.) has space for recording many measured variables, (4) wide range of chart speeds and multispeed recorders, and (5) more data and information on hand for operator and design engineer.

Q   What are the four major classifications or recording devices?

A   (1) Pen with fluid ink, (2) print wheel and pad, (3) chemical or mechanical change in surface coating on chart by stylus, and (4) photographic recording.

Q   Name and illustrate five types of fluid-ink pens.

A   See Fig. 8-6. (a) V-pen, V-shaped pen tip attached to end of lightweight metal pen arm (holds one drop of ink). Must be filled often, usually when chart is changed. Used mostly on circular chart mechanical recorders (thermometers, pressure, flowmeters) to give continuous col-

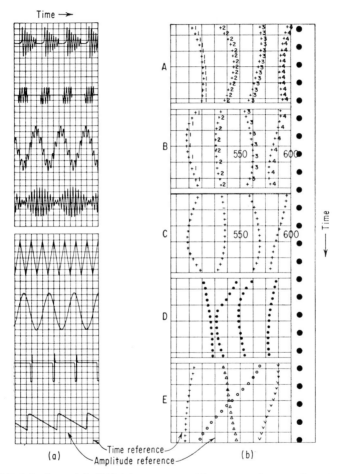

Fig. 8-5. Strip charts: A is divided into segments with continuous line recordings; B shows variety of printed record symbols.

ored ink line. (*b*) Bucket type, used on circular chart potentiometers. Carries 1-week ink supply. (*c*) Fountain pen. This type is moved along a pen carriage across the chart and has an inkwell and small capillary connecting tube through which ink flows by capillary action to the pen tip to give a continuous line. Capacities range from 3 drops for miniature recorders to 6 cu cm for servo-operated wide strip chart recorders. The large-capacity pen, as shown, is made of clear glass, making the ink level visible. For high-speed recording needs, glass, platinum-iridium, or sapphire pen tips (replaceable) are used for longer service. (*d*) Reservoir

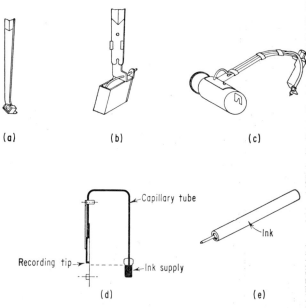

(a)   (b)   (c)

(d)   (e)

Fig. 8-6. Five types of fluid-ink pens.

pens. These have three parts: writing tip, pen tube connecting tip to inkwell (carried by moving element), and a stationary removable inkwell. Capillary action carries ink through the pen tube to the pen tip. Used on miniature recorders for a continuous ink line. (*e*) Ball pen. Used for high-speed recording and for dynamic response. Similar to familiar ball-point pocket pen. Requires hard surface as backup. Produces continuous line.

Q   What are five methods of recording more than one variable on a strip chart?
A   (1) Multiple pens making continuous line records, (2) multiprinted methods, (3) multiple pens on multiple-zone chart, (4) single pen on segmental chart, (5) multiple-mirror galvanometers on a single chart; but each record is separately calibrated.

Q How is recording done with a print wheel and ink pads?

A Multipoint recording wide strip instruments (Fig. 8-17) use a print-wheel recording device. This printing mechanism consists of (1) a print wheel containing in sequence a series of engraved numbers, each having a calibration reference plus sign or dot, and (2) an ink-pad wheel which supports either a single pad or a series of single-color or multicolor ink pads. The two wheels are driven in unison to maintain the correct coincidence between print-wheel numbers and ink-pad colors and identifying indicating numbers. When the variable to be measured is connected through the measuring circuit to the servo-operation mechanism, the proper number on the print wheel contacts first the ink pad and then the chart surface. The proper character is thus printed in a place on the chart representing the measured variable amplitude. Printing mechanisms are used for recording as high as 24 points on one chart, many in multicolor, some in a single color. A variety of identifying characters are used, as shown in Fig. 8-5*b* strip charts.

Q Name and illustrate two types of recording stylus for coated paper charts.

A When medium-speed recording (full pen travel up to 100 times each second) is needed, don't use pen and ink recording devices. Temperature, shock, and vibration extremes give unsatisfactory pen and ink recording. A recording stylus in contact with a treated chart surface is best for this service. Figure 8-7 shows two types: (1) Heated stylus on plastic-coated

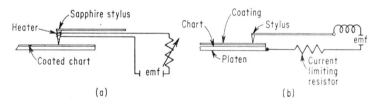

Fig. 8-7. Recording stylus for coated chart.

paper. As the heated stylus melts the plastic coating, a contrasting color below the surface of the paper shows through, producing a clearly defined continuous line record. (2) Electric current through electrically conductive paper. When direct current is passed through a metal stylus in contact with a special conductive coated chart paper, the current burns away the coating, leaving a contrasting colored surface for an intermittent or continuous line record. Some recorders use a stylus and ink recording method where conditions are not so severe as those requiring a heated or electric stylus.

Q Describe a photographic method of recording on paper.
A See Fig. 8-8. Here a light beam is directed onto light-sensitive paper by the mirror on a D'Arsonval moving coil galvanometer, thus producing a continuous line analog record. This means is used for recording on a photographic oscillograph. The frequency response of this system is as high as 6,000 cps, continuous multichannel recording, with instantaneous phase coincidence and overlapping of adjacent recorders. All reference lines are simultaneously photographed during the recording period. Dynamic testing in research, development, and test activities is a frequent use of recording oscillographs.

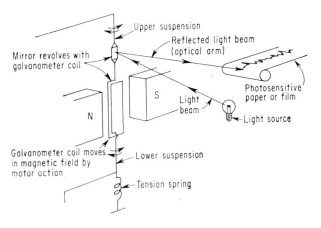

Fig. 8-8. Photographic method of recording.

Q What must the chart drive mechanism accomplish?
A (1) Drive the chart at a uniform rate (keep time as with a clock) with minimum maintenance and (2) provide separation of records with selectable speeds so that overlapping or waste space is avoided.

Q Name and describe four different circular chart drive mechanisms.
A Circular chart drive mechanisms have a center chart-support spindle, containing a device for centering and locking the chart, and a drive motor. Types are: (1) Spring-clock drive. This has a lever escapement and balance-wheel timekeeping device, operated from a manually wound single or double spring. (2) Pneumatic (air) drive. This has a lever escapement and balance-wheel time device with an air-jet impeller-wheel-driven escapement. (3) Electric-motor drives. These are usually self-starting synchronous a-c electric motors for standard voltages and frequencies.

For hazardous conditions, motors are enclosed in explosionproof housings. (4) Externally controlled drives, which are remotely positioned by an externally controlled selsyn or equivalent motor; not often used on circular chart recorders. With hand-wound and electric chart drive, the chart spindle is driven directly or through a gear train. Chart speeds of 30-day, 24-hr, 12-hr, 8-hr, 1-hr, and 15-min revolution are normal for circular chart recorders. Speeds chosen depend on the measured variable speed of response.

Q What are the six major components in a typical industrial strip chart recorder's chart drive system? How do they work?

A As Fig. 8-9 shows: (1) A chart supply roll and flanged supporting arbors or guides provide endwise line-up and reference. (2) A drive roll with accurately positioned guide pins engages holes in the edges of the chart. Printing-type recorders use hard-rubber-coated drive rolls. A slip clutch between the drive roll and the supporting shaft allows the operator to set the chart to read the time marking without disengaging gears between the drive roll shaft and the drive motor. (3) Drive motor and gear train. Spring clock, synchronous electric, or pneumatic motors are used to drive a gear train. Many motor sizes and gear combinations are used, depending on speed and power requirements. Narrow strip chart recorders normally use spring clock, pneumatic, or small electric motors. Wide strip chart recorders, the servo-operated types, use larger (5- to 20-watt) synchronous motors. Externally operated chart drives are often

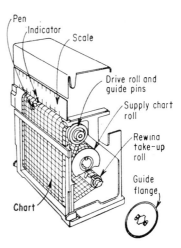

Fig. 8-9. Strip chart recorder.

needed when the chart movement is not a function of time but must be varied from a selsyn-operated function. (4) Speed-changing mechanisms. Chart-speed changes from 1 to 3,600 in. per hr are obtained with interchangeable gears or a combination of change gears. These have manual, electric, ratchet feed, or automatically operated shifting devices. (5) Rewind or chart take-up devices. The chart rewind device keeps the chart taut and flat while rewinding the used portion. This is done by a slip clutch or spring belt stretched between the drive roll and the rewind spindle or grooved pulleys. Torque motor-driven rewind mechanisms are sometimes used.

Q   Why are indicating and recording operating mechanisms needed?
A   (1) To position the pointer, pen, or other recording device at the proper location to identify measured variable response changes. (2) To provide a means of changing the output motion of the measuring element, or circuit, for calibration purposes.

Q   What are the basic characteristics of operating mechanisms for direct-connected instruments? For servo-operated instruments?
A   A direct-connected measuring system produces low torque and has a small output motion. It requires a lightweight low-friction operating mechanism. Servo-operated measuring systems produce relatively high torque and output power. They can actuate sturdy, accurate, positive drive indicating or recording mechanisms.

Q   Name four types of operating mechanisms used with direct-connected indicating instruments.
A   See Fig. 8-10. (*a*) Direct attached pointer support, as in D'Arsonval

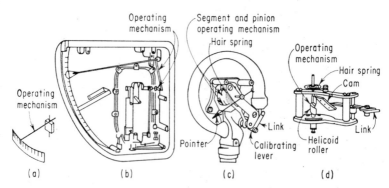

Fig. 8-10. Pointer operating mechanisms.

galvanometer movement. (*b*) Link and lever mechanism; calibration adjusted by varying link length and lever radius. (*c*) Pinion and gear segment; indicator pointer attached to pinion shaft. Motion from measuring element is transmitted from link (multiplied through gear and segment) to pinion. (*d*) Cam and roller, sometimes used to obtain a similar multiplying action.

Q   Name four types of operating mechanisms used with direct-connected recording instruments.
A   (1) Direct-connected (acting) pen where measuring element is connected to base of pen arm; has little adjustment. (2) Link and lever arrangement; provides more adjustment and power for pen arm but gives

loading effect to pen motion. Roberts linkage, used on miniature pneumatic strip chart recorders. (3) Cam and follower; cam profile provides means of changing motion between the measuring element and recording device. Used on flowmeters and as an impulse telemeter transmitter. (4) Combination pinion, gear segment, link, and lever; used on direct-acting strip chart pressure recorder.

Q Name two types of operating mechanisms used in servo-operated measuring instruments.

A (1) Cord and sheave drive, or drive cable, pulley, and pinion system used universally in servo-operated wide strip chart recorders. A sheave or pinion drive from the servo motor converts rotational motion from the measuring servo system into straight-line motion required to position the recording device. As the recording device is positioned across the chart graduations, slide-wire contacts (or other rebalancing device) are positioned so that a feedback signal is provided for servo balancing. (2) Torque motor servo drive directly connected to the arm. Used on miniature strip chart recorders and electric receivers.

Q Describe a direct-connected dial pressure gage. How does it work?

A The dial pressure gage (Fig. 8-11) is one of the most common indicating instruments. It has a thin straight pointer against a 340° semicircular scale graduated in pressure units, a Bourdon tube, segment gear pinion assembly, and a link between the Bourdon tube's tip and the segment gear, all enclosed in a metal case. With pressure applied to the Bourdon tube through a threaded socket, the Bourdon tube tends to straighten out, moving the tip upward. This motion is transmitted to the segment gear through linkage. As the

Fig. 8-11. Direct-connected dial pressure gage.

segment gear moves, the pinion gear, pointer shaft, and pointer across the dial scale are rotated until the resisting force of the Bourdon tube is equal to the force created by the pressure within the tube.

Q Describe a direct-connected circular chart pressure recorder.

A Direct-connected pressure recorders (Fig. 8-12) produce a chart record in pressure units. This recorder works much like the dial pressure indicator. It has a modified Bourdon tube or spiral as the pressure measuring element, a link, lever and shaft, pen arm and V pen, chart drive motor, and case with glass door. Measured pressure is admitted to the spiral, which tends to straighten out, thus causing a rotary motion of the tube tip. This motion is transmitted through linkage to the lever and shaft to which the pen arm is attached. Thus for every value of pressure applied to the pressure element within its range span, there will be a corresponding position of the pen on the chart. The chart is rotated at a predetermined speed by a chart drive motor. The pen arm and lever assembly have zero and span adjustment means. A pen lifter raises the pen from the chart when changing charts.

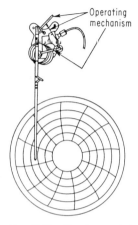

Operating mechanism

Fig. 8-12. Direct-connected pressure recorder.

Q   How does a direct-acting electric temperature indicator work?

A   The millivoltmeter pyrometer (Fig. 2-22) is one of the most widely used temperature indicators. It works on the D'Arsonval deflectional galvanometer principle. A magnetic field, produced by a permanent magnet and pole pieces, surrounds a moving coil which is suspended by pivots and jeweled bearings. An indicator pointer is attached to the coil. When an electric current in millivolts is produced by a change in temperature of a thermocouple passing through the coil, it sets up an opposing magnetic field. This causes the coil to turn and the pointer to move across a curved (arc) scale which is calibrated in temperature units. To retard its movement and to return it to zero when there is no thermocouple current passing through the coil, the coil and pointer deflect against hairsprings. A bimetallic spiral attached to the hairspring mounting and a negative temperature coefficient resistor provide reference junction compensation. Deflectional galvanometers come housed in a variety of cases for surface or panel mountings. Zero adjustment for the galvanometer is made on top of the case. Millivoltmeter pyrometers are easily adaptable to many forms of electric control. Deflectional millivoltmeters may be used to indicate a voltage signal whether it be from a thermocouple or other voltage source.

Q   How do you define indirect-acting (servo-operated) devices?

A   Servo-operated devices are closed-loop systems using feedback that detect an unknown signal and compare it with a reference signal. The resultant difference, or error, signal is amplified and adjusted to zero by a rebalancing mechanism. When rebalancing action takes place continuously and automatically, the instrument is called a continuous null-balance device. Null-balance indicating and recording potentiometers are the most widely used servo-operated devices in industrial plants and processes.

Q How is a potentiometer used? Illustrate it in its most basic form.

A A potentiometer is used to measure a potential difference or voltage. It does this by comparing an unknown voltage with a known reference voltage. In industrial and process applications, potentiometers are used as the most accurate means of measuring temperature with thermocouples (see Chap. 2, "Temperature Measuring Systems"). Figure 8-13 shows the basic potentiometer circuit.

The thermocouple produces an unknown voltage $E_{t/c}$ which is compared with the known battery voltage E_{ref}. Any difference between the two will be indicated as an error e voltage at the deflectional zero-center indicator (error detector). To restore balance, the sliding contactor on a resistor (slidewire voltage divider) must be moved

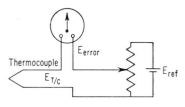

Fig. 8-13. Basic potentiometer circuit.

to a new position until the error voltage becomes zero. Then the indicator pointer reads zero in its center position, which means there is no current flowing in the measuring circuit.

Q What are typical performance characteristics of electronic self-balancing potentiometer recorders?

A Potentiometer recorders measure millivolt signal inputs such as thermocouples (temperature), tachometers (speed), pH, and from many special measuring circuits in ranges from several microvolts (10^{-6} volt) to several volts within accuracies of $\pm\frac{1}{4}$ per cent of full scale. Full-scale indicator and pen travel is as fast as $\frac{1}{4}$ sec to as slow as 24 sec. Records are continuous multicolor ink lines or printed numbers, signs, or characters on 6- or 12-in.-wide strip or circular charts, driven at a great variety of speeds.

Q What are the major components of an electronic self-balancing recording potentiometer?

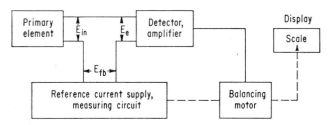

Fig. 8-14. Electronic self-balancing recording potentiometer. E_{in} = input voltage (unknown); E_{fb} = feedback voltage (reference); E_e = error voltage.

A   This potentiometer (Fig. 8-14) works on the same principle as the basic potentiometer. But its error-detecting circuit is an electronic amplifier which amplifies the error signal to a level sufficient to drive a slide-wire contactor to its null-balance position. Drive is continuous through a servomotor and mechanical linkage. Major components are: (1) Servo-drive section consisting of (*a*) reference current supply, (*b*) standardizing means, (*c*) measuring circuit, (*d*) detector and amplifier, and (*e*) rebalancing system. (2) Display section consists of (*a*) indicating and recording means, and (*b*) chart drive mechanism. (3) Enclosure or mounting means.

Q   Describe the servo-drive section of an electronic self-balancing potentiometer and how it works.

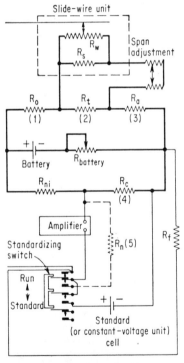

Fig. 8-15. Basic standardizing circuit.

A   The most common type of this unit operates as follows: A reference battery (Fig. 8-15) supplies a standardized current to the measuring slide-wire. Known potential drop across the slide-wire determined by the slide-wire contactor's position is compared with the unknown input voltage (from a thermocouple) and its reference junction temperature compensation, or some other voltage source. If there is a difference between the reference on the slide-wire and the input voltage, an error current will flow; it is detected by an electronic amplifier. Amplified output is applied to an in-phase out-of-phase servo-balancing motor, which drives the slide-wire contactor to rebalance the input voltage so that no current flows in the slide-wire circuit. The balancing motor drive system also positions the indicating and recording means to display the value of the measured variable, in this case temperature. The five basic sections are:

1. *Reference current supply.* This is a dry-cell battery (see sketch) and variable resistor ($R_{battery}$) for adjusting its output.

2. *Standardizing means.* Battery current must be kept constant to obtain reproducible measurements. Since the dry-cell voltage changes with

time and temperature, the potentiometer output emf must be adjusted. This is done by transferring (manually or automatically) the amplifier and motor from the external circuit to the standardizing circuit by means of the standardizing switch. In the standardize position, a standard cell is connected into the measuring circuit where its output (usually 1.019 volts and 2 ma) is compared with the battery current through R_c. If these are not equal, an error system is impressed upon the amplifier, resulting in motor drive of the rheostat R_{battery} until the current is returned to its proper value. In the run position, the potentiometer performs its measuring function. Recent design developments have replaced the battery, standardizing circuit, and standard cell with a constant-voltage unit (CVU) in which the a-c line voltage is reduced by a step-down transformer and converted to an extremely accurate, stable d-c output by a diode rectifier to supply the measuring circuit reference voltage. Regulation is by a two-stage zener diode network.

3. *Measuring circuit.* Basically a Wheatstone bridge circuit, the potentiometer measuring circuit consists of slide-wire R_W (input measured variable signal from a thermocouple is connected between this slide-wire contactor and one side of the amplifier); a voltage divider or range resistor R_t, which determines the range (or limits of measuring) of the instrument; a suppression resistor R_0 to set the lower end of the instrument span (suppression is the calibrated displacement of the zero value from its usual position at the range's lower limit); and current resistor R_a to complete the total resistance value of the bridge. Resistors are changed for each different input range of the instrument. Reference ("cold") junction resistor R_{ni} is used in thermocouple instruments to compensate for any error voltage which might be added to the thermocouple voltage because of a different ambient temperature at the cold junction. This effect is different for each type of thermocouple. It compensates by shifting the point of zero voltage differential between the reference and measuring junctions in accordance with ambient temperature variations. Compensation resistor R_{ni} is changed each time the type of thermocouple is changed. New designs make range changing and actuation changing a simple procedure by mounting the needed measuring circuit resistors on a plug-in mounting board. Other measuring circuits, such as narrow span, multisuppression, center zero, resistance thermometer, follower circuits, and a-c bridge (to name a few), can be used in place of the thermocouple circuit.

4. *Detector and amplifier.* If an error signal (difference voltage between reference emf and unknown thermocouple emf) exists it is fed into the detector-amplifier section to be built up to a signal large enough to drive the balancing motor. The detector, a vibrating-reed "chopper," converts the d-c error signal into a square-wave frequency, identical with

the applied line voltage. This signal is amplified by a hum-bucking step-up transformer that acts as a coupling device between the converter and grid of the first voltage amplifier stage. There are four voltage amplification stages and a power amplifier stage in the vacuum-tube amplifier. Amplifier output is transmitted to the balancing motor in half-wave pulses, which the resonant motor control winding circuit converts to 60-cycle pulses to cause drive in one direction, when below the balance point and in the opposite direction above the balance point. Some recent designs use solid-state (transistors) techniques, high input impedance to accept many different sources, and miniature driven-armature converters.

5. *Balancing action and balancing motor.* Servo-amplifier output is connected to a reversible induction balancing motor which drives the measuring circuit slide-wire contactor (and the indicating and recording device attached to it) to a new position for null balance. The motor drives one direction when the amplifier output is in phase with the supply voltage, and the other direction when 180° out of phase. Acting as the operating mechanism, the balance motor drive gear rotates a large bull gear to which a stainless-steel drive cable is connected. The slide-wire contactor and recording device are connected directly to the drive cable at another position along the cable (Fig. 8-16). Slide-wires are

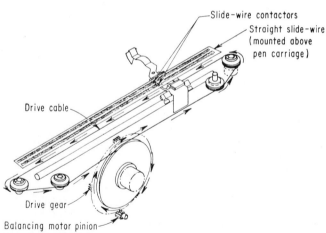

Fig. 8-16. Straight slide-wire drive cable. Arrows indicate direction for threading cable.

helical in form for circular chart and scale instruments, and in straight or helical form for strip chart instruments. Slide-wires are made up of 1,000 to 2,000 turns of wire (convolutions) and the resolution (ability to change current output smoothly in minute steps) depends on the number of convolutions and is finite (as compared with infinite). Rebalancing action can also be done by replacing the slide-wire with (*a*) a capacitance balancing unit and (*b*) a strain gage balancing unit.

Q   Describe the display section of an electronic self-balancing potentiometer. Explain how it works.

A   The servo-operated potentiometer display section has these major parts:

1. *Indicating and recording means.* As explained before, when balancing action takes place, the slide-wire contactor is positioned to the null-balance point. At the same time, the indicating and recording device is also driven to a new position on the chart and scale, corresponding to the value of the measured variable, thus producing a record. Circular chart instruments use bucket-type pens on 12-in.-diameter charts, and 8-in.-long pointers on a 28⅝-in. concentric scale (see Fig. 8-6). Strip chart potentiometers use glass fountain reservoir pens with jeweled or capillary tips on single-record and duplex models, and print-wheel and ink pad device on multirecord models. A triangular index on the pen or print wheel device travels with it across 12-in.-wide calibrated, straight metal scales and paper strip charts. Multirecords are produced by the print wheel in a different color, number, sign, and/or character for each measured variable (Fig. 8-17). Multirecord instruments can switch be-

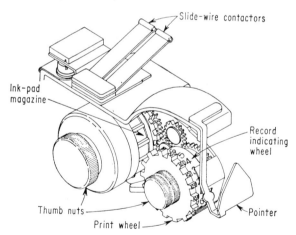

Fig. 8-17. Print wheel carriage.

tween as many as 24 input points, recording a different printed number or character and reference point for each. A rotary commutator switch connects each input signal to the measuring circuit and servo system in sequence. A proper print-wheel character and ink pad is ready to print either at the moment of balance, or on a fixed-cycle basis. Synchro-balance printing permits synchronization of the printing mechanism with the print wheel's motion. It produces faster printing than with the cyclic method. The synchro-balance printing mechanism is actuated through the drive cable, detector arm, clutch, and gears whenever the print carriage comes to a stop at the balance point. Each time the balance is reached, printing takes place. Then the next point in sequence is switched, ready to print when the measuring circuit comes to balance again. Convenient point changing (between 2, 3, 4, 6, 10, 12, 16, 20, and 24 points) is done on recent models by providing a 24-point input terminal plate in every multirecord instrument. To change the point capacity, the proper shorting plug is inserted and the change is made to the correct point on the indicating and print wheels.

Strip chart recorders come with edge-of-chart event marking pens, solenoid-operated printing mechanisms for printing date and time, and special printing mechanisms which skip every other number to spread out the record. Display sections that indicate only take the form of (*a*) circular scales (28⅝ in. long, 12-in.-diameter concentric rotation, 300 to 600 divisions) and stationary triangular index pointer viewed through a large window, (*b*) vertical scales (28⅝ in. long, drum-shaped 2 in. wide, endwise rotation, 300 to 650 divisions) and stationary hairline index. Multipoint indicators have banks of key switches or push buttons for selection of input circuits which are wired to the input terminal either mounted in an indicator case or in a separate housing. Circular scale models usually have integrally mounted switches.

2. *Chart drive mechanism.* Circular charts, or scales, are driven by a synchronous motor through a drive shaft and gear mechanism connected to the chart hub. The hub is tapered and holds the chart with a positioning stud. Strip charts are driven by a synchronous motor through a gear train mechanism, mounted on the chassis side plate. Reroll is done by a reroll chain which drives a reroll spindle, actuated manually by a knob which is disengaged from a friction clutch during reroll. The friction clutch maintains the tension. Chart speeds are changed by changing (*a*) gears, gear trains, and motors; (*b*) switch-operated two-speed chart and print-cycle drive mechanism; (*c*) gear lever-operated four-speed chart drive; (*d*) electrically operated gearshifting; and (*e*) ratchet-operated step drive.

3. *Enclosure section.* Potentiometer instrument cases come in various forms for wall, panel, and relay rack mounting, for bench and table mounting, also as console desks, and with carrying handles for portability.

Q   Name and briefly describe four special-purpose electronic self-balancing strip chart recorders.

A 1. *Adjustable span and suppression recorder.* Similar to the self-balancing potentiometers described before, this recorder has internal fine and coarse knob adjustments for span and zero adjustment. A span adjustment knob makes full-scale pen travel correspond to any voltage within the maximum and minimum range of the instrument. A suppression adjustment knob adjusts the zero by shifting the range up or down.

2. *Extended range recorder.* This increases readability by automatically switching five successive suppression steps into the measuring circuit, depending on the input signal level. This extension of range increases the effective lengths of scale and slide-wire to almost five times those of a single range instrument having the same total range.

3. *Two-pen duplex recorder.* Simultaneously records two independent variables on the same chart, thus simplifying analysis involving comparison measurements. Two separate measuring circuits are used, each having its own pen which traverses the full scale and chart width.

4. *Function plotter* (Fig. 8-18). Automatically plots a curve of the

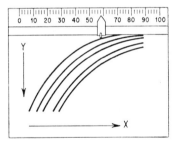

Fig. 8-18. Function plotter.

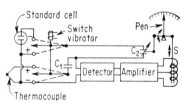

Fig. 8-19. Capacitance self-balancing.

continuous relationship of two variables, one as a function of another $[y = f(x)]$. The recorder has two independent measuring systems: one actuates the recording pen for traversing the chart, while the second actuates the chart movement through a balancing motor. Chart drive can also be a selsyn motor.

All four of these recorders are used in design, development, and scientific test applications, especially in the electronics, environmental testing, and aero-space industries. A duplex function plotter, $y = f(x,x^1)$, is available by adding a second pen and separate measuring circuit for it. Many function plotters use a stationary chart with the recording pen or stylus driven by a resultant (vector) sum of the x and y measuring circuits.

Q   Describe a capacitance balance servo-operated recorder.

A   Another form of self-balancing instrument (Fig. 8-19), this capacitance-balance type compares an unknown emf with a known emf (standard cell, no battery or standardizing circuit) by using each to charge a capacitor. The capacitor balances the resultant charges so the charge is reduced to zero. When the instrument is unbalanced by a change in input signal, an alternating current (produced by a vibrating switch in a capacitor bridge measuring circuit) of appropriate phase is amplified. This current is applied to a phase-sensitive power amplifier which delivers d-c pulses to two solenoids of a balanced solenoid motor. The solenoid motor rotary arm is connected directly to a variable capacitor C_2, which repositions the capacitor to balance the bridge and moves the pen and indicator to indicate the value of the measured variable. Characteristics of this instrument are similar to those of the potentiometer type. An exception is that capacitor rebalancing eliminates the slide-wire and provides infinite resolution and high input impedance measuring circuit and detector. It is used for a great variety of actuations (thermocouple, tachometer, pH, a-c input, capacity, etc.), circular (12-in.-diameter chart) and strip (6-in. width) chart recorders. The circular chart model comes in a unique six-record form, using a single pen arm. A pen-wheel assembly containing styli and associated multicolored ink-impregnated pads, located off the chart area, is keyed to a selector which connects sequentially, for fixed time periods, the input signals to the measuring circuit. The pen wheel is rotated in synchronism with the pen arm motion. The pen arm moves to the pen-wheel assembly, picks up an inked stylus, and moves to a position on the chart by depressing the stylus. The action is repeated in sequence for each input point.

Q   Describe a strain gage balance servo-operated instrument and how it works.

A   Figure 8-20 shows a self-balancing electronic potentiometer circuit. Here the measuring-balancing slide-wire used in the electronic null-balance potentiometers (described before) is replaced by an electromechanical strain gage balancing device. The strain gage balancing transducer is based on the free-wire strain gage principle where the resistance of a wire varies in proportion to the applied tension. It consists of four wire elements (R_{G1}, R_{G2}, R_{G3}, R_{G4}) connected electrically in the form of a resistance bridge, and mechanically to a rotary pivot arm. With a constant current supply across the strain gage device when its resistance is changed by the motion of the balancing motor varying the tension of the wire elements, the proper output voltage is produced to rebalance the measuring circuit. Although the strain gage device does the same work as a slide-wire, it does it better as it provides infinite resolution and trouble-free operation by eliminating the finite, troublesome slide-wire.

1. *Servo-drive module.* Houses measuring circuit (plug-in range and actuation resistor boards), strain gage transducer, detector-amplifier (plug-in miniature converter and transistorized high input impedance amplifier), high stray rejection shield, and balancing motor which drives the strain gage transducer through gear and drive cable combination. This module is used for all models.

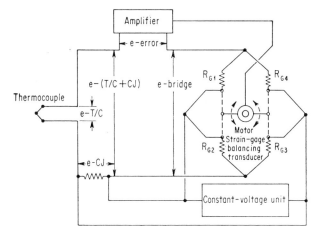

Fig. 8-20. Strain gage transducer self-balancing electronic potentiometer circuit.

2. *Display modules.* There are three interchangeable plug-in sections: 6-in.-wide strip chart, $7\frac{1}{4}$-in.-diameter circular chart, and $20\frac{1}{4}$-in. circular flat scale indicator. They each incorporate the recording and indicating pens and pointers, ink supply, and chart drive system. The circular chart type uses a V pen and plastic reservoir and capillary tubing, and a concentric scale and floating pointer. The chart drive motor is synchronous and drives the chart hub through a gear train connection. The strip chart pen is a jeweled-tip reservoir type, fed from a plastic bottle through a preformed coil capillary tubing. A triangular-shaped indicator rides along a 6-in. calibrated straight scale. Display modules are easily interchangeable and are attached to a pullout (drawer-type) chassis in front of the universal servo-drive module also mounted on the chassis. Modules, chassis mounted, are housed in a metal enclosure with detachable door and window in front, and input terminal on the rear, suitable for panel, relay rack, table mounting, or with carrying handle for portability.

Q What is a recording oscillograph? What is its purpose?

A An oscillograph is a recording instrument which makes a simultaneous continuous recording on a chart of the time variations of analog voltages originating at one or a number of separate points. Analog voltages are produced by electrical transducers which convert physical parameters to be measured into corresponding electrical variations which are either static (slowly varying) or dynamic (rapidly fluctuating) in character. Transducers either are directly connected to the recording means or may be connected to signal conditioning equipment ahead of the recording means. Its purpose is to produce a chart of continuous traces (records) of a number of measured variables with the same time reference from many different types of transducers. This provides research, design, and test engineers with records of different variables which can be analyzed and compared at the same instant, and whose phase relationships, dynamic response characteristics, and calibrated amplitudes can be studied.

Q Who uses multichannel recording oscillographs?

A Anyone who needs detailed information of many measurements whose characteristics are related to each other, particularly when this information is most conveniently obtained from one chart with the same time base. This means that research and development engineers, product and process design engineers, and laboratory, production, and field test engineers in plant, process, and aero-space industries require recording oscillographs. Medical, biological, and life science researchers use recording oscillographs also. Oscillographs measure (1) process variables, (2) mechanical measurements (stress, strain, load, shock, vibration), (3) electrical parameters (current, voltage, phase angle, power), and (4) medical and biological phenomena.

Q What is the basic principle of a recording oscillograph? Name two common types.

A A recording oscillograph uses a galvanometer to measure small magnitudes of current connected directly to it and converts this current signal into a record trace on a chart. The galvanometer uses the D'Arsonval principle of current measurement through the repulsion of the magnetic field of a multiturn galvanometer coil by the field of a permanent magnet. When a current flows through a galvanometer coil placed within the magnetic field of a permanent magnet, the reaction between the current-carrying wire in the coil and the magnetic field produces a rotational torque which twists the coil about its axis. This is the same principle used in an electric meter, or millivoltmeter indicator. If a stylus, or other recording device, is attached to the coil, and a paper strip chart supply is placed under the stylus, there is a continuous recording of the stylus motion. (1) This is called a direct recording (or stylus galvanometer) oscillograph (Fig. 8-21). (2) But if a small mirror is attached to the coil in place of the stylus, it will reflect light from a light source through an optical system of lenses and mirrors onto a photographic paper strip chart supply to produce a continuous trace of the input signal. This is a photographic (mirror galvanometer) oscillograph (Fig. 8-8).

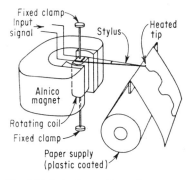

Fig. 8-21. Recording oscillograph.

Q What are typical performance specifications for (1) direct recording oscillographs and (2) photographic oscillographs?

A (1) Most record dynamic signals to 100 cps response, some to 350 cps; maximum deflection is about ±1 in. per channel on a segmental chart (one segment per channel); eight channels maximum; instantaneous continuous record with ink stylus or heated stylus on preprinted charts of from 4 to 18 in. wide. Multiple chart speeds over a wide range are switched by push buttons or a selector switch. (2) Photographic oscillographs record dynamic signals in the high response range up to 6,000 cps, maximum deflections to ±8 in. on all channels with overlapping traces, 50 channels maximum capacity; instantly readable, or chemically developed, continuous traces on photographic-paper charts 5 to 12 in. wide. Amplitude grid and timing reference lines are photographed on the chart at the time of the test recording. Multiple chart speeds over a wide range to maximum 160 in. per sec by push button or switch.

Q Describe a multichannel stylus galvanometer direct-writing oscillograph and how it works.

A A stylus galvanometer oscillograph (Fig. 8-22) consists of (1) galvanometer assembly and driver amplifier, (2) chart and chart drive mechanism, (3) signal conditioning equipment, and (4) enclosure.

1. The galvanometer assembly has a writing arm and attached stylus fixed to and driven by a D'Arsonval moving coil. A permanent magnet surrounds the coil and the entire assembly is mounted in the instrument so that the stylus is heated, for use with a heat-sensitive paper. A different stylus can carry ink from a reservoir for a paper suitable for ink recording. Several galvanometers may be mounted adjacent to each other for multichannel recording. These produce fine, instantly readable traces. Since the stylus galvanometer needs a sizable amount of current to deflect

it full scale (2 in. peak to peak), a driver amplifier is used with it. Strip chart recording paper is mounted below the galvanometers and is pulled over a sharp edge in the paper drive mechanism. The heat stylus wipes over this edge as it swings, thus producing records in true rectangular coordinates (Fig. 8-21).

2. The chart has preprinted reference coordinates in segments since the stylus cannot overlap. A synchronous motor chart drive with electric actuated gear changing provides various chart speeds. Precision is needed to reduce lateral chart motion to a minimum. The other chart drive transmission systems use two synchronous motors, gear trains, and a clutch mechanism. A backing plate allows for making hand notes on the chart. The chart supply roll is positioned on a driven supply spindle, and the chart end is attached to a tension-controlled take-up spindle. The time marker, or event marker, is actuated by a separate synchronous motor and provides time markings on the chart edge. A chart footage indicator shows the unused chart length.

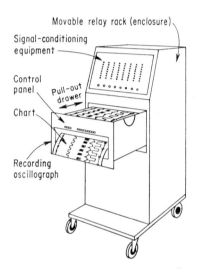

Fig. 8-22. Stylus galvanometer oscillograph.

3. Signal conditioning equipments modify the electrical output signals from any type of measuring element (transducer) so that the proper traces can be produced on the chart. Functions such as amplitude control (attenuation), zero adjustment or suppression, balance controls for resistance, reactance and reluctance bridge transducers, a-c or d-c amplification, and calibration signals are provided by such signal conditioning equipment as pre-amplifiers (a-c and d-c), carrier amplifiers, bridge balance units, servo amplifiers, impedance-matching amplifiers, and logarithmic amplifiers.

4. Enclosures. Direct writing oscillographs are mounted in a drawer-type pullout chassis for relay rack mounting (vertical chart), portable carrying cases (horizontal chart), cases for table or bench mounting, consoles with rubber rollers or wheels for mobile systems, and in shock and vibration mounts for extreme conditions.

Q Describe a multichannel photographic direct recording oscillograph and how it works.

A The photographic, mirror-galvanometer-type oscillograph (Fig. 8-23) differs from the stylus-galvanometer type in these ways: It records higher-frequency phenomena, with wide deflections and overlapping adjacent traces, has higher chart speeds giving better readability, has more sensitive galvanometers requiring reduced current and often eliminating amplifiers, and produces a chart whose reference coordinates are recorded at the same time as the data trace. It consists of (1) a miniature mirror-type galvanometer (or galvanometers), magnetic block (or blocks), optical system, chart, and reference line system as a recording means, (2) chart drive system, (3) signal conditioning equipment, and (4) enclosure.

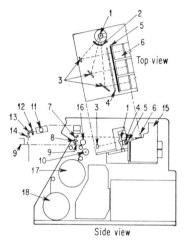

Fig. 8-23. Photographic oscillograph, optical system. (1) Recording lamp; (2) collector lens; (3) parallax elimination mirrors; (4) intensity controllers; (5) trace identifier; (6) galvanometer; (7) recording mirror; (8) dual recording lens; (9) recording plane; (10) grid-line lamp; (11) record number counter, photographic; (12) record number flash tube; (13) record number mirror; (14) record number lens; (15) magnet block; (16) chart drive roller; (17) supply drum; (18) take-up drum.

1. In the miniature galvanometer (smaller than a cigarette), the mirror attached to a multiturn coil is rotated so that a light beam from a light source (incandescent or ultraviolet) is moved laterally in proportion to the current through the coil in the presence of a magnetic field. The galvanometer is "plugged in" to a compact permanent magnet block which provides mounting connections and input signal connections for as many as 12 galvanometers (Fig. 8-24). The coil and mirror are attached to a metallic torsion ribbon that does the two jobs of providing a restoring torque and conducting the input signal current through the coil. Galvanometers have different frequency response characteristics with a useful data range of 60 per cent of the natural frequency. The amount

of current needed to deflect a galvanometer (sensitivity) increases as its frequency response increases. To give the best dynamic response, galvanometers operate at a damping characteristic between free or uncontrolled swing (critical damping) and overdamped deflection with no overshoot. Damping is controlled by electromagnetic means for low-

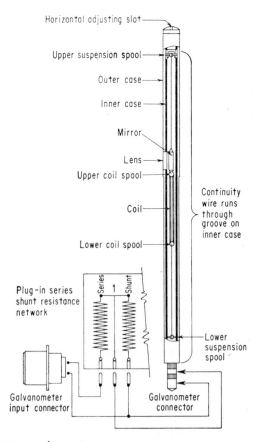

Fig. 8-24. Subminiature galvanometer.

frequency galvanometers (resistor network in input circuit) or fluid means for high-frequency galvanometers (fluid restricts coil motion in galvanometer).

In the optical system a light source, placed at or near the focus of a lens, projects parallel rays from the lens to the galvanometer mirror, which redirects the rays through a lens on the galvanometer case for projection of the source image in the same focal plane, but with lateral displacement corresponding to the mirror's rotation. This system produces a rectilinear relationship between the galvanometer spot motion and the chart motion. The chart is photographic paper sensitive to incandescent or ultraviolet light. The galvanometer light beam produces a continuous trace, which is easy to read in the presence of a small amount of ambient ultraviolet light (as from a fluorescent bulb) on ultraviolet-sensitive paper. Regular photographic paper must be chemically processed. Amplitude reference grids (vertical markings evenly spaced across the chart) are produced by allowing light to shine through a slotted grid bar or film on the chart passing under it (Fig. 8-25). Time lines (horizontal reference every 1, 0.1, 0.01, or 0.001 sec) are produced by an electronic flash timing system to give accurate time references on the chart. Event markers, calibrated traces, and record numbers (four-digit number on the chart's edge) are all photographed on the chart at the time of recording. The chart is viewed at the exact spot of recording and for 12 in. after. Spot and amplitude grid line intensity is adjustable.

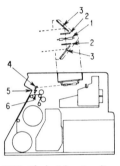

Fig. 8-25. Flash tube time-line system. (1) Time-line flash tube; (2) time-line lens; (3) time-line mirror; (4) recording mirror; (5) recording lens; (6) recording plane.

2. The chart supply roll is mounted on the supply spindle; the chart is brought over the drive roller, to an idler roller at the point where the galvanometer spots and reference lines are photographed on it, and then is clipped to the take-up spindle and drum. The chart is moved by the drive roller, which in turn is driven by a synchronous motor and clutch-operated drive belt and gear combination. The proper gear and belt combination is selected by front panel operated push-button switches, which actuate the clutches. Fifteen speeds can be selected for either forward or reverse chart travel. A clutch on the take-up spindle maintains proper tension on the chart at all speeds and in both directions. Recording lights are blocked out during reverse motion on the chart. An automatic record length device controls the length of chart run in accordance with a preset length.

3. Signal conditioning equipment is similar to that used with the stylus galvanometer oscillograph, except that galvanometer amplifiers are not needed. Often the input signal can be connected directly to the galvanometer.

4. Photographic oscillograph enclosure and mounting facilities are similar to direct-writing oscillographs except that they are more com-

pact, rugged, and versatile. All operating controls and indicators are on the front surface, and all connectors on the rear.

Q   What seven factors must be considered—and what procedure is best for selecting a photographic oscillograph system?

A   Consider the following in order: (1) desired full-scale range and deflection of measured variable; (2) measured variable dynamic response rate, since the selection of transducer and galvanometer depends on these; (3) select primary sensing element (transducer) and type of transmission; (4) galvanometer selection; first select the highest frequency response, then sensitivity, and damping network needed; (5) signal conditioning equipment, if required, including bridge circuit, bridge balance, gage power supply, suppression circuits, and cold-junction compensation; (6) amplifiers; and (7) calibration facilities.

Q   How do you select a multiple-point recorder?

A   You have a choice between multipoint self-balancing potentiometers and direct-writing oscillographs.

1. Determine the dynamic response of the measured variable in time to make a full-scale change. If more than $\frac{1}{2}$ sec, use potentiometer recorder. Use a direct-writing oscillograph in ranges between 1 and 60 cps, and photographic direct recording oscillograph for static data to 6,000 cps. In a multipoint recorder select the instrument for the fastest variable. Ink is used for general-purpose recording but will spatter with high-frequency signals, spill under severe vibration, and freeze at low temperatures. A heated stylus is better for lower frequencies and severe conditions. Photographic light beam recording is excellent for high-speed dynamic recording, somewhat limited in low-speed recording by wider trace.

2. Determine the number of points to be recorded continuously and simultaneously. Select chart width and type of recorder accordingly. Use oscillographs for continuous multichannel recording and potentiometers for two-channel continuous recording, or multichannel sampling and printing. Multirecord potentiometers have a choice of printing mechanism. Choose cyclic printing for slow-moving variables and synchro printing (printing at balance) for faster-moving variables. When an occasional extremely fast change is encountered, a balancing motor cutout switch may be needed so that printing can occur and a smeared record is eliminated.

3. Chart speed determination is important so that the proper compromise between readable, spread-out traces and records and efficient use of chart paper can occur without waste. Slow speeds are acceptable when only broad trends or unusual swing are desired. But if dynamic phenomena are to be recorded, described, and analyzed, you need faster

speeds. Oscillographs have chart speeds as high as 160 in. per sec to make 6,000 cps data readable. The potentiometer printing mechanism can be furnished to print on every other cycle (skip numeral printing), thus allowing a slower chart speed.

4. Signal conditioning equipment. Sensitivity (input signal needed to obtain desired pen, indicator, or galvanometer deflection for full

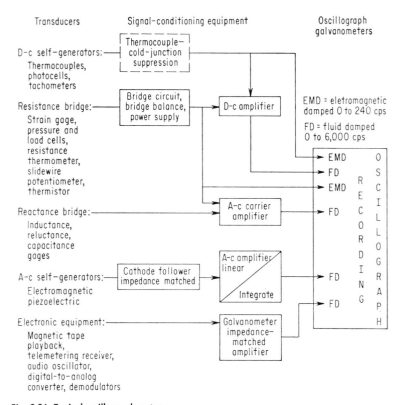

Fig. 8-26. Typical oscillograph systems.

scale) of the recorder determines the need for amplifiers. The type of transducer determines the need for bridge balance, units, carrier, linear, or integrating amplifiers. See Fig. 8-26 for selecting signal conditioning equipment.

Q What is meant by *graphic instrumentation* systems?

A The graphic panel concept (Fig. 8-27) places indicating and recording instruments, as well as control set-point adjustments associated with process measured variables in the process flow diagram, at the location which corresponds to the actual point of measurement and control in the process. It provides a continuous, coordinated panorama of the entire process, or network, within the operator's immediate field of vision. It is a display of process trends and measured variables and thus helps the operator to adjust control points easily. It also reduces the size and

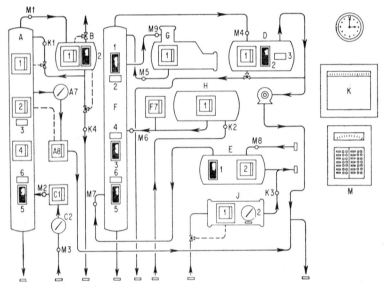

Fig. 8-27. Graphic panel with instruments in flow diagram.

complexity of conventional panel boards (sometimes as long as 200 ft). Graphic panels are usually Formica, anodized or painted steel, with multicolored process lines, process unit symbols, primary sensing and final control element symbols in plastic, or painted on the panel with "miniature" display indicating, recording, and/or controlling instruments and alarm lights. Often graphic instrumentation is combined with conventional size multipoint indicators and recorders.

Q   Name two types of miniature instruments. What do they do?
A   Miniature instruments display process variables measured by a primary sensing element at a process unit in the field and transmitted by air-pressure signal or electrical signal to the miniature receiver on the graphic panel. Indicating and/or recording miniature instruments are either (1) pneumatic receivers or (2) electric receivers. Strip charts 4 in. wide or 3-in. indicating scales display the data as 30-day continuous re-

cording is provided on one chart. The measured variable is also indicated on a graduated scale, and the controller's control set point and control valve position are indicated continuously.

Q Describe a pneumatic miniature recorder and how it works.

A A miniature recorder (Fig. 8-28) is basically a pneumatic receiver which is actuated by a full-scale, 3 to 15 psi, air signal which is proportional to the measured variable full-range value and transmitted from the point of measurement (see Transmitters, Chap. 2). A spring-loaded receiving bellows in the recorder is attached to a pen arm through a linkage which transfers the bellows motion to a pen and indicator pointer motion across an arc scale and a linear 4-in.-wide chart. The reservoir pen is capillary-fed from a 6 months ink supply bottle. Zero and span adjustments for pen and pointer travel

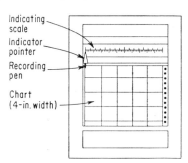

Fig. 8-28. Pneumatic miniature recorder.

are determined by the spring. The chart has sprocket holes along one edge and is driven vertically from the drive drum across a platen to the rewind drum. The chart drive mechanism is either an electric or a pneumatic synchronous motor and is positively geared to the drive drum, providing accurate timing. Pneumatic chart drives are used in hazardous (explosive) atmospheres. A tear-off serrated knife edge provides means for obtaining daily records. Rewind is by thumb wheel, which disengages from the chart drive. The instrument case has a hinged glass door in front and 1/4-in. piping connections in the rear; compact design uses one-fourth the panel-board area as a conventional recorder.

Q Describe an electric miniature recorder and how it works.

A Very similar to pneumatic recorders in display functions, such a recorder differs only in actuation from a measured variable signal. Input signals can be transmitted from d-c or a-c electric transmitters using two- or three-conductor cable. Transmitters are described in Chaps. 2, 3, and 4. The receiver mechanism (Fig. 8-29) is a positioning servo which converts d-c signals into pen and pointer positions across a 4-in.-wide rectangular coordinate chart and straight scale. Input to the recorder (4 to 20 ma d-c) provides a force on a balance beam through a magnet unit. Deflection of this beam changes the air gap in a position detector which has two pieces of ferrite, one on the movable beam, the other rigidly fixed to the chassis. As spacing between the ferrite pieces changes, inductance in the oscillator circuit changes, causing current to flow through the amplifier to drive a torque motor. Since the pen arm is directly attached to the torque motor armature, a change in oscillator output deflects the pen arm in proportion to the input signal. Pen arm deflection acts on a calibrated spring to rebalance the beam. Two pens can be housed in the same case to provide a continuous record of two variables on the same chart. Pens are capillary-fed reservoir type with 6 months ink supply on each. A chart with sprocket holes is driven by a

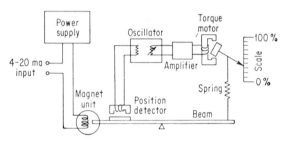

Fig. 8-29. Pen positioning servo system.

drive roller actuated by a fixed gear train and synchronous motor. Speed change is by motor change. Chart supply is carried on a supply spindle and taken up on a reroll spindle with a daily tear-off strip. A reroll spindle knob release clutch provides manual reroll when needed. Recording and indicating mechanisms, chart, chart drive, and servo system are all mounted on a front pullout chassis. A removable tube-tray assembly holds the power supply for five transmitters. Both are mounted in a case with a clear plastic front door and back-mounted terminals for input and power connections. The separate chassis arrangement makes easier servicing and installation of case and connections, without recorder interference.

Q What is a digital display voltmeter (shown in Fig. 8-3)?

A A digital display voltmeter measures an analog voltage input signal and displays a series of lighted digital (arabic numerals) figures in a metal enclosure. Direct- and alternating-current voltages, ratios, or resistances can be measured to accuracies of ±0.01 per cent. Digital voltmeters are used for very rapid readout and display of voltages in analog and digital computers, in scanning and logging systems, in checkout and test systems, in decimal, binary, or hexadecimal numbering systems.

Q Describe a typical digital display voltmeter and how it works.

A Lighted arabic numerals (0 to 9) are displayed in integral windows side by side in a metal enclosure. Four to seven windows are used for numerals, signs, decimal points, or other symbols. Numerals are made by projecting a film slide on ground glass, or edge-lighted plastic numerals, or small light bulbs (neon) arranged in the shape of numbers. Analog voltage input signals are converted to digital pulse signals of specific voltage levels for actuating numeral lights representing the actual voltage value of the input signal. The digital pulse is generated, usually, in a digital potentiometer where the unknown input voltage is amplified and then sequentially compared with a succession of known voltages in a logical procedure, until the analog signal is converted to its digital form to the desired number of significant figures, or decimal places (Fig. 8-30).

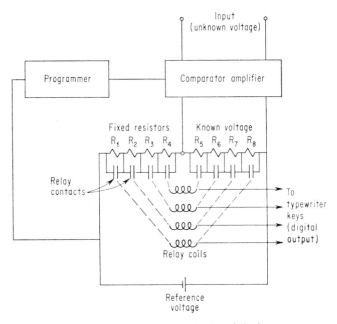

Fig. 8-30. Digital potentiometer measuring circuit for digital display.

The known voltage is obtained from a highly regulated reference supply, impressed across a number of series-connected precision resistors, each shunted by mercury-wetted relay contacts. Instead of moving a contactor across a slide-wire, as in a continuous balance potentiometer to vary the known voltage, relays are used to select and combine the various values of fixed resistors in the voltage input signal. The contact pattern or combination needed to produce a balance condition is interpreted automatically and continuously as the digital value of the measured value, and its output signal actuates the digital display numeral lights. The balancing action is programmed in a logical sequence according to a code set up in the logic section. A typical code would use a combination of the numbers 5-2-2-1 to make up numbers from 0 to 9.

Q What type of device is required to obtain the total area under the curve on a recording chart?

A Integrators are used to determine total area. This total area represents the total flow over a certain period of time under the flow rate curve on a chart from a flowmeter. It can also represent total chromatography sample, electric power, electrolytic cell current, total weight in continuous weighing system, and any other total quantity under a rate curve. If the square root of the differential pressure is extracted by the recorder, as in the case of meters with square-root charts or uniform (linear) chart flowmeters, the total flow is calculated by multiplying the rate of flow by the elapsed time. If the chart reads differential pressure head directly, the computation of charts is simplified by combining all the constant factors in a coefficient to be multiplied by the square root of the differential. Totalizing may be done by a planimeter to compute the area, or automatically by an integrator which is part of the recorder.

Q Name three types of integrators.

A (1) Planimeter, (2) intermittent, and (3) continuous integrators.

Q Describe two types of planimeters.

A Figure 8-31 shows a planimeter which averages the square roots of

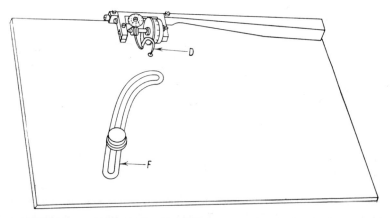

Fig. 8-31. Square-root planimeter for circular charts.

the pressure differential curve on a circular chart. The chart's center is placed on the planimeter hub *F*. The chart is rotated and the hub moved, so that gooseneck pointer *D* follows the chart record. The chart's motion turns a counter mechanism by means of a wheel riding on the chart. The final average read on the counter is then multiplied by a suitable factor to give total flow. A radial-type planimeter similar to this one is used for linear (evenly graduated) charts. A planimeter for integrating the flow rate recorded on miniature strip chart recorders is shown in Fig. 8-32. It also extracts the square-root function. Cursor 1 is made to follow the plotted curve by manual adjustment of knob 2 as the chart paper is driven by a toothed sprocket drum 3 connected to a variable-speed motor 4. The knob moves the cursor through square root cam 5. The angle through which this cam is rotated in following the curve is simultaneously converted to a displacement which is used to position the ball carriage of the integrator 6 which actuates a digital counter 7. Manual reset knob 8 is used to return the counter to zero for

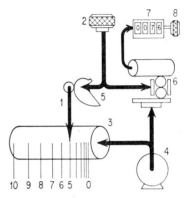

Fig. 8-32. Square-root planimeter for miniature strip charts.

a new reading. Smooth portions of the curve can be traversed at speeds as fast as 1 in 7 sec.

Q Describe a flow recorder automatic intermittent integrator and how it works.

A Figure 8-33 shows schematically a flow recorder with an electronic intermittent integrating mechanism mounted in it. The integrator has three major units: (1) a scanning unit, which checks the flow rate, as shown by the pen position, once every 5 sec, (2) an electronic detector relay, actuated by the scanning unit, which operates a line voltage motor-driven counting mechanism; and (3) a motor-driven counter assembly which totalizes the successive output impulses from the detector relay, thus integrating the flow measurement. The scanning mechanism is composed of a lightweight vane that is positioned by the recording pen through a mechanical linkage, and dual oscillator coils mounted on an arm driven by a cam (for either square-root or linear charts). In operation, the vane is positioned proportional to flow, and twelve times a minute the scanning unit checks the vane position. When the vane's leading edge is intercepted by the oscillator coils on the scanner, the oscillator unit conducts current to the relay, which in turn actuates the counter.

Q Describe a continuous integrator used with electronic strip chart null-balance potentiometers.

A   Figure 8-34 shows an integrator which continuously totalizes the area under the pen record produced on a strip chart potentiometer,

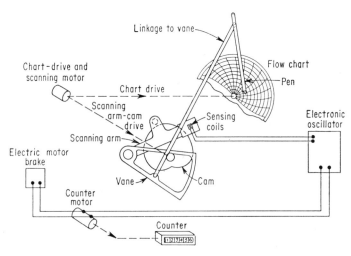

Fig. 8-33. Electronic-type integrator.

where this area is a function of the concentration of the compound producing it when applied to gas chromatography. The instrument can also be actuated by a millivolt producing transducer. This is a ball-and-disk integrator. It operates when a synchronous motor rotates a disk through a gearbox. A pair of hardened steel balls, held in a ball carriage,

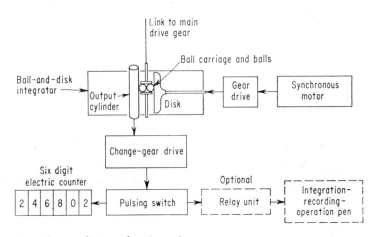

Fig. 8-34. Schematic diagram of continuous integrator.

is located between the disk and an output cylinder with one ball against the disk face and the other pressed against the face of the output cylinder. The balls are in continuous contact with each other. Rotation of the disk causes one ball to rotate. This in turn causes the second ball to rotate at an equal speed, but in the opposite direction. The second ball produces rotation in the output cylinder. Linkage between the main drive gear of the recorder and the ball carriage of the integrator moves the balls farther away from the rotating disk's center as the recording pen moves upscale. This causes the output cylinder to rotate faster, increasing the count rate of the pulsing switch, which actuates a six-digit electric counter. Any output counter (makes up to 1,000 counts per minute) is mounted on the recorder case or can be mounted remotely. Integration pips are also recorded on the left-hand side of the chart by an integration recording operation pen, which makes a maximum of 500 strokes per minute with each tenth pip drawn in the opposite direction. Each set of pips under the recorded peaks is proportional to the area under the peak. This is calibrated in terms of the total measured variable during a specific time period.

Q   What type of recorder would you use to display input signals whose frequency response is greater than 500 to 10,000 cps?

A   Use a cathode-ray oscilloscope with a Polaroid camera, taking a series of photographs. This method provides records to signals of several megacycles per second response (1,000,000 cps). For multichannel recording, a photographic chart is driven very fast over the face of several cathode-ray oscilloscopes mounted adjacent to each other. It provides response to 50,000 cps.

Q   What are the definition and purpose of a transmission system?

A   It provides a means of communicating between the primary sensing element and the controller, and between the controller and the final control element when these elements are located at some distance from each other. Measurement signal transmission is often called telemetering; control signal transmission is sometimes called supervisory control. The definition of telemetering accepted by the AIEE and American Standards Association is: "Telemetering is measurement with the aid of intermediate means, which permits the measurement to be interpreted at a distance from the primary sensing element. Distinctive feature of telemetering is the nature of the translating means, which converts the measured variable into a representative quantity of another kind that can be transmitted for measurement at a distance." The purpose then is to transmit measurement and control signals around the control loop where the control loop elements are separated by relatively long distances. A variety of transmission methods and media are used. Selection is based on distance, signal lag, safety conditions, control-room centralization, and economy.

Q   Name two major types of transmission systems used in process plants and between plants and processes.
A   These are classified by the media used for transmission, which are (1) electric and (2) pneumatic.

Q   What are the basic elements and functions of a transmission system?
A   A primary sensing element which detects the measured variable and whose output signal is fed to a (1) Transmitter (or telemeter transmitter) which consists of a measuring circuit and a transmission circuit where the measured variable signal is converted into a representative quantity of another kind, or medium, to be transmitted over a long distance. (2) Telemetering channel, or communication line, between the transmitter and receiver, often defined as the "route" for conveying the transmitted signal. (3) Telemeter receiver which converts the transmitted signal back to a mechanical motion to position the display means. Display, comparison, computing, and control sections and functions are similar to conventional display and control systems without telemetering. A control transmission system consists of (1) a control transmitter to convert the signal to a suitable signal for transmission and to transmit it through the control channel to (2) a control receiver which converts it to a signal or control energy suitable for actuating the final control element. Often the telemeter receiver, display, control unit, and control transmitter are all enclosed in the same case.

Q   Classify six types of electric transmission systems.
A   (1) Position, or ratio type, (2) voltage type, (3) current type, (4) impulse type, (5) frequency type, and (6) digital type.

Q   Why are electric transmission systems used more than any other type for transmitting over long distances?
A   Electrical telemetering is especially desirable for long distances because of the ease of transmitting through a metallic wire, or microwave, channel. Electric systems have speed, accuracy, and versatility. Wires are usually easier to install and connect than pneumatic tubing or piping. To transmit information outside of a single plant, wire facilities can be leased from the telephone utility. This saves expensive installation costs.

SUGGESTED READING

Recommended Practices, sold by Instrument Society of America, 530 William Penn Place, Pittsburgh, Pa.

    ISA—RP 23.1, *Miniature Recorder Chart Ranges*, 3 pages